# Philosophy
# of Science:
# An
# Introduction

# PHILOSOPHY OF SCIENCE: AN INTRODUCTION

Paul R. Durbin, O.P.
Saint Stephen's College
Dover, Massachusetts

McGraw-Hill Book Company
New York, St. Louis, San Francisco
Toronto, London, Sydney

**Philosophy of Science: An Introduction**

Copyright © 1968 by McGraw-Hill, Inc. All Rights Reserved.
Printed in the United States of America. No part of this
publication may be reproduced, stored in a retrieval system,
or transmitted, in any form or by any means, electronic,
mechanical, photocopying, recording, or otherwise, without
the prior written permission of the publisher.

*Library of Congress Catalog Card Number 68–15466*

18350

1 2 3 4 5 6 7 8 9 0    MAMM    7 5 4 3 2 1 0 6 9 8

# PREFACE

PHILOSOPHY OF SCIENCE AS AN ACADEMIC DISCIPLINE does not have a very long history. In the several decades in which it has been recognized as a separate subject, a number of efforts have been made to produce a manageable undergraduate course—none of them notably successful. The obstacles in the way of such a course are formidable. Normally the science major, who might be expected to take some interest in the course, is so busy acquiring technical competence in his chosen specialty that he simply does not have time for sophisticated criticisms of the methodology of science. The problem is even more severe when it comes to liberal arts majors. Furthermore, interest in the kind of critique that has become the core of philosophical interpretations of science requires an intellectual sophistication that is not normally expected except of graduate students, and is rare enough even among them.

In Catholic colleges the problem of a philosophical introduction to science has most often been taken care of by assigning it to the course in philosophy of nature (or natural philosophy, or cosmology). But the traditional natural philosophy course in Catholic schools has fallen into considerable disfavor today. The course was always said to have a bearing on modern science, and many schools made it compulsory for science majors. Yet students for the most part found the course hopelessly general and failed to see even the remotest connection with science. The result? Many schools have downgraded the course, and the trend is likely to continue in that direction as personalism becomes more and more dominant in Catholic philosophy—an unfortunate irony in our age of technology.

The present text is an attempt to meet the challenge implied in these twin dilemmas without simply discarding the undergraduate introduction to a philosophy of science. It is my belief that such a course, if taught rightly, can have an important bearing on education in science. I would even go so far as to say it can make a contribution to science itself. (I shall not defend the view here; the work as a whole is intended as the best defense.) However, if the course is to have such a bearing on science, it must be conceived as a course in close touch with the contemporary state of scientific knowledge.

To maximize the utility of such a course, the text has been planned in a way that will allow it to be taught according to any one of three methods. (1) It can be taught as a standard *philosophy of science* course in the way this is done in most universities in this country, though with the emphasis on *substantive issues* in science, rather than on methodology or epistemology. (2) It could also serve, in Catholic schools, as a *traditional natural philosophy* course, with more than usual attention paid to problems in science. (3) Finally, there is material enough in the text for an introduction to some key periods in the *history of science*—an approach to philosophy of science that is increasingly important at the present time.

A word on the text: It is built around a set of readings. Many such books justify the inclusion of materials on the ground that they would not otherwise be available. That is not the criterion here. The criterion for inclusion in the present text is *whether or not a particular selection can help raise a problem for discussion.* The availability of material is in fact an advantage—the larger work from which a selection is taken will often be a valuable reference source for further discussions that develop around the problem raised.

Thus the course is deliberately designed to be taught in a discussional, problem-centered fashion. It is not just a selection of readings. Though the bulk of the material is made up of readings—taken from classical, modern, and contemporary contributions to the solution of problems raised by science —these will be introduced in each case in such a way as to highlight as much as possible the problem involved. At the end of each group of selections, the strands of thought are tied together so as to bring out for the student the basic issues involved. In this scheme collateral readings are essential and references are supplied at the end of each section.[1]

The ideal way in which such a course should be taught is purely discussional. In my view, however, this does not rule out the presentation of a definite point of view: I would maintain (for instance) that one who wanted to defend the basic points of Aristotelian natural philosophy could do so *better* in this than in any other way. The course would have to begin with a basic orientation during which the professor could get to know the capabilities and backgrounds of his students. After that, discussion could predominate and the professor's task would be largely one of directing and supplying necessary supplementary readings. In an ideal setup, a group of the better students could be assigned to defend the two or more points of view that give rise to a problem; their task would be to read as much as they can comprehend of the background materials so that they can be leaders in the discussion. However, the rest of the class must also be prepared if discussion is to be fruitful, making the whole process a successful teaching method. This could be done by briefer assigned readings giving the basic points of view, or

---

[1] To promote the continuity and flow of the book, the individual author's footnotes have been incorporated (occasionally in slightly modified form) in brackets in the text. All notes at the bottom of pages are my own, with the exception of the selections from Adolf Grünbaum in which the author's footnotes have been preserved.

else the students defending the various points of view could make up summaries of their own or else pick out representative selections from their broader readings.

Experience has shown, further, that the procedure works best when the teacher actively guides the discussion. This is tied in with a basic point: Students need to be *trained* in discussion. "Rules for the resolution of conflict" must be taught and incorporated in practice in the discussions in such a way as to allow the students themselves to come to a fruitful solution of a problem, or at least to carry on a discussion in an intelligent way. One of the chief functions of such a course, in fact, is precisely to teach students how to see problems, to relate issues, and to come to some sort of solution. The science student in the course might, for instance, learn the relation between his kind of thinking and that of other approaches to reality; he may be better able to see where and why experimentation is required as one of the "rules for resolution," and where and why it is not. The advantages of the approach are numerous.

There are also drawbacks. The most obvious one is lack of time, but there is also the consideration that the teacher himself must have a broad reading knowledge of his field and must know the rules of discussion. Nevertheless, in the present intellectual crisis it seems essential that at least some teachers experiment in this way and come up with dialectical approaches of this sort in *all* fields of knowledge.

Some will also notice omissions. For instance, in a course built around the philosophy of science approach, it may be objected that there is no treatment of induction or the foundations of quantum mechanics or that the treatments of such standard topics as causality and relativity are woefully inadequate, and so on. Similarly, in a historical approach, the objection might be raised that the materials are insufficient, and that there are no references to problems relating science to society. The life sciences, too, have been somewhat slighted, though an effort is made to include *organismic* approaches in Part 3, where these are viewed as overall alternatives in the total interpretation of science. All these are important objections, but I feel that for the course envisioned, a decision must be made. In my view, these more complex problems belong properly to the epistemology, or to the history, or even the sociology of science; or else they should be postponed for graduate-level courses in philosophy of science.[2]

In any case, the course as presented is difficult enough. It may even be suggested that it will work out best as an upper-level undergraduate course, either for science majors or for liberal arts honor students or those with some special interest in the philosophical implications of the sciences.[3]

---

[2] Some of these problems, however, are brought up in the Introduction and given a fuller introduction in two appendixes.

[3] Chapters marked with an asterisk include more difficult material, for science majors or more advanced students.

Finally, I would like here to express my gratitude to a number of people who have had more to do with the final form of the text than they may realize. My thanks are due first to my students, over several years, who by their discussions have helped determine my views on what are the basic philosophical issues in the sciences. Thanks are also due to colleagues who have heard—and criticized—the approach presented from the lecture platform. But I owe a most special debt to William A. Wallace, O.P., and Edward MacKinnon, S.J., for reading the entire manuscript and making very valuable suggestions.

PAUL R. DURBIN, O.P.

# CONTENTS

# INTRODUCTION

SINCE THE PRESENT TEXT HAS BEEN DELIBERATELY DESIGNED so that
it can be taught in any one of three ways—with emphasis on a standard
philosophy of science approach, a historical approach, or a classical Aristotelian interpretation—it will be useful to begin with a somewhat detailed discussion of these three approaches. The result should be at the same time an
*introduction* to the discussions in the main part of the text and a *general
orientation* in terms of possible approaches that can be taken in interpreting
the scientific enterprise as a whole. The three approaches will be briefly introduced, first, and then a more technical survey of the chief problems in each
approach will be given.

The first of the approaches to be discussed—logical empiricism—has a
just claim to being first. It is unquestionably the dominant viewpoint represented in philosophy of science courses in American universities today. However, "logical empiricism," it should be noted at once, is simply a label
attached to many different points of view which, nonetheless, share common
interests. The most important attitudes shared in common are implicit in the
very name—i.e., an unlimited commitment to the *empirical* sciences, and a
passionate belief in the usefulness of *logic* for interpreting the sciences.

There are further points of shared interest. Most of those philosophers who
can in any sense be described as logical empiricists—Nagel, Pap, Scheffler,
Grünbaum, Sellars, etc.—devote a large part of their philosophical attention
to problems concerned with scientific evidence, theory, and explanation, with
scientific method as hypothetico-deductive, and with the problems of induction and confirmation.

Dudley Shapere states the case for this kind of philosophical concern suc-
cinctly and persuasively:

> Surely before asserting (for example) that "scientific method" should
> be applied to political or moral issues, or that science can accomplish
> its aims only if it makes certain "metaphysical" assumptions which it
> itself cannot validate, we should try to be as clear as possible as to
> just what it is we are saying. We should try to be as clear as possible
> about the meanings of terms we might use, both ordinarily and in philo-

sophical and scientific discourse, in characterizing the aims, methods, and structure of science—terms like "theory," "evidence," "explanation," "fact"; and we should try to be as clear as possible about the ways in which evidence and theory and other elements of science are related to one another.[1]

The second of the possible approaches to the course—and to the study of science in general—is the historical. This approach is offered at the present time as the principal challenger to the positivist or logical-empiricist ideal. It takes its stand on the history of science, scientific discovery, and ongoing research in science. Generally speaking, it is a much less narrow approach than the logical, bringing to the understanding of science—in addition to history—contributions from methodology, sociology, psychology, and even metaphysics.

The best contemporary exposition of the view—and the best parallel reading for the present introduction—is Thomas Kuhn's *The Structure of Scientific Revolutions*.[2] Kuhn states his case simply: "The man who takes historic fact seriously must suspect that science does not tend toward the ideal that [the logical-empiricist] image of its cumulativeness has suggested." (p. 95) Further details will be given below.

Another spokesman for this point of view, Norwood Russell Hanson, spells out his opposition to the standard interpretation of science more caustically:

> Why is microphysics misrepresented by philosophers?
> The reason is simple. They have regarded as paradigms of physical inquiry not unsettled, dynamic, research sciences like microphysics, but finished systems, planetary mechanics, optics, electromagnetism and classical thermodynamics. . . . But these are not research sciences any longer, though they were at one time—a fact that historians and philosophers of science are in danger of forgetting. Now, however, they constitute a different kind of physics altogether. Distinctions which at present apply to them ought to be suspect when transferred to research disciplines: indeed, these distinctions afford an artificial account even of the kinds of activities in which Kepler, Galileo and Newton themselves were actually engaged.[3]

The third of the possible approaches to a philosophy of science course is that of traditional Aristotelian natural philosophy. It is an approach that is frankly realist in its belief that science gives true knowledge of the world and its belief that there are absolutes even in scientific research. For the most part the view is dismissed by other philosophers of science as hopelessly naïve.

However, the view does have some hardy defenders, and it is common enough in the cosmology or natural philosophy courses in Catholic schools.

---

[1] Dudley Shapere, *Philosophical Problems of Natural Science*, Introduction, pp. 1–2. Reprinted with permission of The Macmillan Company. Copyright © Dudley Shapere 1965.

[2] University of Chicago Press, Phoenix Books, Chicago, 1964.

[3] N. R. Hanson, *Patterns of Discovery*, Cambridge University Press, London, 1958, p. 1.

*Scientific data in terms of which the three points of view can be compared:*
The following summary of scientific facts and theories is offered as a minimum basis on which to build a set of discussions about science. It is not presumed that the student will be familiar with the details, nor is it even suggested that he should be. These facts and theories are offered as the subject matter upon which debates in the philosophy of science are built; the student can, if he wants, simply take this material as a "given," as something treated elsewhere and borrowed from other courses in the curriculum.

Two further precautions. Although the scientific data are taken as a "given," they are not meant to be *necessary* in the sense that they are immune from critical examination. One of the purposes of philosophical analysis, particularly in the view of logical empiricists, is to offer a critique of the sciences. Again, the data are not intended to be *sufficient* as presented here, for intensive philosophical debate on the professional level. Rather, on this level, it would be presumed that the facts and theories summarized here are only symbolic, standing for whole sciences or areas of science of which they constitute the foundation or classic examples.

Four areas of science will be listed, the first two corresponding to Part 1 of the text, the third covering Part 2 (Chapters 6 to 8), and the fourth corresponding to Chapter 9.

*1. Inertia*  The most basic subject matter for philosophy of science discussions must necessarily be the first great achievement of modern science —the mechanics of motion, proposed by Galileo and reaching full expression in Newton's laws of motion and his theory of universal gravitation.

The laws of motion, in Newton's own words, are:

> *a.* Every body continues in its state of rest or of uniform motion in a right line unless it is compelled to change that state by forces impressed upon it.
> *b.* The change of motion is proportional to the motive force impressed and is made in the direction of the right line in which that force is impressed.
> *c.* To every action there is always opposed an equal reaction; or, the mutual actions of two bodies upon each other are always equal and directed to contrary parts.[4]

The third law, which in its main lines was already known to the pre-Galileo Aristotelians, is an indispensable tool for the measurement of motion. It is one of the chief failures of the Aristotelians that they did not systematically exploit this principle and come up with a science of measurement. The second law in its turn—which can be summarized in the familiar equation, $f = ma$—constitutes the basic system of measurement in the new mechanics of mo-

---

[4] *Principia*, book I; cf. F. Cajori (ed.); *Sir Isaac Newton's Mathematical Principles of Natural Philosophy and His System of the World*, A. Motte (trans., 1729), University of California Press, Berkeley, 1934, p. 13.

tion. And, finally, the first law, the law of inertia, is the indispensable logical presupposition of the second law and therefore of the whole system of measurement built upon it. It is no chance event, then, that the chief philosophical debates about Newtonian mechanics have centered around the law of inertia and its interpretation.

Is it a genuine *law of nature?* Is it a mathematical limit theorem? Is it an idealization from experience, or simply a hypothetical entity useful in predicting measurable results? All these and many other views (including one that would say the law is simply false) have been proposed, and the way in which schools of thought interpret the law is one criterion for distinguishing them from one another.

*2. Atomic structure*    Next to classical mechanics, the most fundamental scientific "given" is the atomic theory, first proposed in its modern, quantitative form by Dalton. At the near end of the historical spectrum, however, no view today of the nature of science could be worth much if it did not account for the latest quantum interpretations of atomic particle structure.

*3. Space-time and units of measurement*    In modern science no one questions the importance of measurement, but there are major disagreements about the instruments and units of measurement and about the interpretation of the very concept of measurement. One of the basic areas of concern is suggested in this quotation from a popular work of a leading physicist:

> Everybody knows that all physical measurements are based on *three basic units.* . . . Length, time, and mass (or less correctly, weight) have been selected in classical physics on some kind of anthropomorphic basis. . . . But the selection of these particular units is really not necessary, and *any three* complex units . . . can serve as basic units, provided they are independent of one another. However, in building a consistent theory of all physical phenomena, it is rational to select three fundamental units, each of which governs a vast area of physics, and to express all other units through them. Which units should be the members of this trio?[5]

Gamow then says two of the units "doubtless should be" the velocity of light, *c*, and Planck's constant, *h*. Others have disagreed on this point, but all agree that candidates for the third universal constant are extremely problematical. This is one kind of problem in the area of measurement.

There is another sort of measurement problem, however, which can even more sharply divide philosophers. A recent discovery in science, the so-called "Mössbauer effect," allows practical measurements of unprecedented accuracy. This effect has also been used for experimental testing of Einstein's general theory of relativity. One of the better present-day science popularizers has written about this:

> The [earlier] victories of Einstein's General Theory were all astronomic

---

[5] George Gamow, *Thirty Years that Shook Physics*, Doubleday, Garden City, N.Y., 1966, pp. 155–157.

in nature. Scientists longed to discover a way to check it in the laboratory under conditions they could vary at will. The key to such a laboratory demonstration arose in 1958, when the German physicist, Rudolf Ludwig Mössbauer, showed that, under certain conditions, a crystal could be made to produce a beam of gamma rays of sharply defined wavelength. . . .[6]

The philosophical bone of contention here is not the remaining details of the Mössbauer-effect experiments, or even Einstein's general theory of relativity itself (though that is widely debated), but the "longing" of physicists "to check it in the laboratory." How does a school interpret this attitude? What view of scientific method is implicit in the attitude?

4. *Population genetics*   The theory of evolution will obviously be important in Chapter 9, on emergence. It is also obviously a subject of some discussion. The fundamental features of such debates, and one attitude on them, can be suggested in a single pointed quotation:

> The way in which selection and the other factors and forces of evolution interact within a population has been worked out in a brilliant series of studies by R. A. Fisher, J. B. S. Haldane, Sewall Wright, and others. It is these studies, more than anything else, that have made possible the synthesis of generations of observations and experiments in a wide variety of fields into a coherent and comprehensive *modern* theory of evolution. For the reader who may have browsed widely in the literature of evolution and who may have become bewildered by continuing divergences of opinion, here is a touchstone: *I think it fair to say that no discussion of evolutionary theory need now be taken seriously if it does not reflect knowledge of these studies.*[7]

What Simpson is saying is that an accurate knowledge of population genetics—of the *"modern theory of evolution"*—is presupposed to any intelligent discussion of evolution today. Arguments about evolution that do not take the new view into account can still be heard. They may be interesting, but they do not belong to philosophy of science in the sense in which it is taken here.

In addition to these four areas of scientific fact and theory, scientific method itself is a subject of philosophical debate. In one sense, there is no such thing as *a* scientific method (in the singular)—the methods and procedures of the various sciences are all different. They differ even in different parts of the same science. Such variety, however, does not prevent philosophers from speaking of a basic model of scientific thinking found as a theme running throughout all the differences of special methods. It is the so-called "hypothetico-deductive method," commonly summed up in terms of four steps: *observation* of facts, *hypotheses* (entertained tentatively at first) to

---

[6] Isaac Asimov, *The New Intelligent Man's Guide to Science*, Basic Books, New York, 1965, p. 323.

[7] G. G. Simpson, *The Meaning of Evolution*, Yale, New Haven, Conn., 1949, pp. 225–226 (italics added).

explain the facts, *predictions* of consequences of the hypotheses which can be experimentally tested, and *verification* of these experimental predictions. Verification *confirms* the hypothesis or theory; falsification obviously eliminates it as a possible explanation.[8] Nearly every major term in this formulation is the subject of debate among philosophers, but the scheme as a whole is accepted in some sense by all. The words "in some sense" are the key: different approaches to science can be distinguished from one another in terms of what they make of the hypothetico-deductive method just as clearly as they can in terms of what they make of the scientific data themselves.

Against this background, it is now possible to give something of the flavor of the three approaches—logical empiricist, historical, and Aristotelian—in terms of some chief problems to which they address themselves.

### Logical Empiricism

The philosophers who can today be rather loosely grouped as "logical empiricists" trace their origin to the much more tightly knit group of the famous Vienna Circle (1929). As the philosophers of the original circle moved to America, during the rise of Nazism, the tone of the group changed to suit their new intellectual climate. From a rigid exclusivism with respect to all traditional philosophical problems, judged "nonsense" in terms of the criterion of "verifiability," the empiricists softened their approach, spoke of confirmation rather than verification, and gradually became more and more tolerant of traditional problems of philosophy—though always treating them in terms of logic and empiricism. Today an empiricist like Ernest Nagel can be quite tolerant in his attitude toward nonempiricists and quite broad in the topics he thinks worthy of logical-empiricist discussion. And he is not untypical of present-day philosophers of science who espouse a general logical-empiricist view.

The greatest of the philosophers holding such a view, and the most influential, is undoubtedly Ludwig Wittgenstein. It is tempting, then, to think of describing the typical problems of logical empiricism through a presentation of Wittgenstein's views. Wittgenstein is, however, a very difficult thinker, his approaches are markedly different in the early *Tractatus Logico-Philosophicus* and the later *Philosophical Investigations*, and his influence has been greater on general analytic philosophy than specifically on the analysis of science.

There are, however, two thinkers who represent the logical-empiricist view in its purest form—Rudolf Carnap and Carl Hempel. By considering some of the key problems to which they have devoted their attention, we can get a very good picture of typical logical empiricist concerns. Fortunately, two collections

[8] For an excellent, more detailed summary, which is still modestly introduced as "merely a [mnemonic] device that may be helpful in thinking about some recurring and related features of scientific procedure," cf. G. Holton and D. Roller, *Foundations of Modern Physical Science*, Addison-Wesley, Reading, Mass., 1958, pp. 252–257.

of their discussions have recently been published which make excellent source materials for anyone who wants to follow up these discussions in detail. They are: Carl G. Hempel, *Philosophy of Natural Science*, Prentice-Hall, Englewood Cliffs, 1966; and Rudolf Carnap, *Philosophical Foundations of Physics: An Introduction to the Philosophy of Science*, Martin Gardner (ed.), Basic Books, New York, 1966.

Four key problems can be mentioned here:

1. *"The theoretician's dilemma"*   This extremely difficult problem, often associated with an article by Hempel of the same name, has to do with the relation between theoretical and observational terms in a scientific explanation. It can be summarized in this way:

> One of the chief motivations behind the attempt to defend a distinction between theoretical and observational terms has been the desire to explain how a theory can be tested against the data of experience, and how one theory can be said to "account for the facts" better than another; that is, to give a precise characterization of the idea, almost universally accepted in modern times, that the sciences are "based on experience," that they are "empirical."[9]

This problem was perhaps the single most vexing source of controversy in the early days of logical empiricism because of the fundamental character of the issues involved. On the one hand, there was the desire to be empirical; on the other hand, there was the undoubted fact that science does use such unverifiable theoretical terms as "inertia." How can such terms be reduced to the data of experience?

Logic offers the most obvious solution, through the *translatability* of theoretical and observational terms (preferably with the observational terms as "primitives"). This leads directly to the paradox. Translation would be effected by a *logical equivalence* between two sets of terms; but, by clear rules of mathematical logic, this leads to the embarrassing consequence that the equivalence remains true *even if the datum described by an observational term is not observed.* Thus nonobservation seems to support theoretical terms equally as well as observation!

This obviously will not do for an empiricist, and many solutions of the difficulty have been proposed. Carnap, for instance, suggested restricting the translatability, i.e., he suggested a "partial interpretation" of theoretical terms. (Symbolically, this would be done by rearranging the logical equivalence.) Whatever the solution, however, it is obviously a thorny problem for one who wants at the same time to be empirical and to apply logic to the analysis of science.

2. *"Lawlike statements"*   Granted that theoretical terms can somehow be based on or related to observations, there remains a problem for the logical empiricist about the logical status of laws or theories. How are they to be

[9] Shapere, *op. cit.*, p. 15.

analyzed in logical terms? And more particularly, how are we to distinguish between statements that are admissible as laws or theories in science and those that are not?

The problem is a problem for the logical empiricist chiefly because he would want to associate his views with the historical empiricism of someone like Hume. In such a view it is difficult to justify at all the universal and supratemporal character of law statements as they are used in science. Furthermore, once the difficulty is gotten round—usually by reducing law statements to functional universal correlations of terms in a nonfinite class—there remains the further difficulty of distinguishing, logically, between "lawlike" universal conjunctions and those that are not.

One common response is the following:

> I shall call statements of the first type "law statements" and statements of the second type "nonlaw statements." Both law and nonlaw statements may be expressed in the general form, "for every x, if x is S, x is P." Law statements, unlike nonlaw statements, seem to warrant inference to statements of the form, "If a, which is not S, were S, a would be P" and "For every x, if x were S, x would be P."[10]

This is the "problem of counterfactual conditionals," and both Hempel and Carnap (as well as most other logical empiricists) have devoted much attention to it. The most obvious example of a counterfactual formulation of a scientific theory is the law of inertia, but it will be immediately apparent to anyone who accepts the hypothetico-deductive formulation of scientific method that a great many scientific theories have something like the counterfactual logical structure. Yet as the controversies show, not all agree on how such counterfactuals are to be interpreted.

*3. "Explanation-prediction symmetry"*   Apart from problems of fact and theory, logical empiricists are much concerned with problems of scientific explanation. Most of the recent problems derive from what has become the classical logical formulation of the explanation structure—the so-called "covering-law" model of Hempel and Paul Oppenheim. The problem here is not the model; most philosophers of science accept it in some form. The problem is, rather, that the model seems to imply that explanation is logically the same as prediction of an event after the fact, and prediction is simply explanation before the fact. Such, however, would be quite a paradox for an empiricist, for it would imply that, given suitable initial laws and conditions, future discoveries of science could be anticipated and even predicted.

As a response to the problem, some authors attempted to deny the symmetry, others restricted the scope of this type of explanation. Hempel himself

[10] R. M. Chisholm, "Law Statements and Counterfactual Inference," in E. Madden (ed.), *The Structure of Scientific Thought*, Houghton Mifflin, Boston, 1960, p. 229.

clarifies and amends his position as a result of these controversies in a "Postscript to Studies in the Logic of Explanation."[11]

4. *"The problem of confirmation"* As a final typical concern of logical empiricism, we can list here the modern version of the old logical positivism "verifiability" controversy—i.e., granting the structure of the hypothetico-deductive method, how can we say that a theory in science is ever truly verified? The general answer is, of course, that we cannot, and logical empiricists now speak rather of *confirmation* than of verification.

In spite of this general tendency to agree on the use of terms, however, many problems remain. The most fundamental are associated with the names of Hempel and Carnap—namely, Hempel's work on problems of confirmation, and Carnap's attempt to give confirmation a strict interpretation by way of the theory of probability. The former includes a great deal of discussion on the so-called "paradoxes of confirmation" (most formulations end up confirming too much or not enough); the latter includes a vast modern literature on the "problem of induction."

These brief references to a vast literature, however inadequate because of their brevity, do serve to indicate the kinds of problems with which logical empiricists are concerned. They also indicate how rigorously connected most of the problems are with empiricism and with logical analysis.

## Historical Approaches

Although the logical approach is most common today in philosophy of science, it does have its challengers. And the best responses to logical empiricism in recent years have come from the quarter of history of science. Among the critics of empiricism, Michael Polanyi is the most radical; he takes his stand on a "subjective" or "personal" interpretation of science, opposing his view to the traditional glorification of scientific objectivity. He feels that the historical approaches of Hanson and Kuhn (mentioned earlier), as well as the approaches of Stephen Toulmin, J. Bronowski, and Gerald Holton, are basically similar to his own view.

This may in fact be so, but for the present we shall limit this introduction to the strictly historical approach. It needs to be complemented by the discovery approach of Hanson (and the need for completion will be duly noted), but the emphasis will be on Thomas Kuhn as the best contemporary exponent of an anti-empiricist, historically grounded interpretation of science.

Kuhn introduces his essay as follows:

> History, if viewed as a repository for more than anecdote or chronology, could produce a decisive transformation in the image of science by

---

[11] C. Hempel, *Aspects of Scientific Explanation and Other Essays in the Philosophy of Science*, Free Press, New York, 1965, pp. 291–295.

> which we are now possessed. That image has previously been drawn, even by scientists themselves, mainly from the study of finished scientific achievements as these are recorded in the classics and, more recently, in the textbooks from which each new scientific generation learns to practice its trade. . . . This essay attempts to show that we have been misled by them in fundamental ways. Its aim is a sketch of the quite different concept of science that can emerge from the historical record of the research activity itself.[12]

Kuhn then, immediately, points out two preliminary and key notions that some historians of science have discovered:

> The more carefully they study, say, Aristotelian dynamics, phlogistic chemistry, or caloric thermodynamics, the more certain they feel that those once current views of nature were, as a whole, neither less scientific nor more the product of human idiosyncracy than those current today. (p. 2)

And:

> What differentiated these various schools was not one or another failure of method—they were all "scientific"—but what we shall come to call their incommensurable ways of seeing the world and of practicing science in it. (p. 4)

Kuhn is explicit in his opposition to the logical-empiricist ideal; he intends his central concept of revolutions in science to be itself revolutionary in the interpretation of science. Opposition is expressed to "the most prevalent contemporary interpretation" of science, and to the logical-empiricist "philosopher's inquiry about the testing, verification, or falsification of established scientific theories."

One of his most basic conceptions is that "scientific fact and theory are not categorically separable," that in the revolutionary transition from one "paradigm-based" scientific tradition to another the very empirical data themselves are "incommensurable." Obviously, a key to the understanding of Kuhn is what he means by a "paradigm-based scientific tradition."

Kuhn explains his crucial term *paradigm* historically, maintaining that pre-Galilean science (which he recognizes to be truly scientific, though in a restricted sense) is distinguished from that after Galileo largely on the basis of the absence and presence of a paradigm. This he defines as "an achievement . . . sufficiently unprecedented to attract an enduring group of adherents away from competing modes of scientific activity. Simultaneously, it [must be] sufficiently open-ended to leave all sorts of problems for the redefined group of practitioners to resolve" (p. 10). Such paradigmatic achievements in science, which are usually a quantitative improvement on their predecessors, give birth to "traditions of scientific research" (p. 11), and include law, theory, instrumentation, and particular facts to work with, all together. A paradigm is

[12] Kuhn, *op. cit.*, p. 1.

thus more of a spirit or *zeitgeist* of experimental research than merely a new theory to be elaborated and reconciled with older theories.

Given these preliminaries, Kuhn's overall view can now be rather briefly summarized. A particular science, he would say, can be in one of two states—normal or crisis. Before the establishment of a paradigm, a science must be by definition in a crisis state; once one is found, "normal science" can begin. This rather closely approximates what we normally think of as science, but according to Kuhn it is to be thought of as "puzzle solving"—essentially a mopping-up operation, according to strict rules like those of a puzzle or game, with respect to the problems left over by the paradigm. These operations are usually of three kinds: determination of which facts are significant, explanation of the facts in terms of the theory or theories associated with the paradigm, and further extension of theory.

Puzzle solving, however, is not the whole of normal science. For such science must inevitably (at least according to patterns thus far historically apparent) generate crises which equally inevitably lead to progress through revolution. The very rigidity of the rules of puzzle solving and the ingenuity engendered in scientists force them to the discovery of anomalies and the invention of new theories in the face of anomaly-induced crisis. When things reach a state of complete breakdown, the stage is set for revolutionary advance.

In the real heart of the essay—the sections on scientific revolution proper (IX-X)—Kuhn insists that the history of science demands the rejection of the positivist interpretation according to which later scientific theories are seen as either logically including or excluding earlier theories—a "cumulative" view of scientific progress (pp. 95–97). This must be rejected, he maintains, in favor of a view that would interpret theories in terms of the struggle from which they emerge.

> The remainder of this essay aims to demonstrate that the historical study of paradigm change reveals very similar characteristics in the evolution of the sciences. Like the choice between competing political institutions, that between competing paradigms proves to be a choice between incompatible modes of community life. . . . Each group uses its own paradigm to argue in that paradigm's defense.
> The resulting circularity does not, of course, make the argument wrong or ineffectual. . . . Yet, whatever its force, the status of the circular argument is only that of persuasion. It cannot be made logically or even probabilistically compelling. (p. 93)

There is a point to criticize here in Kuhn's exposition (in addition to the many points of difference logical empiricists would attack); it is the view that the arguments involved in major scientific advances are mere "persuasion." Other authors, notably Hanson, while recognizing the difficulty in categorizing such arguments, would maintain that discovery, and scientific breakthroughs in terms of ongoing research, can be formulated—even in a *logic* of discovery.

This latter point has been one of Hanson's main contentions in a long series of articles. The least that can be said here is that, if there are aspects of science that have been missed by logical empiricism, then surely discovery is one of them, and very likely the most important one. If a logic of discovery is not possible, then at least some formulation of the actual thinking processes of creative scientists is worth philosophical investigation (with the help of the history, psychology, and sociology of science).

## Aristotelian Natural Philosophy

The third of the possible approaches to a philosophy of science course is that of traditional Aristotelian natural philosophy.[13] As mentioned, it is an approach that is frankly realist in its belief that science gives true knowledge of the world and its belief that there are absolutes even in scientific research.

For the most part the view is dismissed by other philosophers of science as hopelessly naïve. Yet the view does have defenders. One of the most interesting is John Herman Randall, Jr. In a selection included in Chapter 1, Randall claims that the present state of physical theory (after Einstein) can best be explained in Aristotelian terms—although this state of affairs, he adds, "is mostly unrealized."

> Then, in the twentieth century, the physicists themselves found their billiard balls, the Newtonian mass-particles following the simple laws of molar masses, dissolving into complex functional systems of radiant energy. They discovered that the subject matter of physics itself must be treated in functional and contextual terms, in terms of concepts appropriate to "the field." And what this means is that in his basic concepts the physicist himself must think like the biologist.
>
> Today, the concepts of Aristotle's physics, those notions involved in his analysis of process, have been driving those of Newton out of our theory. That our revolution in physical theory can be so stated is mostly unrealized; but it is often explicitly recognized that the ideas of Aristotle's physics are far closer to present-day physical theory than are the ideas of the nineteenth century.[14]

Randall is obviously referring here to the basic "process philosophy" of Aristotle's *Physics*, and not to the archaic science of the *De caelo*. And even here there is exaggeration, for, while Aristotle's views are intended to describe *things as they are*, post-Einsteinian physics remains a highly abstract *theory*. Nevertheless, Aristotle's view does remain a perennially possible option in the interpretation of knowledge of the world. This "realist option" can be sum-

---

[13] There are other realist approaches, of course, but none of these has as widespread an influence as that of Aristotelian natural philosophy in Catholic schools. There are, in addition, many versions of Aristotle. For discussional purposes a single version is best, and the one preferred here is that of John Herman Randall, Jr.

[14] J. Randall, *Aristotle*, Columbia, New York, 1960, pp. 166–167.

marized in terms of three basic questions faced by Aristotle himself, as well as the implications of the answers he gave.

1. What makes a *changeable being* be what it is?

Various answers had been given to this question by the ancients—most of them difficult for us to understand today. Aristotle was one of the first to treat the question critically, and all that he accepted from his predecessors was their general consensus that the changeable world can be explained by a basic "stuff" with contrary qualities.

Aristote based his own answer on the existence and various types of change:

> Accidental change: local, qualitative, or vital; and
> Substantial change (such as death or corruption)

His whole conception of the changeable world was based on an attempt to safeguard the reality of substantial change. Arguing from a comparison with artificial changes (such as that of molding clay into a statue) he said that beings are made up of a material element capable of receiving a form, and the form received. To account for substantial change, the material element must be conceived as pure capacity for forms, nothing more: It is that aspect of a being that allows it to be able to change into something else substantially different. It is not a physical, real material element, as in the case of accidental or artificial changes. Thus it cannot be equated with atoms, but is something more radical, something that can only be conceived by the mind—the mere possibility of receiving forms (*both* the one it has in an individual being and the forms that that being can turn into), including the form of an atom. (This material element is called *primary matter,* because it is the most radical kind of material out of which things are made.)

Modern science for the most part does not take this factor into consideration; it has no need to. It has chosen to limit itself to the quantitative aspect of things, and this is satisfactorily explained on the assumption of atoms. Yet the modern scientist does accept the difference between accidental chemical changes (mixtures, for instance) and true substantial changes (those that yield genuine chemical compounds), and thus he implicitly recognizes that the elements of a compound include in their makeup the possibility of entering into the compound—a possibility that is there both before and after the change (in the latter case as *realized*). Hence the scientist implicitly and on a commonsense basis admits something very like primary matter.

In order, however, that *matter* and *form* not be conceived in too naïve a fashion, it is best to avoid thinking of them except in terms of the next question.

2. What is *nature?*

Basing his view on common language usage and a contrast with artificial things, Aristotle arrived at a definition of nature as "the intrinsic principle or cause of change and rest that belongs to a thing essentially." Translating this into more modern terminology, we might restate the definition: nature is the condition of the possibility of change (or rest) which belongs to a thing essentially. As such it is an entirely relative term: Nature cannot exist without change (or rest) and change cannot exist without nature.

Accordingly, the best definition of *primary matter* would be: It is the condition of the possibility of substantial change (which remains in a thing even after the change is over)—it is thus the principle of corruption in things. *Form,* on the other hand, is the condition of the possibility of the accidental changes (and of all the characteristics presupposed by or acquired by means of these changes) *which are peculiar to each type of thing*—it is thus the principle of stability in a thing explaining what a thing is and why it stays as it is as long as possible.[15]

3. What is *change*?

To answer this question Aristotle had to fall back on some very difficult language—the definition must reflect the dynamic character of change and yet it cannot use words that simply say, circularly, that "change is change." The definition that Aristotle gave is that change is the (continuous) actualization of a potential precisely insofar as it is potential. The last phrase is the key one, and it indicates that the actualization is not complete but still in the process of completion—it is on the way, so to speak, to a term or goal.

This definition immediately suggests a connection with matter and form, as possibilities (potentials) for change. Change is, in fact, nothing more than the actualization of the capacity of a thing to change—almost so obvious that it does not need saying. Yet it is important, for it implies that every material being will have a specific type of change in accord with its form *which must be found with that being in some way.* (Any other changes it has will be artificial—results of and built upon its natural changes.)

4. Implications and the foundations of the special sciences:

The principal implication of this view is that Aristotle's world is dynamic through and through. There is no possibility of conceiving the world, as Newton did, as a gigantic clock that God first created and then set in motion. Material beings simply cannot exist without the natural changes that belong to them.

A second implication is that the world is an interrelated system of bodies all acting on one another and each carrying out its assigned role in the whole —there is no place for a vacuum or empty space between bodies: they always extend as far as the next body so that the two can act on one another in accord with the role of each. Thus each natural being has its natural place in

---

[15] Aristotle and the scholastics have, of course, said many other very technical things about matter and form—and these are not necessarily being opposed. What is being suggested is merely that we make as sure as possible that these constituents not be reified as if they were things in themselves.

its own system, and it will either move to that place or resist being moved from it. A modern version of this notion would yield a realist explanation of gravity, and a realist would say that the so-called "force of gravity" is merely a very helpful theoretical construct to explain the quantitative effects of natural local motion.

Two other implications follow. Within a molecule or *chemical* compound the atoms that make it up must be considered as parts of a new system, and not the same as in the free state. Their natural changes are now subordinated to (and help explain) the natural changes that belong to the whole compound. Again in *biology* the important factor is the functional role a part plays in the organism or the organism plays in its environment—Aristotle would have been impatient with any final causality outside things; for him "purpose" meant a functional role in a particular process, especially the functional structure or adaptation aimed at by a given process.

These three conceptions—natural local motion, natural chemical change, and functional processes in biology—are for Aristotle the foundations of a realist interpretation of the special sciences of physics, chemistry, and the life sciences.

As a final note to end this Introduction, I would like to cite a remarkably balanced statement of Hanson on alternative approaches to the interpretation of science. Hanson can be caustic in his denunciation of the logical-empiricist approach, but in this case he speaks eloquently for the fact that there is truth in more than one approach. (Such an attitude should be borne in mind in all the discussions to follow.)

> Activities on the scientific battleground are of many different kinds. Some scholar could be interested in studying the attitudes of researchers before and while winning scientific encounters. Such a scholar would be concerned with the psychology of discovery—as were Wertheimer, Hadamard, and Polya. The thought processes of discoverers would be the focus here. Or perhaps it is the rational strategies invoked during such encounters that capture the imagination of philosophers. Contributors to this area of inquiry would be Toulmin, Peirce, and Whewell, among others. "Good reasons for entertaining as-yet-unestablished hypotheses" would be the watchword here. Still others will address the necessity of coming to understand what conceptual moves must be made in order for the scientific terrain, once achieved, to be related and integrated with the larger logical geography of the scientific enterprise. Such scholars will set out the logical justification for such new territories being adjudged properly acquired, with claims on them fully and justifiably established. "The logical underpinning of scientific knowledge" is the motto here. In this department of inquiry names like those of Carnap, Tarski, Reichenbach, and Hempel are the ones to be reckoned with. And this comports well with *dramatis personae* within the scientific epic itself. There are those whose discoveries came in a flood of inspiration—the Rutherfords, the Poincarés, the Kékulés, and the Keplers. There are also those whose

unprecedented work at the frontiers was suported by brow-breaking initial arguments of considerable cogency—the Clerk Maxwells, the Newtons, and the Galileos. And, finally, there are those whose great and necessary contributions consisted in fortifying, strengthening, and holding the scientific ground already won by scholars in the vanguard. These are the Eulers, the Laplaces, and the Lagranges.[16]

## BIBLIOGRAPHY

### Standard Texts in Logical Empiricism

Nagel, Ernest: *The Structure of Science,* Harcourt, Brace & World, New York, 1961.

Pap, Arthur: *An Introduction to the Philosophy of Science,* Free Press, New York, 1962.

Scheffler, Israel: *The Anatomy of Inquiry,* Knopf, New York, 1963.

### Anthologies Covering Principal Issues

Danto, Arthur, and Sidney Morgenbesser (eds.): *Philosophy of Science,* Meridian, New York, 1960.

Feigl, Herbert, and May Brodbeck (eds.): *Readings in the Philosophy of Science,* Appleton-Century-Crofts, New York, 1953.

Madden, E. H. (ed.): *The Structure of Scientific Thought,* Houghton Mifflin, Boston, 1960.

### Fundamental Works in the Historical Mode

Hanson, N. R.: *Patterns of Discovery,* Cambridge University Press, London, 1958.

Holton, Gerald, and D. H. D. Roller: *Foundations of Modern Physical Science,* Addison-Wesley, Reading, Mass., 1958, chaps. 8, 13–15.

Kuhn, Thomas S.: *The Structure of Scientific Revolutions,* University of Chicago Press, Phoenix Books, Chicago, 1964.

### Philosophy of Science Texts Sympathetic toward the Historical Approach

Nash, Leonard K.: *The Nature of the Natural Sciences,* Little, Brown, Boston, 1963.

Toulmin, Stephen: *The Philosophy of Science,* Harper & Row, New York, 1960.

### Classics of the Aristotelian Natural Philosophy Tradition

Aristotle: *Physics,* available in several versions: (1) W. D. Ross (ed.): *Aristotle's Physics,* Oxford, London, 1936 (1960), Greek text and commentary that has become standard; (2) Richard McKeon (ed.): *The Basic Works of*

---

16 N. R. Hanson, "A Philosopher's Philosopher of Science," *Science,* vol. 152, p. 193, Apr. 8, 1966. Copyright 1966 by the American Association for the Advancement of Science.

*Aristotle,* Random House, New York, 1941, standard English translation; (3) Richard Hope (trans.): *Aristotle's Physics,* University of Nebraska Press, Lincoln, Nebr., 1961, a new translation.

Aquinas, St. Thomas: *Commentary on Aristotle's Physics,* also available in several versions: (1) P. M. Maggiolo (ed.): *In Octo libros physicorum Aristotelis expositio,* Marietti, Turin, 1954, Latin text; (2) R. J. Blackwell, R. J. Spath, and W. E. Thirlkel (trans.): *Commentary on Aristotle's "Physics,"* Yale, New Haven, Conn., 1963, English translation, complete; (3) J. A. McWilliams: *Physics and Philosophy,* American Catholic Philosophical Association, Washington, D.C., 1945, pp. 53–121, précis.

### Contemporary Proponents of the Aristotelian View

Randall, J. H., Jr.: "The Understanding of Natural Processes," *Aristotle,* Columbia, New York, 1960, chap. 8.

Smith, V. E.: *The General Science of Nature,* Bruce, Milwaukee, 1958.

Solmsen, Friedrich: *Aristotle's System of the Physical World,* Cornell, Ithaca, N.Y., 1960.

Wallace, W. A.: *Einstein, Galileo and Aquinas: Three Views of Scientific Method,* Thomist, Compact Studies, Washington, D.C., 1963.

# Philosophy of Science: An Introduction

Part

# 1

# THE FOUNDATIONS
# OF SCIENCE

# Section

# 1

# MECHANISM, NATURALISM, AND POSITIVISM

ALL THE PROBLEMS TO BE CONSIDERED in this section are reducible to a perennial problem in philosophy—the interpretation of the objects of sensation. How intelligible is the world of the senses?

There are only a limited number of possible answers to this generalized version of the question, "Can the objects of sensation be known as they are?"—"yes" or "no"; if "yes," then the intelligibility must be either *absolute* or *relative*.

A "no" answer to the question of knowing the objects of sensation as they are is the essence of *positivism*. The projection of a simple, absolute intelligibility—say that of mathematics or geometry—onto the physical world is the basic option of *mechanism*. An intermediate answer, affirming a qualified, relative intelligibility of sense objects, is the position of Aristotelian naturalism (so called because the view stands or falls on Aristotle's basic conception of "nature").

The way in which controversies on these questions developed in the ancient, medieval, and modern worlds will be the subject of the three chapters in this section.

# Chapter

# 1

# Mechanism,
# Naturalism, and
# Positivism in the
# Ancient World

AS A BACKGROUND FOR DISCUSSIONS on the foundations of science in the ancient world, the student should consult a good history of Plato's academy. (An excellent one is Friedländer's *Plato: An Introduction*.) It was in that milieu that actual historical discussions of these issues took place.

Especially in Plato's old age, the Academy was an influential intellectual center where the great minds of the age—including Aristotle, the great mathematician Eudoxus, and many others—gathered for discussion. The breadth of interest of these men suggests the breadth of interest of the Academy: classification of plants and animals, foundations of physics and cosmology, spherical geography, and advanced mathematics (all, in Plato's mind, subject to a basic metaphysical and political orientation).

Within the general context of these Platonic discussions, one version of the problem of the intelligibility of sense objects was debated in terms of the question, "Is there any such thing, in the world of our experience, as 'natural change'?" (This would really be an Aristotelian formulation of the question, but it will be seen further on that it allows the best presentation of opposing views.)

The term *change* is used here as a class including *motion* as a subclass, but that does not prejudice the discussion—an ancient atomist would explain other types of change by reducing them to the basic type, motion. The term *natural change* refers to two things: change in accord with the *nature* of a given object, and change as a *function* within a larger system of naturally changing bodies. The entire question, as posed, is intended to leave open the possibility that change may be only an appearance, the question whether we can know the realities underlying change as they really are.

The basic defender of natural change and its knowability is Aristotle. The foundation of his view was experience: We do experience things as changing in accord with their nature—smoke rises, wood is buoyant in water, heavy objects fall toward the earth, iron rusts, and, most obviously, living beings function and generate so regularly in the same way that we interpret any deviation as "freakish" or "monstrous." The selection representing Aristotle's view here is taken from the *Commentary on Aristotle's Physics* of St. Thomas Aquinas, the best known of the medieval interpreters of Aristotle. This selection has been chosen because it shows more clearly than Aristotle himself the logical connections between sections. (These are clearly indicated by headings supplied in the text.)

These logical connections reveal a structure which carries out, to the letter, Aristotle's prescription that the *material definition* of a property is equivalent to a *demonstration* of that property as a necessary characteristic of the subject. This allows St. Thomas to claim that Aristotle has *demonstrated* the necessity of change in accord with the nature of physical objects.

Many objections can be raised against this view. Historically, one of the most persistent has been the rejoinder that, since the essential natures of things are not ordinarily known by us, Aristotle's definition attempts to explain the more known through the less known. The objection, however, is not really very cogent in context, for Aristotle was perfectly well aware of the fact that nature and change are *correlative,* that natures are only known through natural change (as in chemistry, for instance, where we determine the nature of chemical substances through their typical reactions, in qualitative analysis). The selection from Randall, appended to the basic Aristotelian selection, is intended to show that such relative contextual definition is still a valuable tool in science today.

A more cogent objection is that Aristotle's view claims to have *proved* that natures *must* have characteristic changes—in the future as well as in the experienced present and past. For Aristotle, this is an inescapable conclusion if one comprehends his definitions. This is not so obvious for the modern interpreter of science, who may admit that very likely nature *will* always operate in a lawlike way but will resolutely deny that we can prove it *must.* Even in Aristotle's time there were doubting Thomases questioning the certainty of our knowledge of the world. The selection from Plato's *Timaeus* is offered as an example; it places explicit limitations on knowledge of the physical world, calling such knowledge no more than a "likely story." Taylor, in his commentary, sees this as an anticipation of the contemporary scientific attitude.

Opposition can come, moreover, from a different vantage point. Aristotle's view would treat the world of change as *radically potential and relative*—all its intelligibility is found indirectly, through reduction of dynamic potential to its static term, and through reduction of sensible objects to universal categories. The mechanist tends to view all this as very fuzzy indeed. If we know potentiality only in terms of directly intelligible actuality, why bother with potentiality at all? Clear, nonfuzzy intelligibility is the goal here, and the clearest intelligibility to be found in the world is that of mathematics. The most obvious extension of this view is to presume that there are in the world discrete *units of measurement*, and this is the psychologically attractive appeal of atomism, ancient or modern. Though Aristotle was opposed to ancient atomism (since for him there were no indestructible units in the world—all the elements could change into one another), his presentation of their position is the best historical source we have. Heisenberg's essay is added to show something of the perennial appeal of the atomistic idea.

In summary, the discussions of this section revolve around the question, "Is there any such thing, in the world of our experience, as 'natural change'?" The possible answers to the question are "yes" or "no" with respect to the existence of such changes in the world, and if an affirmative answer is given, only "probable" (a "likely story") or "demonstrative" with respect to the logical status of the knowledge of natural change. Atomists deny the existence of natural change, reducing all changes to motion. Aristotelians defend the existence of natural change, and in addition, argue that the knowledge of natural change can be demonstrative. Plato would deny this last point, though he would admit the usefulness of the idea of "natural" changes in his total, organic view of the world; his view is best summed up in his willingness to accept "likely stories" in the interpretation of the world.

## LEUCIPPUS [5th century B.C.] AND DEMOCRITUS [460–370? B.C.][1]

*Aristotle (384–322 B.C.)*

There is, further, another view—that of Leucippus and Democritus of Abdera. . . . The primary masses, according to them, are infinite in number and indivisible in mass: one cannot turn into many nor many into one; and all things are generated by their combination and involution. Now this view in a sense makes things out to be numbers or composed of numbers.

---

[1] Selections from Aristotle on ancient atomism, taken from the works cited after each passage, are from *The Oxford Translation of Aristotle*, by permission of the Clarendon Press, Oxford.

The exposition is not clear, but this is its real meaning. And further, they say that since the atomic bodies differ in shape, and there is an infinity of shapes, there is an infinity of simple bodies. But they have never explained in detail the shapes of the various elements, except so far as to allot the sphere to fire. Air, water, and the rest they distinguished by the relative size of the atom, assuming that the atomic substance was a sort of master-seed for each and every element.

*On the Heavens,* Book III, Chapter 4

Leucippus and his associate Democritus say that the full and the empty are the elements, calling the one being and the other non-being—the full and solid being being, the empty non-being (whence they say being no more is than non-being, because the solid no more is than the empty); and they make these the material causes of things. And as those who make the underlying substance one generate all other things by its modifications, supposing the rare and the dense to be the sources of the modifications, in the same way these philosophers say the differences in the elements are the causes of all other qualities. These differences, they say, are three— shape and order and position. For they say the real is differentiated only by "rhythm" and "inter-contact" and "turning"; and of these rhythm is shape, inter-contact is order, and turning is position; for A differs from N in shape, AN from NA in order, Ⴎ from H in position. The question of movement—whence or how it is to belong to things—these thinkers, like the others, lazily neglected.

*Metaphysics,* Book I, Chapter 4

The most systematic and consistent theory, and one that applied to all bodies, was advanced by Leucippus and Democritus: and, in maintaining it, they took as their starting-point what naturally comes first. . . .

Leucippus thought he had a theory which harmonized with sense-perception and would not abolish either coming-to-be and passing-away or motion and the multiplicity of things—he made these concessions to the facts of perception. On the other hand, he conceded to the Monists that there could be no motion without a void. The result is a theory which he states as follows: "The void is a 'not-being,' and no part of 'what is' is a 'not-being'; for what 'is' in the strict sense of the term is an absolute *plenum.* This *plenum,* however, is not 'one': on the contrary, it is a 'many' infinite in number and invisible owing to the minuteness of their bulk. The 'many' move in the void (for there is a void): and by coming together they produce 'coming-to-be,' while by separating they produce 'passing-away.' Moreover, they act and suffer action wherever they chance to be in contact (for *there* they are not 'one'), and they generate by being put together and becoming intertwined. From the genuinely-one, on the other hand, there never could have come-to-be a multiplicity, nor from the genuinely-many a 'one': that is impossible. But (just as Empedocles and some of the other philosophers say that things suffer action through their pores, so) all 'alteration' and all 'passion' take place in the way that has been explained: breaking-up (i.e. passing-away) is effected by means of the void, and so too is growth—solids creeping in to fill the void places.". . .

Such, approximately, are the current explanations of the manner in which some things "act" while others "suffer action." And as regards the Atomists, it is not only clear what their explanation is: it is also obvious that it follows with tolerable consistency from the assumptions they employ.

*On Generation and Corruption*, Book I, Chapter 8

Does, then, configuration and colour constitute the essence of the various animals and of their several parts?[2] For if so, what Democritus says will be strictly correct. For such appears to have been his notion. At any rate he says that it is evident to every one what form it is that makes the man, seeing that he is recognizable by his shape and colour.

*Parts of Animals*, Book I, Chapter 1

Some have inferred from observation of the sensible world the truth of appearances. For they think that the truth should not be determined by the large or small number of those who hold a belief, and that the same thing is thought sweet by some when they taste it, and bitter by others, so that if all were ill or all were mad, and only two or three were well or sane, these would be thought ill and mad, and not the others.

And again, they say that many of the other animals receive impressions contrary to ours; and that even to the senses of each individual, things do not always seem the same. Which, then, of these impressions are true and which are false is not obvious; for the one set is no more true than the other, but both are alike. And this is why Democritus, at any rate, says that either there is no truth or to us at least it is not evident.

And in general it is because these thinkers suppose knowledge to be sensation, and this to be a physical alteration, that they say that what appears to our senses must be true.

*Metaphysics*, Book IV, Chapter 5

[2] This selection and the next are included to show that Democritus held a relatively consistent atomism, extending it into biology, psychology, and epistemology.

# THE ROOTS OF ATOMIC SCIENCE[1]

*Werner Heisenberg (1901– )*

The concept of the atom goes back much further than the beginning of modern science in the seventeenth century; it has its origin in ancient Greek philosophy and was in that early period the central concept of materialism taught by Leucippus and Democritus. On the other hand, the modern interpretation of atomic events has very little resemblance to genuine materialistic philosophy; in fact, one may say that atomic physics has turned science away from the materialistic trend it had during the nineteenth century. It is therefore interesting to compare the development of Greek philosophy toward the concept of the atom with the present position of this concept in modern physics.

The idea of the smallest, indivisible ultimate building blocks of matter first came up in connection with the elaboration of the concepts of Matter, Being and Becoming which characterized the first epoch of Greek philosophy. This period started in the sixth century B.C. with Thales, the founder of the Milesian school, to whom Aristotle ascribes the statement: "Water is the material cause of all things." This statement, strange as it looks to us, expresses, as Nietzsche has pointed out, three fundamental ideas of philosophy. First, the question as to the material cause of all things; second, the demand that this question be answered in conformity with reason, without resort to myths or mysticism; third, the postulate that ultimately it must be possible to reduce everything to one principle. Thales' statement was the first expression of the idea of a fundamental substance, of which all other things were transient forms. The word "substance" in this connection was certainly in that age not interpreted in the purely material sense which we frequently ascribe to it today. Life was connected with or inherent in this "substance" and Aristotle ascribes to Thales also the statement: All things are full of gods. Still the question was put as to the material cause of all things and it is not difficult to imagine that Thales took his view primarily from meteorological considerations. Of all things we know water can take the most various shapes; it can in the winter take the form of ice and snow, it can change into vapor, and it can form the clouds. It seems to turn into earth where the rivers form their delta, and it can spring from the earth. Water is the condition for life. Therefore, if there was such a fundamental substance, it was natural to think of water first.

The idea of the fundamental substance was then carried further by Anaximander, who was a pupil of Thales and lived in the same town.

[1] From Werner Heisenberg, *Physics and Philosophy*, Harper & Row, New York, 1958, pp. 59–69; 73–75. Copyright © 1958 by Werner Heisenberg. Reprinted by permission of Harper & Row, Publishers. For a treatment of Heisenberg's philosophy, cf. Patrick Heelan, *Quantum Mechanics and Objectivity: A Study of the Physical Philosophy of Werner Heisenberg*, Nijhoff, The Hague, 1965.

Anaximander denied the fundamental substance to be water or any of the known substances. He taught that the primary substance was infinite, eternal and ageless and that it encompassed the world. This primary substance is transformed into the various substances with which we are familiar. Theophrastus quotes from Anaximander: "Into that from which things take their rise they pass away once more, as is ordained, for they make reparation and satisfaction to one another for their injustice according to the ordering of time." In this philosophy the antithesis of Being and Becoming plays the fundamental role. The primary substance, infinite and ageless, the undifferentiated Being, degenerates into the various forms which lead to endless struggles. The process of Becoming is considered as a sort of debasement of the infinite Being—a distintegration into the struggle ultimately expiated by a return into that which is without shape or character. The struggle which is meant here is the opposition between hot and cold, fire and water, wet and dry, etc. The temporary victory of the one over the other is the injustice for which they finally make reparation in the ordering of time. According to Anaximander, there is "eternal motion," the creation and passing away of worlds from infinity to infinity.

It may be interesting to notice at this point that the problem—whether the primary substance can be one of the known substances or must be something essentially different—occurs in a somewhat different form in the most modern part of atomic physics. The physicists today try to find a fundamental law of motion for matter from which all elementary particles and their properties can be derived mathematically. This fundamental equation of motion may refer either to waves of a known type, to proton and meson waves, or to waves of an essentially different character which have nothing to do with any of the known waves or elementary particles. In the first case it would mean that all other elementary particles can be reduced in some way to a few sorts of "fundamental" elementary particles; actually theoretical physics has during the past two decades mostly followed this line of research. In the second case all different elementary particles could be reduced to some universal substance which we may call energy or matter, but none of the different particles could be preferred to the others as being more fundamental. The latter view of course corresponds to the doctrine of Anaximander, and I am convinced that in modern physics this view is the correct one. But let us return to Greek philosophy.

The third of the Milesian philosophers, Anaximenes, an associate of Anaximander, taught that air was the primary substance. "Just as our soul, being air, holds us together, so do breath and air encompass the whole world." Anaximenes introduced into the Milesian philosophy the idea that the process of condensation or rarefaction causes the change of the primary substance into the other substances. The condensation of water vapor into clouds was an obvious example, and of course the difference between water vapor and air was not known at that time.

In the philosophy of Heraclitus of Ephesus the concept of Becoming occupies the foremost place. He regarded that which moves, the fire, as the basic element. The difficulty, to reconcile the idea of one fundamental principle with the infinite variety of phenomena, is solved for him by recognizing that the strife of the opposites is really a kind of harmony. For Heraclitus the world is at once one and many, it is just "the opposite tension" of the opposites that constitutes the unity of the One. He says: "We must know that war is common to all and strife is justice, and that all things come into being and pass away through strife."

Looking back to the development of Greek philosophy up to this point one realizes that it has been borne from the beginning to this stage by the tension between the One and the Many. For our senses the world consists of an infinite variety of things and events, colors and sounds. But in order to understand it we have to introduce some kind of order, and order means to recognize what is equal, it means some sort of unity. From this springs the belief that there is one fundamental principle, and at the same time the difficulty to derive from it the infinite variety of things. That there should be a material cause for all things was a natural starting point since the world consists of matter. But when one carried the idea of fundamental unity to the extreme one came to that infinite and eternal undifferentiated Being which, whether material or not, cannot in itself explain the infinite variety of things. This leads to the antithesis of Being and Becoming and finally to the solution of Heraclitus, that the change itself is the fundamental principle; the "imperishable change, that renovates the world," as the poets have called it. But the change in itself is not a material cause and therefore is represented in the philosophy of Heraclitus by the fire as the basic element, which is both matter and a moving force.

We may remark at this point that modern physics is in some way extremely near to the doctrines of Heraclitus. If we replace the word "fire" by the word "energy" we can almost repeat his statements word for word from our modern point of view. Energy is in fact the substance from which all elementary particles, all atoms and therefore all things are made, and energy is that which moves. Energy is a substance, since its total amount does not change, and the elementary particles can actually be made from this substance as is seen in many experiments on the creation of elementary particles. Energy can be changed into motion, into heat, into light and into tension. Energy may be called the fundamental cause for change in the world. But this comparison of Greek philosophy with the ideas of modern science will be discussed later.[2]

---

[2] See Chapter 4, the selection from Heisenberg, below.

Greek philosophy returned for some time to the concept of the One in the teachings of Parmenides, who lived in Elea in the south of Italy. His most important contribution to Greek thinking was, perhaps, that he introduced a purely logical argument into metaphysics. "One cannot know what is not—that is impossible—nor utter it; for it is the same thing that can be thought and that can be." Therefore, only the One is, and there is no becoming or passing away. Parmenides denied the existence of empty space for logical reasons. Since all change requires empty space, as he assumed, he dismissed change as an illusion.

But philosophy could not rest for long on this paradox. Empedocles, from the south coast of Sicily, changed for the first time from monism to a kind of pluralism. To avoid the difficulty that one primary substance cannot explain the variety of things and events, he assumed four basic elements, earth, water, air and fire. The elements are mixed together and separated by the action of Love and Strife. Therefore, these latter two, which are in many ways treated as corporeal like the other four elements, are responsible for the imperishable change. Empedocles describes the formation of the world in the following picture: First, there is the infinite Sphere of the One, as in the philosophy of Parmenides. But in the primary substance all the four "roots" are mixed together by Love. Then, when Love is passing out and Strife coming in, the elements are partially separated and partially combined. After that the elements are completely separated and Love is outside the World. Finally, Love is bringing the elements together again and Strife is passing out, so that we return to the original Sphere.

This doctrine of Empedocles represents a very definite turning toward a more materialistic view in Greek philosophy. The four elements are not so much fundamental principles as real material substances. Here for the first time the idea is expressed that the mixture and separation of a few substances, which are fundamentally different, explains the infinite variety of things and events. Pluralism never appeals to those who are wont to think in fundamental principles. But it is a reasonable kind of compromise, which avoids the difficulty of monism and allows the establishment of some order.

The next step toward the concept of the atom was made by Anaxagoras, who was a contemporary of Empedocles. He lived in Athens about thirty years, probably in the first half of the fifth century B.C. Anaxagoras stresses the idea of the mixture, the assumption that all change is caused by mixture and separation. He assumes an infinite variety of infinitely small "seeds," of which all things are composed. The seeds do not refer to the four elements of Empedocles, there are innumerably many different seeds. But the seeds are mixed together and separated again and in this way all change is brought about. The doctrine of

Anaxagoras allows for the first time a geometrical interpretation of the term "mixture": Since he speaks of the infinitely small seeds, their mixture can be pictured as the mixture between two kinds of sand of different colors. The seeds may change in number and in relative position. Anaxagoras assumes that all seeds are in everything, only the proportion may change from one thing to another. He says: "All things will be in everything; nor is it possible for them to be apart, but all things have a portion of everything." The universe of Anaxagoras is set in motion not by Love and Strife, like that of Empedocles, but by "Nous," which we may translate as "Mind."

From this philosophy it was only one step to the concept of the atom, and this step occurred with Leucippus and Democritus of Abdera. The antithesis of Being and Non-being in the philosophy of Parmenides is here secularized into the antithesis of the "Full" and the "Void." Being is not only One, it can be repeated an infinite number of times. This is the atom, the indivisible smallest unit of matter. The atom is eternal and indestructible, but it has a finite size. Motion is made possible through the empty space between the atoms. Thus for the first time in history there was voiced the idea of the existence of smallest ultimate particles —we would say of elementary particles, as the fundamental building blocks of matter.

According to this new concept of the atom, matter did not consist only of the "Full," but also of the "Void," of the empty space in which the atoms move. The logical objection of Parmenides against the Void, that not-being cannot exist, was simply ignored to comply with experience. From our modern point of view we would say that the empty space between the atoms in the philosophy of Democritus was not nothing; it was the carrier for geometry and kinematics, making possible the various arrangements and movements of atoms. But the possibility of empty space has always been a controversial problem in philosophy. In the theory of general relativity the answer is given that geometry is produced by matter or matter by geometry. This answer corresponds more closely to the view held by many philosophers that space is defined by the extension of matter. But Democritus clearly departs from this view, to make change and motion possible.

The atoms of Democritus were all of the same substance, which had the property of being, but had different sizes and different shapes. They were pictured therefore as divisible in a mathematical but not in a physical sense. The atoms could move and could occupy different positions in space. But they had no other physical properties. They had neither color nor smell nor taste. The properties of matter which we perceive by our senses were supposed to be produced by the movements and positions of the atoms in space. Just as both tragedy and comedy can be written by using the same letters of the alphabet, the vast variety of events in this world can be realized by the same atoms through their different arrangements and movements. Geometry and kinematics, which were made possible by the void, proved to be still more important in some way than pure being. Democritus is quoted to have said: "A thing merely appears to have color, it merely appears to be sweet or bitter. Only atoms and empty space have a real existence."

The atoms in the philosophy of Leucippus do not move merely by chance. Leucippus seems to have believed in complete determinism, since he is known to have said: "Naught happens for nothing, but everything from a ground and of necessity." The atomists did not give any reason for the original motion of the atoms, which just shows that they thought of a causal description of the atomic motion; causality can only explain later events by earlier events, but it can never explain the beginning.

The basic ideas of atomic theory were taken over and modified, in part, by later Greek philosophers. For the sake of comparison with modern atomic physics it is important to mention the explanation of matter given by Plato in his dialogue *Timaeus*. Plato was not an atomist: on the contrary, Diogenes Laertius reported that Plato disliked Democritus so much that he wished all his books to be burned. But Plato combined ideas that were near to atomism with the doctrines of the Pythagorean school and the teachings of Empedocles.

The Pythagorean school was an offshoot of Orphism, which goes back to the worship of Dionysus. Here has been established the connection between religion and mathematics which ever since has exerted the strongest influence on human thought. The Pythagoreans seem to have been the first to realize the creative force inherent in mathematical formulations. Their discovery that two strings sound in harmony if their lengths are in a simple ratio demonstrated how much mathematics can mean for the understanding of natural phenomena. For the Pythagoreans it was not so much a question of understanding. For them the simple mathematical ratio between the length of the strings *created* the harmony in sound. There was also much mysticism in the doctrines of the Pythagorean school which for us is difficult to understand. But by making mathematics a part of their religion they touched an essential point in the development of human thought. I may quote a statement by Bertrand Russell about Pythagoras: "I do not know of any other man who has been as influential as he was in the sphere of thought."

Plato knew of the discovery of the regular solids made by the Pythagoreans and of the possibility of combining them with the elements of Empedocles. He compared the smallest parts of the element earth with the cube, of air with the octahedron, of fire with the tetrahedron, and of water with the icosahedron. There is no element that corresponds to the dodecahedron; here Plato only says "there was yet a fifth combination which God used in the delineation of the universe."

If the regular solids, which represent the four elements, can be compared with the atoms at all, it is made clear by Plato that they are not indivisible. Plato constructs the regular solids from two basic triangles, the equilateral and the isosceles triangles, which are put together to form the surface of the solids. Therefore, the elements can (at least partly) be transformed into each other. The regular solids can be taken apart into their triangles and new regular solids can be formed of them. For instance, one tetrahedron and two octahedra can be taken apart into twenty equilateral triangles, which can be recombined to give one icosahedron. That means: one atom of fire and two atoms of air can be combined to give one atom of water. But the fundamental triangles cannot be considered as matter, since they have no extension in space. It is only when the triangles are put together to form a regular solid that a unit of matter is created. The smallest parts of matter are not the fundamental Beings, as in the philosophy of Democritus, but are mathematical forms. Here it is quite evident that the form is more important than the substance of which it is the form.

After this short survey of Greek philosophy up to the formation of the concept of the atom we may come back to modern physics and ask how our modern views on the atom and on quantum theory compare with this ancient development. Historically the word "atom" in modern physics and chemistry was referred to the wrong object, during the revival of science in the seventeenth century, since the smallest particles belonging to what is called a chemical element are still rather complicated systems of smaller units. These smaller units are nowadays called elementary particles, and it is obvious that if anything in modern physics should be compared with the atoms of Democritus it should be the elementary particles like proton, neutron, electron, meson. . . .

We may add an argument at this point concerning a question which is frequently asked by laymen with respect to the concept of the elementary particle in modern physics: Why do the physicists claim that their elementary particles cannot be divided into smaller bits? The answer to this question clearly shows how much more abstract modern science is as compared to Greek philosophy. The argument runs like this: How could one divide an elementary particle? Certainly only by using extreme forces and very sharp tools. The only tools available are other elementary particles. Therefore, collisions between two elementary particles of extremely high energy would be the only processes by which the particles could eventually be divided. Actually they can be divided in such processes, sometimes into very many fragments; but the fragments are again elementary particles, not any smaller pieces of them, the masses of these fragments resulting from the very large kinetic energy of the two colliding particles. In other words, the transmutation of energy into matter makes it possible that the fragments of elementary particles are again the same elementary particles.

After this comparison of the modern views in atomic physics with Greek philosophy we have to add a warning, that this comparison should not be misunderstood. It may seem at first sight that the Greek philosophers have by some kind of ingenious intuition come to the same or very similar conclusions as we have in modern times only after several centuries of hard labor with experiments and mathematics. This interpretation of our comparison would, however, be a complete misunderstanding. There is an enormous difference between modern science and Greek philosophy, and that is just the empiristic attitude of modern science. Since the time of Galileo and Newton, modern science has been based upon a detailed study of nature and upon the postulate that only such statements should be made, as have been verified or at least can be verified by experiment. The idea that one could single out some events from nature by an experiment, in order to study the details and to find out what is the constant law in the continuous change, did not occur to the Greek philosophers. Therefore, modern science has from its beginning stood upon a much more modest, but at the same time much firmer, basis than ancient philosophy. Therefore, the statements of modern physics are in some way meant much more seriously than the statements of Greek philosophy. When Plato says, for instance, that the smallest particles of fire are tetrahedrons, it is not quite easy to see what he really means. Is the form of the tetrahedron only symbolically attached to the element fire, or do the smallest particles of fire mechanically act as rigid tetrahedrons or as elastic tetrahedrons, and by what force could they be separated into the equilateral triangles, etc.? Modern science would finally always ask: How can one decide experimentally that the atoms of fire are tetrahedrons and not perhaps cubes? Therefore, when modern science states that the proton is a certain solution of a fundamental equation of matter it means that we can from this solution deduce mathematically all possible properties of the proton and can check the correctness of the solution by experiments in every detail. This possibility of checking the correctness of a statement experimentally with very high precision and in any number of details gives an enormous weight to the statement that could not be attached to the statements of early Greek philosophy.

All the same, some statements of ancient philosophy are rather near to those of modern science. This simply shows how far one can get by combining the ordinary experience of nature that we have without doing experiments with the untiring effort to get some logical order into this experience to understand it from general principles.

# COMMENTARY ON THE EIGHT BOOKS OF ARISTOTLE'S *PHYSICS*: A PRÉCIS[1]

*St. Thomas Aquinas (1225–1274)*

## Book One—PRINCIPLES[2]

LESSON 1. SUBJECT MATTER OF NATURAL SCIENCE

Physics is the study of material substances—not, indeed, in all their aspects, but as subjects of continuous processes, or changes. Now, every organized study starts with certain "principles" determined by the subject-matter under investigation. For physics, the principles are: (a) the constituent elements of which bodies are composed; and (b) the causes involved in continuous processes. A cause is that which is necessary for the production of a thing. Physics has to do with all the causes: the extrinsic (efficient and final); the intrinsic (material and formal). In this, physics differs from metaphysics, which, since it studies substance as such, leaves to physics the study of what is peculiar to material substances. Material things, though the objects of our immediate experience, require the greatest amount of observation and inductive study, before they can be organized into a science.

"Nature" is a principle of activity or change, actual or possible. Thus the material world, where change is most obvious, is called "Nature."

---

[1] This summary is taken from J. A. McWilliams, *Physics and Philosophy: A Study of Saint Thomas' Commentary on the Eight Books of Artistole's Physics*, American Catholic Philosophical Association, Washington, D.C., 1945, pp. 53–65, with some omissions and stylistic changes for the sake of uniformity in the text.

[2] The headings in McWilliams's summary have been generally replaced by a new set designed to bring out the order of the sections. A brief run-through of these sections reveals the following topics:

A determination of the *subject matter* for discussion: whatever there is that can change
A dialectical search for the defining constituents of these "changeable beings"
Aristotle's *definition*, in terms of primary matter and substantial form
Thus defined, changeable being is related to *nature*, the condition of the possibility of change; matter allows what Aristotle distinguishes as "substantial change;" form allows the other types of change recognized by Aristotle, as well as all the characteristics essential for these changes
At this point Aristotle interposes special questions on the "causes" or possible scientific explanations of natural objects, with special sections devoted to chance and finality
Change, the principal characteristic or *property* of changeable beings, is *defined* formally (nominal definition) as the realization of a potential as potential, then materially (properly) as the realization in a subject and according to the nature of the subject
Collecting these items (and eliminating the parenthetical sections which prepare for demonstrations to come later in natural science), we have the following structure of the first part of the *Physics*:

Subject and definition
Defined subject as explanation of essential characteristics:         S is M
Identity between the definition of the subject and an aspect of the
   formal definition of a property:         M is P
Subject as explaining, requiring the existence of, the property (or
   conversely, property materially defined through its subject):         S is P

And the study thereof is called "natural science" (or the philosophy of nature). . . .[3]

### LESSONS 2–11. DIALECTICAL SEARCH FOR DEFINING CONSTITUENTS OF THE SUBJECT

Parmenides did not make any distinction between substance and accident, nor between the potential and the actual. And even granted that what "truly is" is substance, *ens*, still there is another sense in which "ens" includes accident. Again, on his supposition that there is no such thing as potency, to say that "ens est unum" is to exclude extended being; because extended being is in a sense many, since it is divisible. Lastly, of accidents, some (the contingent) are separable from their subject, others (the proper) are inseparable, as the fact that man is a biped. With Parmenides, all would have to be inseparable.

The Platonists made the continuum consist of indivisible ultimates, and also took *ens* as a genus, whereas it is substance that is the genus. On that basis, accident is in a sense *non-ens*. Now, accident is not "ens simpliciter," but that does not mean it is absolute "non ens."

Now come the "natural philosophers" or "physici," those who admit change. Yet, even these want to derive everything from a single principle, namely from one of the elements. They all neglected earth, as too gross. They took one of the other three, or something midway between a pair of them (as [for instance] something denser than fire and more subtle than air). Generation was just by rarefaction and condensation, as air by condensation became water, and by rarefaction became fire. The rarer had less of matter, and so were more excellent. Empedocles finally won the day with his four elements.

All the "physicists" took it as true that nothing comes from nothing, so they explained becoming by rarefaction and condensation or by separation and conjunction. That was because they did not advert to potency and act. Entity in potency is as it were intermediate between pure non-entity and actual entity. Natural products are therefore not produced from mere non-entity, but from entity in potency, not from entity in act.

---

[3] Several paragraphs of the summary are omitted here because they do not give the flavor of the highly schematic review St. Thomas gives of the pre-Socratics:

| Constituent principles of material things can be | one | immutable: | *Parmenides* |
| | | mutable | water: *Thales* |
| | | | "the indefinite": *Anaximander* |
| | | | air: *Anaximenes* |
| | | | fire: *Pythagoras, Heraclitus* |
| | many | finite | ("four elements"): *Empedocles* |
| | | infinite | homogeneous: *Atomists* |
| | | | heterogeneous: *Anaxagoras* |

Note: From Heraclitus on, in the outline, the view should be taken as referring to the material principle only; St. Thomas was aware that these later philosophers held more complex doctrines, but his outline does not make room for greater subtleties.

So it is not necessary that when water becomes air, there be pre-existing actual particles of air in the water, which are liberated.

There cannot be an actually infinite number of parts in an animal or plant; nor can the parts be indeterminate in size. Whatever may be said of the mathematical continuum, in a natural body there is found a natural form, which requires a determinate size, just as it requires other accidents. Hence there must be a limit to the size of the particles that make up any natural body. This does not impugn the mathematical continuum, because there the parts can be progressively smaller without limit.

Some totals are compounded and resolved into parts of the same kind (and these are the elements), as a house is compounded of bricks and resolved into the same; but not so with other things, as houses are not made of other houses. In compounds, as also in transmutation of elements, the product is different from what it is generated from and from what it is resolved into. Thus there is no need of either only one principle or of an infinite number of principles.

Having done with unacceptable explanations, Aristotle now turns to the quest of the true position to take. But he first sets the problem of Democritus. The full and the void, he said, were the principles of nature; the full he ascribes to being, the void to non-being. Also, though the indivisible bodies were all of one nature, yet diverse things were composed out of them by reason of their diversity of shape, position and arrangement.

All the physicists admit some sort of contraries, and everything that is produced is produced from something not identical with the product. Anything that is produced or destroyed did not exist before it was produced, nor exists after it is destroyed. Hence that which becomes something else and that into which the something else is resolved, must not include the actuality of the thing that became or was corrupted. That things thus come from and are resolved into their contraries is clear enough in the case of transmutation of elements, but not so clear in the formation of compounds, since these latter are mediate between the elements; yet it is true of the compounds, too, because they are derived from the elements, and these are contraries to one another. Aristotle credits his adversaries with following reason, even though their reasons were not clear to them. For the true is the good of the intellect, toward which it is naturally directed. So man's intellect sometimes tends by natural inclination to the truth. Aristotle then shows the different ways his predecessors regarded the contraries.

How many principles must we accept? Not one only, because change involves contraries. Not an infinite number because: (a) we could never know nature if we had to learn an infinite number of its principles; (b) the first principle must be substance, and that is one genus; but a genus has a first pair of contraries, so not an infinite number; (c) if a finite number is sufficient, then an infinite number is to be rejected (Empedocles, with his four elements is to be preferred to Anaxagoras, with his infinite number); (d) the principles are contraries, but if (with Empedocles) we deny the transmutation of elements, we must make all the principles prime principles and contraries; yet it is evident that some contraries are posterior to others, and some contraries do come mutually from one another, as sweet and bitter. Here Aristotle argues from given doctrines of his adversaries; also when contraries come one from the other, there is a subject common to both. Not otherwise; white itself does not become black. But since there must be a subject, the principles are at least three.

Discussing the question in the context in which his predecessors left it, Aristotle says that none of the elements can be that third principle, because complete substance is a genus that has no contrary. The entire generation of things can be accomplished by positing one material principle and two formal principles; because for receptivity one material principle suffices. And since there are but two contraries (contraries being the two extremes), three principles (subject and two contraries) are sufficient.

LESSONS 12–15.  ARISTOTLE'S DEFINITION: RESPONSE TO EARLIER VIEWS

Nature means the power of activity, change, becoming. And the principles of change are three: the two terms and the subject. The *terminus a quo* may be simply negative, as nonmusical, or it may be privative, as unmusical. In every change that which is not opposed to either term remains; but since the terms come and go, neither they remain, nor does the compound remain which each of them forms with the subject.

Becoming *simply* is only the becoming of substances, but other things are said to become *in a limited sense*. That is because becoming means the beginning of existence. For a thing to become simply, it is required that the thing previously simply was not. This happens in substantial change. That which becomes a man, not only previously was not a man, but it is true to say that he simply was not at all. But when a man becomes white, it is not true to say that he previously was not, but that he previously was not thus. The reason is that accidents (quantity, quality and others) require a subject, substance does not. Yet even substances are produced out of a subject.

Kinds of change: alteration of shape (statue from brass); addition (river from rivulets); cutting away (statue by sculpture); composition, putting together (house); change of nature, accidental and substantial. But all these require a subject.

The principles and causes of natural things are the constituents of which they consist and are made, not the concomitants. These constituents are subject and form. Privation is a concomitant of the subject, and it remains even when the subject has a form, that is, there still remains the privation of other forms. In generation the opposites are privation and form; in corruption, form and privation; in accidental change the opposites are both positive, e.g., motion in opposite directions.

Prime matter is not known in itself but through a form. Thus when we see that what is air, becomes at times water, we must say that something existing under the form of air is at times under the form of water, and this we call prime matter. This therefore is one principle of nature, which is not a one, like "this something," that is, not like a denominated individual, as though it had form and oneness in reality; but it is called "being" and "one" in that it is in potency to form. Another principle is form. The third principle is privation, which is the contrary of form.

The neglect of these principles of change was what led the ancients to deny change and multiplicity. They said being cannot come from non-being. Aristotle answered: From a being *in potency* something [else can truly come to be; thus] matter enters the substance of the thing made. . . .

## Book Two—CAUSES

LESSONS 1–4.   SUBJECT-NOW-DEFINED AS SCIENTIFIC SUBJECT, I.E., AS
EXPLANATION OR CAUSE OF ESSENTIAL PROPERTIES
(ESPECIALLY CHANGE)

Having declared what are the principles of natural things, we now consider the principles of natural science; first its material object, then its formal object.

Things are: by nature; by art; by accident. By nature: animals; plants; elements. Natural things have within themselves a principle of change and rest: with respect to place; to increment; to alteration. This principle is either active or passive; thus the celestial bodies have a natural motion, even though they be moved by a separate mover.[4] In the heavy and light bodies however there is a formal principle of their motion; but this formal principle cannot be called an active potency, to which that motion belongs, but is included under passive potency. . . . Not that the motor is the form, for the motor is the generator (generating the element outside its proper sphere). Nature then is nothing else than the principle of change and rest—of itself and not contingently. Nature means "nata," inborn. Nature is the subject [when it refers to] matter; and it is *in* the subject [when] it is called form. . . .

4 This is the antiquated astronomy of Aristotle as interpreted generally in the Middle Ages.

Physical science studies natural bodies and their accidents, but these latter include the subject matter of astronomy; and astronomy is a part of mathematics (geometry).[5] But physics is not a part of mathematics, because the mathematician considers lines, points and surfaces in abstraction from bodies. Mathematics considers quantity apart from change and "sensible matter" (but not from "substance" or "intelligible matter," i.e., imaginary extension). The natural philosopher abstracts from individuals, but not from sensible matter. The application of pure mathematics to music and astronomy [however] does not make these "intermediate sciences" mathematical, because their term is natural matter. Geometry and arithmetic are the only purely mathematical sciences. . . .

LESSONS 5–15. TYPES OF NATURAL EXPLANATION (THE FOUR CAUSES)[6]

Having determined the subject matter of physics, we now turn to the formal object; and this is a quest for the causes or reasons. Material cause is in the product. Exemplar cause determines the species. Species is not the form only but form and (common) matter; it is in this species that the individuals participate. Efficient cause is fourfold: (a) perfecting, finishing, gives the substantial form; (b) preparing, disposing, makes the matter apt for the form; (c) adjuvant cause works not for its own end but for the end of the other; (d) advising, imparts [to an agent] a form by which [it] acts. . . . Lastly there is end as a cause, the "why" of things; and ends are both intermediate and ultimate. . . .

A resume of the causes treated in physics: primarily the material and the mover; these result in the form, which is the end sought in generation, and embodies the final cause. . . .

**Book Three—CHANGE**

LESSONS 1–4. DEFINITION OF CHANGE AS NATURAL

*a. Introduction*

After having settled what are the principles of natural things and the principles of the science of [these natural things], Aristotle turns to the [properties of the] subject matter. This, he says, is beings susceptible to change. [The first property then is change] itself. How accidental change

[5] Another common doctrine in the Middle Ages, derived from the Platonic doctrine of "saving the appearances." The mathematician, by clever geometrical manipulations, could predict movements of the heavens, but this account did not *explain* the motions. It is this kind of astronomy that is said to be part of mathematics.

[6] This section includes three parts: the causes in general, hidden causes (Aristotle's teaching on chance and luck), and special questions on finality in nature. The latter two are reluctantly omitted here.

differs from substantial change will be explained in the Fifth Book. Since change is a continuum, and therefore divisible infinitely, the infinite is a concomitant of change. The extensive continuum, "quantity" in the categories, can be defined as composed of parts (because parts added to parts can be fused into one total), but change must be defined as resolvable into parts (because a change once stopped can never be made continuous with the next change). Change also implies place, vacuum, time—the last being the measure of motion. [These, then, are the other properties to be considered after change.] . . .

### b. Change defined absolutely (formally)

What is in potency only is not changing; what is already in perfect act is not changing either, but has already changed. Water at its lowest temperature is in potency only, at the boiling point is in perfect act; in between, it is moving toward its term, toward further act. If the ordination to further act ceases, the very actuation (which it then has), however imperfect, is a terminus, and not change; as when anything is halfway heated. But the ordination to further actuation belongs to the existent-in-potency to that further actuation. But the potency alone is not change, it is the start of change; the completed act is the end, and change is therefore act, but imperfect, incomplete. To what precedes, it is act; to what follows, it is potency. *Change is the actuation of a thing existing in potency* (to further actuation), *precisely as such*. This last phrase is added [to indicate that] . . . the subject must be taken [precisely] as *in potency to further actuation.*

The actuation which is change is such only while there is change. To say that change is mere "otherness" or "inequality" or "non-ens" [definitions current in Aristotle's day] is ambiguous, because these can also be said of things that are not change. Change is an incomplete, imperfect act. That such an act is difficult to form a concept of is due to the mixture of act and potency; yet that there is such is not impossible, it is a fact.

### c. Change defined relatively to subject and agent (material and proper definition)[7]

Having defined change, [Aristotle] here determines whose act the change is, whether it is that of the changeable thing or the mover [responsible for the change]. It can be said that he now gives another defi-

---

[7] This is the crucial culmination of the entire passage; unfortunately, it is very confused in McWilliams's summary. The version given here is taken from another passage in McWilliams's study (pp. 37–38), but even so it had to be rather drastically revised. What is crucial about the passage is that a material definition of a property in terms of its proper subject is, for Aristotle and St. Thomas, the equivalent of a demonstration of the property as necessarily belonging to the subject.

nition of change which, to the previous definition, is as the material to the formal, and as conclusion to the premise. Here is the definition: change is the actuation of the changeable thing [as such]. This definition follows from the previous one. For change is the actuation of a thing existing in potency, precisely as in potency; but such a thing existing in potency is the changeable thing, and not the mover—because the mover as such is a thing existing in act; therefore change is the actuation of the changeable thing precisely as changeable.[8]

## THE SIGNIFICANCE OF ARISTOTLE'S NATURAL PHILOSOPHY[1]

*John Herman Randall, Jr. (1899–    )*

From the limited point of view of early modern physics, seventeenth-century and Newtonian mechanics, Aristotle's physics, and especially his astronomy, in the *De Caelo,* seemed perverse and barren. Aristotle was judged by those pioneers as far behind his contemporaries. His physics was qualitative, not mathematical; it was teleological and functional, not exclusively mechanical. The Pythagoreans and the Platonists had developed a mathematical physics and astronomy, which were judged in the seventeenth century to be "real science," a combination of atomism and mathematics. Out of their activities there developed Alexandrian mathematical physics. In later antiquity Aristotle's physics enjoyed in fact little influence outside the Aristotelian school, and was hardly known except in the Lyceum. It came to be enormously influential during the Middle Ages; and during the modern era since the seventeenth century this influence has been judged to have been very unfortunate. It has been assumed that when the moderns, first in the thirteenth century, and then again in the sixteenth, turned from Aristotle to Platonic and Pythagorean ideas, they immediately began to secure fruitful results.

In the nineteenth century the attitude toward Aristotle as a scientist began to change. As biology came to the fore, it was realized that Aristotle was the greatest biologist until the eighteenth century. Darwin made the enthusiastic remark, "Linnaeus and Cuvier have been my two gods; but they were mere schoolboys compared to old Aristotle." In biology, Aristotle's mistakes and failures come from his lack of detailed observation, his lack of a microscope, his trust in common opinion; all these things could be easily remedied by time. But in physics and astronomy it was Aristotle's aim itself that was "unfruitful." His method was

---

[8] I.e., as *natural*, in accord with the specific nature of the subject.

[1] From John Herman Randall, Jr., *Aristotle*, Columbia, New York, 1960, pp. 165–171.

"wrong," his direction "barren"—judged, that is, by the modern aim of seeking practical techniques for the control of nature.

Hence while he was an object of execration to the early modern scientists who were concerned exclusively with mathematics and mechanics, Aristotle's greatness as a scientific observer and theorist began to be appreciated as biology felt the impact of Darwin and Wallace; for the central Aristotelian ideas of process and function are fundamental in biology. But during the whole nineteenth century it was still held that as a physicist Aristotle was a first-rate biologist. This view prevailed, despite the fact that Aristotle maintains that any science of nature that fails to explain the most complex natural processes, living and knowing, is wholly inadequate; and that nineteenth-century physics, face to face with the problems of dealing with living and knowing, broke down miserably.

Then, in the twentieth century, the physicists themselves found their billiard balls, the Newtonian mass-particles following the simple laws of motion of molar masses, dissolving into complex functional systems of radiant energy. They discovered that the subject matter of physics itself must be treated in functional and contextual terms, in terms of concepts appropriate to "the field." And what this means is that in his basic concepts the physicist himself must think like the biologist.

Today, the concepts of Aristotle's physics, those notions involved in his analysis of process, have been driving those of Newton out of our theory. That our revolution in physical theory can be so stated is mostly unrealized; but it is often explicitly recognized that the ideas of Aristotle's physics are far closer to present-day physical theory than are the ideas of the nineteenth century. Thirty years ago it was still possible to regard Aristotle's physics as the least valuable part of his thought, and as of mere historical interest. Today, his analysis of the factors and concepts involved in process strikes us as one of the most valuable parts of his whole philosophy, one of his most illuminating and suggestive inquiries. Far from being obviously "wrong," it seems today far truer and sounder than the basic concepts of Newton. And it is fascinating to speculate how, had it been possible in the seventeenth century to reconstruct rather than abandon Aristotle, we might have been saved several centuries of gross confusion and error.

The exclusively mechanical emphasis during early modern science, from the age of Newton through the end of the nineteenth century, is now beginning to seem a kind of transitory interlude in scientific thought. The functional concepts of Aristotle were not necessary for the simple molar mechanics of the seventeenth and eighteenth centuries; they were discarded in large part because they were not manageable by the available mathematical techniques. With the advance of mathematical methods themselves, and above all with the carrying of scientific methods into the much more concrete, rich, and less abstract fields, like radiant energy, we have been forced to return to Aristotle's functional and contextual concepts—this time, of course, in exact, analytical and mathematical formulation.

Thus the temporary eclipse of Aristotle's physics is emerging as a kind of adolescent stage in the development of our own physical theory, a mere passing blindness. Today it is Aristotle who often seems strikingly modern, and Newton who appears "of mere historical interest." Newton, despite his epoch-making contributions to "natural philosophy," that is, to the science of dynamics, seems in the notions and concepts of his more general "philosophy of nature" to have been confused, in many of his ideas barren, and even wrong in his aim. It is Aristotle who strikes the present-day student as suggestive, enlightening, and sound.

Hence Aristotle's philosophy of nature, his analysis of the factors involved in process, and of the concepts of physical theory by which they can be rendered intelligible, as contrasted, of course, with his antiquated cosmology and astronomy, deserves the most careful study. And he is to be studied in the light of our own enterprise of revising and reconstructing the confused concepts we have inherited from Newton's "philosophy of nature." Where we are often still groping, Aristotle is frequently clear, suggestive, and fruitful. This holds true of many of his analyses: his doctrine of natural teleology; his view of natural necessity as not simple and mechanical but hypothetical; his conception of the infinite as potential, not actual; his notion of a finite universe; his doctrine of natural place; his conception of time as not absolute, but rather a dimension, a system of measurement; his conception that place is a coordinate system, and hence relative. On countless problems, from the standpoint of our present theory, Aristotle was right, where the nineteenth-century Newtonian physicists were wrong.

Aristotle has various physical writings, dealing with the analysis of natural processes. The *archai* of all natural change and process, *metabole*, are considered in the first two books of our *Physics*, which the other texts usually refer to as "the books on Nature." The analysis of the factors and concepts involved in "motion," *kinesis*, which includes not only motion in place, *phora*, but also growth or quantitative change and alteration or qualitative change, is carried on in our *Physics*, Books III to VIII, usually referred to as the "Books on Motion." The analysis of the most fundamental change of all, substantial change, "coming into being and passing away," is undertaken in the *De Generatione et Corruptione*. A description of the order and movements of the heavens occupies the *De Caelo*, Books I and II. The analysis of the elements and of chemical change is found in *De Caelo*, Books III and IV, and in the *Meteorologica*, Book IV.

The *Physics* is really a philosophical introduction to the concepts of natural science. As such, it is directly relevant to the criticisms we have now been making for a generation of the concepts of our inherited Newtonian philosophy of nature. For Aristotle is a thoroughgoing functionalist, operationalist, and contextualist, criticizing the views of those whom in our day we call the reductive mechanists. He is trying to reinstate, reconstruct, and defend the ancient Ionian conception of "Nature," *physis*, and of natural career or process, against the critics who had discredited it, Parmenides and the Eleatics, whose criticism had culminated in the mechanistic views of Empedocles and the atomists. These critics had used Parmenides' test of thinkability to conclude that there is no "nature," no *physis*, no process in the world: there is no genuine coming into being, no genesis. For it is not thinkable that anything should come to be out of what is not. There is only a mixing and unmixing of elements which themselves do not change. There are no "powers" in things coming into "operation," but only a sheer succession of actual states and their rearrangement.

As against this view, Aristotle insists that the world displays real geneses, real comings into being, with a fundamental unity and continuity, a basic temporal pattern or structure. Wherever we cut into these processes, we find them, in the words of Leibniz, the seventeenth-century Aristotelian, "heavy with the past and big with the future." We find that in a significant sense, every process *is* not what it will be. It has genuine temporal parts and relations which are essential to its being that process, and not merely incidental to it. The process cannot be adequately understood apart from this temporal character and pattern.

Now this, as Whitehead has made clear, is precisely our own criticism of the Newtonian philosophy of nature. That philosophy makes time an accident, we say; it does not take time seriously. It regards motion as a succession of instantaneous states, as just one state after another. This view, as Whitehead pointed out, culminates in the structureless world of Hume, in which "anything may be followed by anything."

To such a view, which he found maintained by the Megarians, Aristotle answers, No! Every process involves the operation of determinate powers. There is nothing that can become anything else whatsoever. A thing can become only what it has the specific power to become, only what it already is, in a sense, potentially. And a thing can be understood only as that kind of thing that has that kind of a specific power; while the process can be understood only as the operation, the actualization, the functioning of the powers of its subject or bearer. Aristotle generalizes: even local motion, motion in place, *phora*, the "motion" of

Galileo and Newton, is the operation of a power, a genuine process: it is a passing from one position to another. Such motion in place is not to be understood in the terms in which the structuralists try to understand it, the Eleatics, the Newtonians, in our day Bertrand Russell, as a "distance traversed," a succession of successive points occupied at successive instants of time. It is rather "the traversing of a distance." It is not a succession of determinations, but the determining of a succession, a continuous operation or process.

## TIMAEUS (Selections)[1]

*Plato (427–347? B.C.)*

*Critias* Let me proceed to explain to you, Socrates, the order in which we have arranged our entertainment. Our intention is, that Timaeus, who is the most of an astronomer amongst us, and has made the nature of the universe his special study, should speak first, beginning with the generation of the world and going down to the creation of man; next, I am to receive the men whom he has created of whom some will have profited by the excellent education which you have given them; and then, in accordance with the tale of Solon, and equally with his law, we will bring them into court and make them citizens, as if they were those very Athenians whom the sacred Egyptian record has recovered from oblivion, and thenceforward we will speak of them as Athenians and fellow-citizens.

*Socrates* I see that I shall receive in my turn a perfect and splendid feast of reason. And now, Timaeus, you, I suppose, should speak next, after duly calling upon the Gods.

*Timaeus* All men, Socrates, who have any degree of right feeling, at the beginning of every enterprise, whether small or great, always call upon God. And we, too, who are going to discourse of the nature of the universe, how created or how existing without creation, if we be not altogether out of our wits, must invoke the aid of Gods and Goddesses and pray that our words may be acceptable to them and consistent with themselves. Let this, then, be our invocation of the Gods, to which I add an exhortation of myself to speak in such manner as will be most intelligible to you, and will most accord with my own intent.

First, then, in my judgment, we must make a distinction and ask, What is that which always is and has no becoming; and what is that which is always becoming and never is? That which is apprehended by intelligence and reason is always in the same state; but that which is

1 From Benjamin Jowett (trans.), *The Dialogues of Plato*, Clarendon Press, Oxford, 1953, vol. III, pp. 715–745 and 780; 27a–29d, 31b–32d, 37d–38a, 41d–42c, 47e–50a, 53c–d, 55e–56c, 57d–58c, and 92c.

conceived by opinion with the help of sensation and without reason, is always in a process of becoming and perishing and never really is. Now everything that becomes or is created must of necessity be created by some cause, for without a cause nothing can be created. The work of the creator, whenever he looks to the unchangeable and fashions the form and nature of his work after an unchangeable pattern, must necessarily be made fair and perfect; but when he looks to the created only, and uses a created pattern, it is not fair or perfect. Was the heaven then or the world, whether called by this or by any other more appropriate name—assuming the name, I am asking a question which has to be asked at the beginning of an enquiry about anything—was the world, I say, always in existence and without beginning? or created, and had it a beginning? Created, I reply, being visible and tangible and having a body, and therefore sensible; and all sensible things are apprehended by opinion and sense and are in a process of creation and created. Now that which is created must, as we affirm, of necessity be created by a cause. But the father and maker of all this universe is past finding out; and even if we found him, to tell of him to all men would be impossible. And there is still a question to be asked about him: Which of the patterns had the artificer in view when he made the world,—the pattern of the unchangeable, or of that which is created? If the world be indeed fair and the artificer good, it is manifest that he must have looked to that which is eternal; but if what cannot be said without blasphemy is true, then to the created pattern. Every one will see that he must have looked to the eternal; for the world is the fairest of creations and he is the best of causes. And having been created in this way, the world has been framed in the likeness of that which is apprehended by reason and mind and is unchangeable, and must therefore of necessity, if this is admitted, be a copy of something. Now it is all-important that the beginning of everything should be according to nature. And in speaking of the copy and the original we may assume that words are akin to the matter which they describe; when they relate to the lasting and permanent and intelligible, they ought to be lasting and unalterable, and, as far as their nature allows, irrefutable and immovable—nothing less. But when they express only the copy or likeness and not the eternal things themselves, they need only be likely and analogous to the real words. As being is to becoming, so is truth to belief. If then, Socrates, amid the many opinions about the gods and the generation of the universe, we are not able to give notions which are altogether and in every respect exact and consistent with one another, do not be surprised. Enough if we adduce probabilities as likely as any others;[2] for we must remember that I who am the speaker, and you who are the judges, are only mortal men, and we ought to accept the tale which is probable and enquire no further. . . .

---

[2] This thought should be noted carefully; it is a persistent theme throughout the discourse.

Now that which is created is of necessity corporeal, and also visible and tangible. And nothing is visible where there is no fire, or tangible which has no solidity, and nothing is solid without earth. Wherefore also God in the beginning of creation made the body of the universe to consist of fire and earth. But two things cannot be rightly put together without a third; there must be some bond of union between them. And the fairest bond is that which makes the most complete fusion of itself and the things which it combines; and proportion is best adapted to effect such a union. For whenever in any three numbers, whether cube or square, there is a mean, which is to the last term what the first term is to it; and again, when the mean is to the first term as the last term is to the mean,—then the mean becoming first and last, and the first and last both becoming means, they will all of them of necessity come to be the same, and having become the same with one another will be all one. If the universal frame had been created a surface only and having no depth, a single mean would have sufficed to bind together itself and the other terms; but now, as the world must be solid, and solid bodies are always compacted not by one mean but by two, God placed water and air in the mean between fire and earth, and made them to have the same proportion so far as was possible (as fire is to air so is air to water, and as air is to water so is water to earth); and thus he bound and put together a visible and tangible heaven. And for these reasons, and out of such elements which are in number four, the body of the world was created, and it was harmonized by proportion, and therefore has the spirit of friendship; and having been reconciled to itself, it was indissoluble by the hand of any other than the framer. . . .

When the father and creator saw the creature which he had made moving and living, the created image of the eternal gods, he rejoiced, and in his joy determined to make the copy still more like the original; and as this was eternal, he sought to make the universe eternal, so far as might be. Now the nature of the ideal being was everlasting, but to bestow this attribute in its fulness upon a creature was impossible. Wherefore he resolved to have a moving image of eternity, and when he set in order the heaven, he made this image eternal but moving according to number, while eternity itself rests in unity; and this image we call time. For there were no days and nights and months and years before the heaven was created, but when he constructed the heaven he created them also. They are all parts of time, and the past and future are created species of time, which we unconsciously but wrongly transfer to the eternal essence; for we say that he "was," he "is," he "will be," but the truth is that "is" alone is properly attributed to him, and that "was" and "will be" are only to be spoken of becoming in time, for they are motions, but that which is immovably the same cannot become older or younger by time, nor ever did or has become, or hereafter will be, older or younger, nor is subject at all to any of those states which affect moving and sensible things and of which generation is the cause. These are the forms of time, which imitates eternity and revolves according to a law of number. . . .

Thus he spake, and once more into the cup in which he had previously mingled the soul of the universe he poured the remains of the elements, and mingled them in much the same manner; they were not, however, pure as before, but diluted to the second and third degree. And having made it he divided the whole mixture into souls equal in number to the stars, and assigned each soul to a star; and having there placed them as in a chariot, he showed them the nature of the universe, and declared to them the laws of destiny, according to which their first birth would be one and the same for all,—no one should suffer a disadvantage at his hands; they were to be sown in the instruments of time severally adapted to them, and to come forth the most religious of animals; and as human nature was of two kinds, the superior race would hereafter be called man. Now, when they should be implanted in bodies by necessity, and be always gaining or losing some part of their bodily substance, then in the first place it would be necessary that they should all have in them one and the same faculty of sensation, arising out of irresistible impressions; in the second place, they must have love, in which pleasure and pain mingle; also fear and anger, and the feelings which are akin or opposite to them; if they conquered these they would live righteously, and if they were conquered by them, unrighteously. He who lived well during his appointed time was to return and dwell in his native star, and there he would have a blessed and congenial existence. But if he failed in attaining this, at the second birth he would pass into a woman, and if, when in that state of being, he did not desist from evil, he could continually be changed into some brute who resembled him in the evil nature which he had acquired, and would not cease from his toils and transformations until he followed the revolution of the same and the like within him, and overcame by the help of reason the turbulent and irrational mob of later accretions, made up of fire and air and water and earth, and returned to the form of his first and better state. . . .

Thus far in what we have been saying, with small exception, the works of intelligence have been set forth; and now we must place by the side of them in our discourse the things which come into being through necessity—for the creation is mixed, being made up of necessity and mind. Mind, the ruling power, persuaded necessity to bring the greater part of created things to perfection, and thus after this manner in the beginning, when the influence of reason got the better of necessity, the universe was created. But if a person will truly tell of the way in which the work was accomplished, he must include the other influence of the variable cause as well. Wherefore, we must return again and find another suitable beginning, as about the former matters, so also about these. To which end we must consider the nature of fire, and water, and air, and earth, such as they were prior to the creation of the heaven, and what was happening to them in this previous state; for no one has as yet explained the manner of their generation, but we speak of fire and the rest of them, whatever they mean, as though men knew their natures, and we maintain them to be the first principles and letters or elements of the whole, when they cannot reasonably be compared by a man of any sense even to syllables or first compounds. And let me say thus much: I will not now speak of the first principle or principles of all things, or by whatever name they are to be called, for this reason,—because it is difficult to set forth my opinion according to the method of discussion which we are at present employing. Do not imagine, any more than I can bring myself to imagine, that I should be right in undertaking so great and difficult a task. Remembering what I said at first about probability, I will do my best to give as probable an explanation as any other,—or rather, more probable; and I will first go back to the beginning and try to speak of each thing and of all. Once more, then, at the commencement of my discourse, I call upon God, and beg him to be our saviour out of a strange and unwonted enquiry, and to bring us to the haven of probability. So now let us begin again.

This new beginning of our discussion of the universe requires a fuller division than the former; for then we made two classes, now a third must be revealed. The two sufficed for the former discussion: one, which we assumed, was a pattern intelligible and always the same; and the second was only the imitation of the pattern, generated and visible. There is also a third kind which we did not distinguish at the time, conceiving that the two would be enough. But now the argument seems to require that we should set forth in words another kind, which is difficult of explanation and dimly seen. What nature are we to attribute to this new kind of being? We reply, that it is the receptacle, and in a manner the nurse, of all generation. I have spoken the truth; but I must express myself in clearer language, and this will be an arduous task for many reasons, and in particular because I must first raise questions concerning fire and the other elements, and determine what each of them is; for to say, with any probability or certitude, which of them should be called water rather than fire, and which should be called any of them rather than all or some one of them, is a difficult matter. How, then, shall we settle this point, and what questions about the elements may be fairly raised?

In the first place, we see that what we just now called water, by condensation, I suppose, becomes stone and earth; and this same element, when melted and dispersed, passes into vapour and air. Air again, when inflamed, becomes fire; and again fire, when condensed and extinguished, passes once more into the form of air; and once more, air, when collected and condensed, produces cloud and mist; and from these, when still more compressed, comes flowing water, and from water comes earth and stones once more; and thus generation appears to be transmitted from one to the other in a circle. Thus, then, as the several elements never present themselves in the same form, how can any one have the assurance to assert positively that any of them, whatever it may be, is one thing rather than another? No one can. But much the safest plan is to speak of them as follows:—Anything which we see to be continually changing, as, for example, fire, we must not call "this" or "that" but rather say that it is "of such a nature"; nor let us speak of water as "this," but always as "such" nor must we imply that there is any stability in any of those things which we indicate by the use of the words "this" and "that," supposing ourselves to signify something thereby; for they are too volatile to be detained in any such expressions as "this," or "that" or "relative to this," or any other mode of speaking which represents them as permanent. We ought not to apply "this" to any of them, but rather the word "such"; which expresses the similar principle circulating in each and all of them; for example, that should be called "fire" which is of such a nature always, and so of everything that has generation. That in which the elements severally grow up, and appear, and decay, is alone to be called by the name "this" or "that"; but that which is of a certain nature, hot or white, or anything which admits of opposite qualities, and all things that are compounded of them, ought not to be so denominated. . . .

In the first place, then, as is evident to all, fire and earth and water and air are bodies. And every sort of body possesses solidity, and every solid must necessarily be contained in planes; and every plane rectilinear figure is composed of triangles; and all triangles are originally of two kinds, both of which are made up of one right and two acute angles; one of them has at either end of the base the half of a divided right angle, having equal sides, while in the other the right angle is divided into unequal parts, having unequal sides. These, then, proceeding by a combination of probability with demonstration, we assume to be the original elements of fire and the other bodies; but the principles which are prior to these God only knows, and he of men who is the friend of God. . . .

To earth, then, let us assign the cubical form; for earth is the most immovable of the four and the most plastic of all bodies, and that which has the most stable bases must of necessity be of such a nature. Now, of the triangles which we assumed at first, that which has two equal sides is by nature more firmly based than that which has unequal sides; and of the compound figures which are formed out of either, the plane equilateral quadrangle has necessarily a more stable basis than the equilateral triangle, both in the whole and in the parts. Wherefore, in assigning this figure to earth, we adhere to probability; and to water we assign that one of the remaining forms which is the least moveable; and the most moveable of them to fire; and to air that which is intermediate. Also we assign the smallest body to fire, and the greatest to water, and the intermediate in size to air; and, again, the acutest body to fire, and the next in acuteness to air, and the third to water. Of all these elements, that which has the fewest bases must necessarily be the most moveable, for it must be the acutest and most penetrating in every way, and also the lightest as being composed of the smallest number of similar particles: and the second body has similar properties in a second degree, and the third body in the third degree. Let it be agreed, then, both according to strict reason and according to probability, that the pyramid is the solid which is the original element and seed of fire; and let us assign the element which was next in the order of generation to air, and the third to water. We must imagine all these to be so small that no single particle of any of the four kinds is seen by us on account of their smallness: but when many of them are collected together their aggregates are seen. And the ratios of their numbers, motions, and other properties, everywhere God, as far as necessity allowed or gave consent, has exactly perfected, and harmonized in due proportion. . . .

Unless a person comes to an understanding about the nature and conditions of rest and motion, he will meet with many difficulties in the discussion which follows. Something has been said of this matter already, and something more remains to be said, which is, that motion never exists in what is uniform. For to conceive that anything can be moved without a mover is hard or indeed impossible, and equally impossible to conceive that there can be a mover unless there be something which can be moved;—motion cannot exist where either of these are wanting, and for these to be uniform is impossible; wherefore we must assign rest to uniformity and motion to the want of uniformity. Now inequality is the cause of the nature which is wanting in uniformity; and of this we have already described the origin. But there still remains the further point— why things when divided after their kinds do not cease to pass through one another and to change their place—which we will now proceed to explain. In the revolution of the universe are comprehended all the four elements, and this being circular and having a tendency to come together, compresses everything and will not allow any place to be left void. Wherefore, also, fire above all things penetrates everywhere, and air next, as being next in rarity of the elements; and the two other elements in like manner penetrate according to their degrees of rarity. For those things which are composed of the largest particles have the largest void left in their compositions, and those which are composed of the smallest particles have the least. And the contraction caused by the compression thrusts the smaller particles into the interstices of the larger.

And thus, when the small parts are placed side by side with the larger, and the lesser divide the greater and the greater unite the lesser, all the elements are borne up and down and hither and thither towards their own places; for the change in the size of each changes its position in space. And these causes generate an inequality which is always maintained, and is continually creating a perpetual motion of the elements in all time. . . .

We may now say that our discourse about the nature of the universe has an end. The world has received animals, mortal and immortal, and is fulfilled with them, and has become a visible animal containing the visible—the sensible God who is the image of the intellectual, the greatest, best, fairest, most perfect—the one only-begotten heaven.

## A COMMENTARY ON PLATO'S "TIMAEUS"[1]

*A. E. Taylor (1869–1945)*

Timaeus begins his discourse with a distinction which it is vital to keep in mind all through, and to which he recurs repeatedly when he enters on a new division of his subject-matter. He wishes it to be made clear from the outset that the whole of his cosmology makes no claim to be regarded as "exact science." Properly speaking it is not "science" but "myth," not in the sense that it is baseless fiction, but in the sense that it is the nearest approximation which can "provisionally" be made to exact truth. Cosmology and biology, and "pure" physics itself for the matter of that, can never, in his or in Plato's opinion, be rigorously "exact." You can never arrive at any finality in these studies, as you can in absolutely pure mathematics, because the things they study are incessantly undergoing variation, or, as Timaeus puts it, "never are but are always becoming." In pure mathematics you get absolute finality and exactitude, just because there is no change or movement or life in the objects you are studying, integers, triangles, ellipses, and the like. They are once for all just what they are, or rather, time has not to be taken into account at all in studying them. Consequently they never "turn out," as things which change or move or grow are always doing, to be more or less than we had supposed them to be, and so we do not need to be perpetually revising and improving on the results we have once reached about them, as Plato rightly held we have to do in all the "natural" sciences, even the most abstract of them. What Timaeus wants to insist on is that, to use a phrase of Dr. Whitehead's, "passage" is the fundamental fact about "Nature." This is why all natural science is

[1] From A. E. Taylor, *A Commentary on Plato's "Timaeus,"* Clarendon Press, Oxford, 1928, pp. 59–60, 61. By permission of the Clarendon Press, Oxford.

"provisional," whereas arithmetic, for instance, is "final," or, to put it in a more complimentary way, it is why natural science is "progressive" in a sense in which pure mathematics is not. Physical "laws" are always being revised and "corrected" in the light of newly-discovered "facts" or of more accurate measurements of "facts" which were already familiar. But no proposition of the multiplication table is exposed to any possibility of "correction" or "revision." There is nothing inherently absurd in the suggestion that Newton's gravitation-formula is not absolutely exact but only a "first approximation," but it *would* be absurd to suggest that 4 may yet turn out to be only a "close approximation" to the product of 2 $\times$ 2. There is nothing disparaging to the "natural" sciences in this correct Platonic view. What their results lose in the way of "finality" they gain in another way in interest.

This correct perception that there is no finality in natural science is one of the things which most markedly distinguish Plato from Aristotle for the better. The account of the world Plato puts into the mouth of Timaeus is in many ways crude, but in its general outlines it is much more like such an account as might be given today than Aristotle's scheme of concentric "spheres" rotating with constant velocity on unchanging axes. Also Plato is careful to make Timaeus remind us many times over that his doctrines are tentative—the best that can be devised in our present state of imperfect acquaintance with the "facts," but nothing more—whereas Aristotle really believed the mythology of his *De Caelo* to be exact science and the last word of astronomy. Plato was kept right by his clear understanding of the functions of scientific hypothesis. Its business, as the phrase of the Academy went, is *sozein ta phainomena*, "to save the appearances," that is to find a coherent expression which does full justice to the whole of the ascertained "facts.". . .

He holds that though we can never reach finality in natural science, it is our business to get as near to it as we can. We must make our method of studying "that which becomes" as nearly as possible that of strictly rational science. Mathematical physics is what he is dreaming of.

## SUMMARY OF POINTS FOR DISCUSSION

1. A *mechanist* should be able to make a good case for the simple clarity of the atomistic approach; he should have most difficulty in explaining the stability of aggregates composed of atoms, and particularly in explaining the uniform activity of normal macroscopic bodies in the world. Can he do so at all without invoking a principle of order in addition to atoms and the void?

2. An *Aristotelian naturalist* should be able to make an overwhelming case for the experience of changes in accord with the natures of bodies; he will have greatest difficulty in defending the necessity of the natural order of events. Cannot the scientist's faith in the orderliness of nature be justified?

3. A *skeptical positivist* should be able to show at least that, if there is any

necessity in the order of nature, it is not the sort of necessity that makes it logically inconceivable for the laws of nature to fail; he would have most difficulty in satisfying himself as to the basis of the scientist's unquestioned belief in order. Can this belief be justified?

4. Presuming that in any given discussion these questions will not be answered to the satisfaction of all the parties involved, it seems, nevertheless, that each view can make a valid contribution to the basic question, "Is there any such thing as natural change?"

a. Whether or not there is, mechanical-atomistic explanations will still be possible and easier than a naturalist explanation.

b. There is a great deal to be said for an attempt to justify science's belief in an orderly world.

c. The necessity of such order, whatever it may be, is not such as to make a disorderly world logically inconceivable.

## BIBLIOGRAPHY

### General

The works from which the selections have been taken:

Heisenberg's *Physics and Philosophy;* Aristotle's *Physics,* in R. McKeon (ed.), *The Basic Works of Aristotle,* Random House, New York, 1941; St. Thomas Aquinas' *Commentary on Aristotle's Physics,* R. Blackwell *et al.* (trans.), Yale, New Haven, Conn., 1963; Randall's *Aristotle;* Plato's *Dialogues;* and Taylor's *Commentary.*

Adler, M. (ed.): "Change," *The Great Ideas: A Syntopicon of Great Books of the Western World,* vol. I, "Great Books" series, vol. 2, Enclyclopaedia Britannica, Chicago, 1952.

Solmsen, F.: *Aristotle's System of the Physical World,* Cornell, Ithaca, N.Y., 1960.

### Atomism

Whyte, L.: *Essay on Atomism,* Wesleyan University Press, Middletown, Conn., 1961.

### Aristotle

Weisheipl, J.: *Nature and Gravitation,* Albertus Magnus Lyceum, River Forest, Ill., 1955.

### Plato

Blake, R.: "Theory of Hypothesis among Renaissance Astronomers, I. Ancient and Medieval Background," in E. Madden (ed.), *Theories of Scientific Method,* University of Washington Press, Seattle, 1960, pp. 22–25.

Cornford, F.: *Plato's Cosmology,* Bobbs-Merrill, Indianapolis, 1957.

Crombie, I.: *An Examination of Plato's Doctrines,* vol. II, Humanities Press, New York, 1963.

Friedländer, P.: *Plato: An Introduction,* Pantheon, New York, 1958.

# Chapter

# 2

# Scholasticism and Early Modern Science

THIS CHAPTER CONSTITUTES SOMETHING of a transition. The basic outlines of the perennial controversy over the intelligibility of the sensible world were clearly drawn in ancient times. The issues raised so long ago are still very much alive today, and the controversy takes a very lively form in our own time. In between stand several centuries of lively discussion on the nature of scientific knowledge. The issues were not always set in the same terms as in the ancient world, and still more clearly not in the terms of the modern controversies. Nevertheless, as an undercurrent, these issues were very much at stake in the clash between late scholasticism and early modern science. The best generally available sources for a background to these discussions are Crombie's *Medieval and Early Modern Science* and Randall's *The Career of Philosophy from the Middle Ages to the Enlightenment.*

In the clash between scholasticism and early modern science, one element of the classical debate was more or less absent—the skeptical, prepositivist attitude of Plato's "likely story" or "saving of the appearances." The doctrine was by no means unknown; it was a commonplace in astronomical theorizing all through the Middle Ages and well into the Renaissance. But the real clash was that between two dogmatisms, Galileo's mechanistic philosophy and late Aristotelianism.

In spite of this, Isaac Newton's actual procedures—as opposed to his intellectual predilections, which were something of an odd combination of mechanism and spiritualism—can be thought of as excellent instances of the "saving of appearances" method. In addition, there are a few places in his works in which he makes statements, about theories derived by induction from experiments, which anticipate the logical-empiricist views of today. It is for this reason that Blake's article on Newton, attempting to make him out a positivist-before-the-time, is included here.[1]

Nevertheless, the basic point at issue in the clash between scholastics and the followers of Galileo was not the hypothetical status of science but something entirely different. The point can be suggested by two quotations. Galileo himself is the author of the first:

> *Salviati:* The present does not seem to be the proper time to investigate the *cause* of the acceleration of natural motion concerning which various opinions have been expressed by various philosophers. . . . Now, all these fantasies, and others too, ought to be examined; but it is not really worth while. [*Dialogues Concerning Two New Sciences*, p. 160.]

The other quote comes from a contemporary Thomist:

> The "new science" discovered by Galileo, and developed by Newton, . . . can be recognized as a legitimate science in the Aristotelian sense of the term. At the same time we can reject the mechanical philosophy which happened to predominate in the seventeenth, eighteenth, and nineteenth centuries. [J. Weisheipl, in the article used as a selection below.]

The issue is crystal clear: Galileo denies that causal explanation is "really worth while," yet Weisheipl interprets Galileo's own science as a type of causal explanation. The issue is not, as in the ancient world, the existence of "natural motion"—both Galileo and Newton use the term. The issue is whether a causal explanation of natural motions, an explanation in terms of the natures of bodies, is possible or worthwhile using scientific methods, especially experimentation.

In the selections that follow Weisheipl defends his view of a basic continuity between Aristotelian and modern science in terms of causal explanations. Randall offers a brilliant outline of some of the developments in the theory of scientific method which, historically, led up to Galileo. Randall's work would offer material either for a defense of Weisheipl's position, or for a modified Aristotelian view much closer to modern positivist views of scientific method as hypothetico-deductive. Finally, there is Blake's article on Newton as a forerunner of pragmatic positivism. Thus the selections in this chapter are suggestive of possible approaches more than materials for debate.

---

[1] Including the article does not imply acceptance of its thesis. It is historically implausible, considering the intellectual climate of the times, to think that Newton would have remained skeptically uncommitted in the heat of the discussions surrounding him.

In addition, the selections suggest something of the importance of accurate historical research in overcoming long-standing stereotypes in the history of science.

## THE METHOD OF GALILEO GALILEI[1]

*James A. Weisheipl (1923–     )*

The scientific revolution of the seventeenth century is commonly summed up under the caption "The Downfall of Aristotle." Not infrequently this "downfall" is credited to a new scientific method based on observation and experimentation. However, some years ago Ernst Cassirer suggested that Galileo's method was really the Aristotelian *compositio-resolutio* employed by Jacopo Zabarella. This view has recently been defended by J. H. Randall, A. C. Crombie, and N. W. Gilbert. For the present I would like to pass over both of these views and direct attention to two methodological innovations of Galileo which can more suitably culminate our discussion of scientific method.

The first innovation to be considered is the very point discussed by Aristotle in the *Posterior Analytics* and in the *Physics*, namely, the value of mathematical middle terms in the explanation of physical phenomena. It was Galileo more than anyone else who was chiefly responsible for introducing the mathematical middle term as the *only* true, certain, and *propter quid* demonstration in natural science. This is implied in his famous panegyric on mathematics:

> Philosophy is written in that vast book . . . the universe. . . . It is written in mathematical language, and the letters are triangles, circles and other geometrical figures, without which means it is humanly impossible to comprehend a single word. [*Il Saggiatore*, q. 6.]

The origin of this innovation can be seen vaguely in the mathematical ideal of Robert Grosseteste and Roger Bacon, as A. C. Crombie has pointed out. It can be seen more clearly in the kinematics and dynamics of Thomas Bradwardine. . . . It is even more conspicuous in the cryptic notebooks and drawings of Leonardo da Vinci, for whom "no human inquiry can be called true science, unless it proceeds through mathematical demonstrations." But none of these current claimants as "precursors of Galileo" can adequately account for Galileo's unshakeable conviction in the power of mathematics. The origin of this innovation must be sought elsewhere.

[1] From James A. Weisheipl, "The Evolution of Scientific Method," in V. Smith (ed.), *The Logic of Science*, St. John's University Studies: Philosophical Series #4, pp. 81–86. Copyright 1964, St. John's University, New York.

Historically and doctrinally, Galileo's basic conviction that he had discovered "an entirely new science in which no one else, ancient or modern, has discovered any of the most remarkable laws which I demonstrate to exist in both natural and violent movement" must be traced to Copernicus. It must be traced to Copernicus' own conviction that he had found, not merely another way in which "to save" the phenomena of the heavens, but the *only* way. Osiander's Preface notwithstanding, Copernicus himself and many of his supporters were not content to consider the new system as a mere theory, a mere "saving of the appearances." The real point was that Copernicus and many Copernicans, including Galileo, insisted that it was the *only true* system of the system of the heavens. This was the understanding of the Holy Office in 1616 when the *De revolutionibus orbium* was placed on the *Index* "until corrected." In order to prove the absolute truth of the Copernican system, Galileo frequently resorted to sensible proofs, such as the motion of the tides and telescopic evidence of corruptibility in the heavenly bodies. Nevertheless he was convinced that mathematics alone sufficiently demonstrated the necessary truth of the Copernican system.

But if mathematics could demonstrate so perfectly the true world system in astronomy, why not in terrestrial physics as well? Many factors led Galileo and his contemporary, John Kepler, to believe that terrestrial and celestial phenomena must be governed by the same mathematical laws of nature. Those factors need not concern us here. The important point is that for Galileo only mathematics could give true and certain *propter quid* demonstrations in natural science. The basis for this conviction was his conception of quantity, which was thoroughly Platonic. Instead of considering mathematical entities as abstractions from nature, as Aristotle and St. Thomas had done, Galileo conceived the ideal geometrical bodies as the true substrate of all reality. During the second day of the *Dialogue Concerning the Two Chief World Systems* Galileo explains that there is no real difference between abstract and concrete geometric figures:

> Just as the computer who wants his calculations to deal with sugar, silk, and wool must discount the boxes, bales and other packings, so the mathematical scientist (*filosofo geometro*), when he wants to recognize in the concrete the effects which he has proved in the abstract, must deduct the material hindrances, and if he is able to do so, I assure you that things are in no less agreement than arithmetical computations.

Consequently Galileo did not consider quantity and quantified aspects to be a "remote cause" of natural phenomena,[2] but the immediate, proper cause of everything that counts in objective nature: "size, shape, quan-

---

[2] As they were considered by Aristotelians.

tity and motion, swift or slow." For this reason the so-called secondary sense qualities—tastes, smells, sounds, colors, heat, etc.—were eliminated from Galileo's objective world and reduced to individual sensations; they "are nothing more than mere names, and exist only in the sensitive body." [*Il Saggiatore*, q. 48.]

However, if we overlook Galileo's Platonic view of quantity, and if we discount his optimism in the matter of demonstration, we must admit that he did discover a new method, a new *modus*, namely the mathematical way to nature. Because this method is determined by the objectively measurable aspects of physical phenomena, he did indeed discover "an entirely new science." This "new science" was, in fact, an extension of celestial mechanics, the ancient science of astronomy, to the world of terrestrial phenomena.

The method of this new science is still the analytical or "resolutive method" of Aristotle, as Galileo himself states on the first day of the *Dialogue*. We should not have expected anything different, since mathematical physics is a speculative science, requiring the general method of all speculative knowledge. The special characteristics of the *modus proprius* are determined by the objective measure. Among the more important characteristics are:

1. The indispensable role of mathematics in all demonstrations of measurable quantities;
2. The impossibility of dealing with anything but measurable quantities;
3. The need to search for more and more suitable hypotheses to account for the facts, as did the astronomers of old; and
4. The necessity of experimentation (a) to obtain the necessary measures, and (b) to verify or falsify the hypotheses proposed.

Historians of seventeenth-century science, I think, would admit that these characteristics were universally recognized and enthusiastically praised by the founders of classical physics.

The second innovation in seventeenth-century science need only be considered briefly to establish a very important point concerning the "new science." It is generally recognized that the seventeenth century gave birth not only to a new mathematical physics, but also to a new *mechanical philosophy* [cf. M. B. Hall, "Matter in XVIIth-Century Science," in E. McMullin (ed.), *The Concept of Matter*, University of Notre Dame Press, Notre Dame, Ind., 1963, pp. 344–367]. What is not so clearly recognized is that there is no necessary connection between these two. There was no necessary connection between these two even in the seventeenth century. The foremost proponents of the mechanical philosophy, namely, Descartes, Gassendi, Francis Bacon, and Robert Boyle, can hardly be listed as mathematical physicists. However, like Galileo, these philosophers recognized only two first principles in natural science —matter and motion. Like Galileo, they recognized no motion in nature other than mechanical. The truth of the matter is that in the seventeenth, eighteenth, and nineteenth centuries there was a comfortable compatibility between a mechanical philosophy and mathematical physics. To use Whitehead's felicitous phrase, we might say that they were oblivious to "the fallacy of misplaced concreteness."

The essential feature of this mechanical philosophy was the rejection of *phusis*, or nature, as an explanatory principle in natural science. With this rejection also went potency and act, substance, formal and final causality, and even the ontological reality of true causality. In their place, as is well known, the seventeenth-century philosophers substituted quantified matter (corpuscular, atomic, or continuous), mechanical agencies (like impulse, attractions, repellents, adhesive forces and various energies), and local motion. But the important point is that these substitutes for the concept of nature were, in fact, principles proposed for a new natural philosophy. They were not the principles of the new mathematical physics actually discovered by Galileo. The principles of the new physics were and still are mathematical. In other words, the "new science" discovered by Galileo, and developed by Newton, and perfected in our own day by the theories of relativity and quantum, can be recognized as a legitimate science in the Aristotelian sense of the term. At the same time we can reject the mechanical philosophy which happened to predominate in the seventeenth, eighteenth, and nineteenth centuries.


## PADUA METHOD AND GREEK MATHEMATICS[1]

*John Herman Randall, Jr. (1899–    )*

During the sixteenth century attention was increasingly focused on this double process involved in scientific procedure. It came to be known by the Averroistic term of "regress"; the dependence of all strict demonstration on the prior investigation of principles was increasingly em-

[1] From John Herman Randall, Jr., *The Career of Philosophy, I. From the Middle Ages to the Enlightenment*, Columbia University Press, New York, 1962. The chapter from which the selection was taken bears the full title, "The Padua Tradition of Method and the Revival of Greek Mathematics." It begins with an outline statement: "If the concepts of a mathematical physics were arrived at by a criticism of Aristotelian ideas, the 'new method,' the logic and methodology actually taken over by Galileo . . . , was even more clearly the result of a fruitful critical reconstruction of the Aristotelian logic, undertaken at Padua in particular, and fertilized by the methodological discussions of the commentators on the received medical writers." As mentioned by Weisheipl at the beginning of his selection, Randall's classical researches are based on an original suggestion of the German philosopher Ernst Cassirer. The selections here are from pp. 288–290, 292–295, and 296–297.

phasized, and the details of that establishment were carefully examined. The fullest account of these problems is to be found in the commentary of Niphus on the *Physics* (1506).

After explaining the three kinds of demonstration in Averroes' prohemium, and assigning to natural philosophy the two procedures, "one from the effect to the discovery of the cause, the other from the cause discovered to the effect" [*Expositio de physico auditu*, book I, text 4], Niphus takes up at once the question of whether this is a circular proof, and cites Philoponus, Themistius,[2] and Averroes[3] in defense of such a *regressus*.

> Recent writers maintain that there are four kinds of knowledge (*notitia*): the first is of the effect by the senses, or observation; the second is the discovery of the cause through the effect, called demonstration of sign; the third is knowledge of the same cause by an examination (*negotiatio*) of the intellect, from which is first derived such knowledge of the cause as makes it fit to serve as the middle term of demonstration *simpliciter*; the fourth is a knowledge of the same effect *propter quid*, through that cause known so certainly as to be a middle term. (I, 4)

Since the second knowledge of the effect differs widely from its initial observation, this is no circle, but a regress. Niphus then asks, what is this *negotiatio* or examination of the intellect? It is not a demonstration, nor a definition, nor is it induction.

> This *negotiatio* is composition and division. For when the cause itself has been discovered, the intellect composes and divides until it knows the cause as a middle term. For though cause and middle term be the same, they differ in their reason: a cause is so called in so far as the effect proceeds from it, whether it be better known than the effect or not. But it is called a middle term, in so far as it is a definition. From effect to cause is the procedure of discovering the cause; *negotiatio* leads to the cause as a middle term and a definition. But since the definition is not discovered except by composition and division, it is by them that the cause is discovered under the aspect of a middle term, from which we can then proceed to the effect. (I, 4)

In his *Recognitio*, added later, Niphus suggests another view of what he calls "demonstrative regress."

> It is customary to treat at length the regress in physical demonstrations; I say physical, because there is no regress in mathematics. The younger men (*iuniores*) in this difficulty conceive three kinds of knowledge in demonstrative regress, of which the first is about the effect, that it is; that is, that the proposition signifying the effect is true; and this knowledge comes from the senses. That man has the capacity for science is known by

---

2 Philoponus (ca. A.D. 490–530) and Themistius (4th century A.D.), famous Greek commentators on Aristotle.

3 Spanish Mohammedan philosopher (1126–1198) whose works strongly influenced the Middle Ages.

sense. The second kind of knowledge is the reason why (*propter quid*) of that which is observed by sense. Thus we consider the reason why man has the capacity for science, and not the brute, and we say, because he has a rational soul. Therefore of the effect, or of the proposition signifying the effect, there are two kinds of knowledge, the one, that it is true, and this is clear to sense; the other, why it is, and this is known to us by the discovery of the cause. Of the cause, or of the propositions signifying the cause, there is one kind of knowledge, and this is discovery (*inventio*), which is nothing else than that it is the cause, or that the propositions are true which signify it to be the cause. They conceive therefore that by this knowledge which is the discovery of the cause, is secured the reason why of the effect, or the reason why the conclusion is true. Thus in the regress in physical demonstration there are three kinds of knowledge, of which two are of the effect, and the third is the discovery of the cause, which when related to the effect is its reason why, but which when related to the cause is the fact that it is cause; this discovery is acquired through the effect. [*Recognitio*, book I, text 4.]

Niphus cites significantly examples from the *History of Animals*, the most empirical of the Aristotelian writings.

From this it is clear that there is no need of any *negotiatio*, to render greater our knowledge of the cause, as we formerly held, for the mere knowledge that it is a cause is the reason why of the effect. Yet when I more diligently considered the words of Aristotle, and the commentaries of Alexander and Themistius, of Philoponus and Simplicius, it seemed to me that in the regress in physical demonstrations the first procedure, by which the discovery of the cause is syllogized, is a mere conjectural (hypothetical) syllogism, since by it the discovery of the cause is syllogized merely in conjectural fashion; but the second, by which is syllogized the reason why of the effect through the discovery of the cause, is demonstration *propter quid*, not that it makes us know *simpliciter*, but on condition that that really is the cause, or that the propositions are true which represent it to be the cause, and nothing else can be the cause.... Alexander asserts that the discovery of the cause is conjectural, while going from the discovery of the cause to the effect is demonstrative, not *simpliciter*, but on the condition that that is the cause, and that nothing else can be the cause.... But you object, that in that case the science of nature is not science at all. We must say that the science of nature is not science *simpliciter*, like the science of mathematics; yet it is science *propter quid*, because the discovery of the cause, gained by a conjectural syllogism, is the reason why of the effect.... That something is a cause can never be so certain as the effect, whose existence is known to the senses. That it is a cause remains conjectural (hypothetical).

Here at the beginning of the sixteenth century is clearly expressed the structure of a science of hypothesis and demonstration, with the dependence of its first principles upon empirical investigation plainly set forth —the one element in the Aristotelian theory of science that had remained obscure....

With the same simplicity and lucidity with which he summed up the collective wisdom of the Padua school on all their other problems, Zabarella [1532–1589] formulated the classic version of their teaching on method, in the terms and with the distinctions fruitfully employed and consciously expressed by Galileo. Out of this long and patient critique of the Aristotelian theory of science there developed the method that was to issue in fresh triumphs over nature. Logic Zabarella regards, following the Greeks, not as a science, but purely as an instrument.

> The whole treatment of logic is about second notions; but these are our own work, and by our will can either be or not be. They are therefore not necessary things, but contingent, and hence do not fall under science, since science is only of necessary things. [De natura logicae, book I, chap. iii.]

Logic is a tool, sought not for its own sake but for its utility in furthering science.

> Logic is an instrumental intellectual state (habitus), or instrumental discipline, created by philosophers for the sake of philosophy, which constructs second notions in the concepts of things, and makes them into instruments by which in all things the true may be known and the false discerned. [I, xx]

In this sense it is like the other instrumental discipline, grammar. But logic is double, "one applied to things, and already to put to use; the other separate from things"; and the former is identical with science itself. For the sciences are "nothing else than logical methods put to use" [De methodis, I, 1].

For Zabarella, therefore, logic and method are interchangeable terms; and he criticizes the logicians, who therefore ought to treat method carefully, for leaving it to the physicians, who in turn neglect Aristotle for their Galen. Method is "an intellectual instrument producing knowledge of the unknown from the known.... Method has the force of inference (vim illatricem), and connects this with that." (III, 2, 1) Method is therefore the same as the syllogism: "the definition of method does not differ from the definition of the syllogism." The syllogism is, in fact, "the common genus of all methods and logical instruments." (III, 3) Since all necessary connection is causal in character, all method must be from cause to effect or from effect to cause. There are therefore only two possible methods, composition and resolution.

> For all scientific progress from the known to the unknown is either from cause to effect, or from effect to cause; the former is the demonstrative method, the latter resolutive; there is no other procedure which generates a certain knowledge of things. For if we progress from something to something else, of which neither is the cause of the other, there cannot be between them any essential and necessary connexion, whence no certain knowledge can follow that progress. It is thus clear that there can be no scientific method except the demonstrative and the resolutive. (III, 17)

> Demonstrative method is a syllogism generating science from proposi-
> tions that are necessary, immediate, better known, and the causes of the
> conclusion. . . . Resolutive method is a syllogism consisting of necessary
> propositions, which leads from posterior things and effects better known
> to the discovery of prior things and causes. (III, 18)

Zabarella makes the Averroistic distinction between the resolutive
method suitable for natural science and the "analytic" method of mathematics. In the latter, both the principles and the consequences have the
same certainty and are coordinate, so that whether we start with one or
the other is merely a technical question. In natural science, however, we
must start with effects observed by the senses.

> Since because of our mental weakness the principles from which proof
> is to be derived are unknown to us, and since we cannot take our depar-
> ture from the unknown, we must follow another way on which we are led
> by means of the resolutive method to the discovery of principles, so that
> after they are once found we can prove the natural phenomena and effects
> from them. (III, 18)

The resolutive method is thus the servant of the demonstrative.

> The end of the demonstrative method is perfect science, which is knowl-
> edge of things through their causes; but the end of the resolutive method
> is discovery rather than science; since by resolution we seek causes from
> their effects so that we may afterwards know effects from their causes,
> not so that we may rest in a knowledge of the causes themselves. (III, 18)

There are two kinds of resolution or ways of discovery, "demonstration from effects, which in its proper function is most efficacious, and
induction, which is much weaker than resolution." (III, 19) By induction
we know only principles known according to nature. But Zabarella
sometimes follows his teacher Tomitanus in identifying induction with
resolution. . . .

The originality of Zabarella, and of the whole development of which
he is the culmination, is thus to set off scientific experience from mere
ordinary observation, the accidental and planless collection of single
cases. The weakness of the logic of the Schoolmen lay precisely in establishing first principles uncritically from such mere observation. Zabarella, and with him the whole new science, insisted that experience
must be first carefully analyzed to discover the principle or cause of the
observed effects. After this way of discovery has been followed, we can
then deductively demonstrate how facts follow from this principle or
cause: we can pursue the way of proof. Science proceeds, that is, from
the rigorous analysis of a few selected instances to a general principle,
and then from that principle to the systematized or ordered facts or
science. Zabarella calls this the combination of the resolutive and com-
positive methods; and such was precisely the procedure and terms of

Galileo. The presupposition of this method, of course, is that there exists an intelligible structure in the subject-matter under examination; Zabarella makes this perfectly clear.

> Demonstrative induction takes place in a necessary subject-matter and in things that have an essential connexion with each other. It therefore does not consider all the particulars, since after a few have been inspected our mind perceives at once the essential connexion and thus disregarding the remaining particulars at once collects the universal. [De regressu, chap. 4.]

No clearer statement could be made of the procedure of the seventeenth-century scientists. . . .

The theory of science set forth in Aristotle's *Analytics* is a theory of proof, not of discovery. Here within the school of Padua Aristotelians there has been added what was so sorely needed, a logic of investigation and inquiry. No longer are the first principles of natural science taken as indemonstrable and self-evident: they have become hypotheses resting upon the facts they explain. If Zabarella did not follow up the suggestion of Niphus that all natural science therefore remains conjectural and hypothetical, it was because he believed that an examination of particular instances would reveal an intelligible structure there present; and that was precisely the faith of which modern science was born. Zabarella distinguishes between the principles of logic and the principles of physics.

> Those are most properly called principles whose truth cannot be demonstrated in their science in any way, either a priori or a posteriori; for these are properly called *principia cognoscendi*, than which in that science nothing is more known. But *principia essendi* are not propositions but things, nor are they of necessity known beforehand, but often they are unknown, and can be demonstrated a posteriori, though not a priori, for if they had prior principles they would not themselves be principles. [De tribus praecognitis, chap. 4.]

But these physical principles are no mere conveniences of knowledge; they belong to their subject-matter, and are a part of the intelligible structure of the world.

> Propositions accepted in demonstrations from effects, if we consider things themselves, are not less necessary, less *per se*, nor less certain than propositions of strict demonstration; but if we consider our mind, they are not so known by us to be necessary, as the propositions of strict demonstration. Still we recognize some necessity in them; if not so much as is really there, at least so much as suffices for that syllogism to have the name and nature of demonstration. [De speciebus demonstrationis, chap. 10.]

It is not surprising that Galileo should so often sound like Zabarella. For he arrived in Padua in 1592, while the echoes of the great controversies over method between Zabarella and Francesco Piccolomini and Bernardino Petrella in the 1580s were still resounding.

# ISAAC NEWTON AND THE HYPOTHETICO-DEDUCTIVE METHOD[1]

*Ralph M. Blake (1889–1950)*

## 1. The General Nature of Newton's Achievement

Newton was not primarily a student of the theory of scientific method, but an active experimental investigator. We are consequently not surprised to discover that there are comparatively few passages in his works in which he discusses, in any connected or systematic fashion, his views of the subject. He was, however, by no means unconscious of the nature of the methods he was employing, and scattered through his writings there are numerous remarks concerning the matter, from which it is not too difficult to gather his doctrine. When his teaching is thus reconstructed, moreover, it can scarcely fail, despite certain lingering confusions, to strike us as representing a very notable advance. Not only is there abundant evidence that Newton has profited to the full by all that his predecessors have had to say on questions of method, but to a remarkable degree he shows himself capable of separating the gold from the dross, utilizing all that is valuable in their views, and at the same time freeing himself from all that is extravagant, one-sided, or perverse. Moreover, in the clearness and fullness of his grasp of the subject, he goes considerably beyond anything they have to offer. Indeed to such an extent was he in advance of his age that his followers themselves by no means always grasped the true significance of a point of view that even to us of today still seems quite essentially modern.

Newton's achievement is twofold. In the first place he has completely emancipated himself from the current notion that our understanding of nature can ever reach embodiment in an absolutely certain and definitive science. And in the second place he gives us for the first time a thoroughly clear and well-balanced account, to say nothing of a brilliant exemplification, of the analytic-synthetic method of mathematical physics.

## 2. Newton and the Theory of Scientific Certitude

In respect of his frank abandonment of the possibility for natural science of any absolute certitude and finality Newton must, however, share the honors with his contemporary Christian Huygens, who had independently arrived at the same position. Huygens expresses his conclusions in the matter in the Preface to his *Treatise of Light* (published in 1690, but representing work completed some years before that date), in

[1] Reprinted from *The Philosophical Review*, vol. XLII, pp. 453–454, with excerpts from pp. 467–475, 1933, with the permission of the editors. The article is also reprinted in E. Madden (ed.), *Theories of Scientific Method*, University of Washington Press, Seattle, 1960. (Cf. pp. 119–128, 130–135.)

a passage which also in other respects embodies views akin to those of Newton. One finds in this subject, he writes, speaking of the physics of light,

> ... a kind of demonstration which does not carry with it so high a degree of certainty as that employed in geometry: and which differs distinctly from the method employed by geometers in that they prove their propositions by well-established and incontrovertible principles, while here principles are tested by the inferences which are derivable from them. The nature of the subject permits of no other treatment. It is possible, however, in this way to establish a probability which is little short of certainty. This is the case when the consequences of the assumed principles are in perfect accord with the observed phenomena, and especially when these verifications are numerous; but above all when one employs the hypothesis to predict new phenomena and finds his expectations realized.

With the spirit of this passage Newton is really in thorough agreement at every point. To one approaching his writings for the first time, however, this agreement will not always be readily apparent; and in fact much confusion has often been felt with regard to Newton's true position in the matter. A careful study can scarcely fail to disclose the real state of his mind; but there are at the same time features of his work that may easily give rise to misapprehensions.

In the first place, the mathematical and deductive form with which Newton increasingly invested his works undoubtedly belies the true spirit of his method, and is only too likely to mislead the reader into supposing that his theory of science is substantially one with that of Descartes. Nothing could really be further from the truth. In fact there are not wanting signs that Newton, apart from the influence of external circumstances, would never spontaneously have chosen to throw his exposition into the strict geometrical form of a system which, starting with a set of definitions and axioms, proceeds to a series of lemmas, propositions, and corollaries. In this connection L. Bloch [La philosophie de Newton, Alcan, Paris, 1908] points to the frequency and length of the scholia in the Principia. These sections, which interrupt the logical sequence of the demonstration for a variety of purposes, testify to the embarrassment Newton feels at being confined within that rigid schematism; and it is significant that in one of them he tells us how it was by means of certain experiments that he has just described, and in advance of any formulation of the matter, that he really discovered, concerning the resistance of fluids, facts that at an earlier stage he has already expounded as necessary consequences of certain theoretical principles [Principia, II, sec. 7 (Motte-Cajori, p. 357)].

In the Opticks, too, Newton finds the mathematical form in which the work is cast so unsuitable that he is obliged to intercalate into his series of deductions sets of experiments that supply the necessary premises of the demonstrations that follow. Moreover, in a notable passage of the third book of the *Principia* he writes:

> Upon this subject I had, indeed, composed the third Book in a popular method, that it might be read by many; but afterward, considering that such as had not sufficiently entered into the principles could not easily discern the strength of the consequences, nor lay aside the prejudices to which they had been many years accustomed, therefore, to prevent the disputes which might be raised upon such accounts, I chose to reduce the substance of this Book into the form of Propositions (in the mathematical way), which should be read by those only who had first made themselves masters of the principles established in the preceding Books. [Motte-Cajori, p. 397.]

Newton here tells us, in effect, that demonstration *more geometrico* is so little essentially necessary to the subject that another form would actually be clearer to most readers, and that he had himself at first found it natural to adopt another style of exposition. Why then, we may ask, if this is the true state of the case, did he persist in throwing his work into this more or less uncongenial and misleading form? He himself supplies the answer in the latter portion of the passage just quoted. He had found, namely, by bitter experience, that to present his conclusions merely as a result of experimental investigation did not suffice to produce conviction of their truth. Only by casting his argument in a severely deductive form could he hope to carry with him his more reluctant readers. Hence the procedure that he actually adopted.

In other words, as Bloch sums up the matter, the geometrical mode of exposition is not for Newton a definitive form insuring a grasp of absolute fact. It is rather a means of persuading those whom dogmatic prejudice renders incredulous, by the use of a language which they find clearer than that of the facts themselves.

Similar polemical motives led Newton frequently to insist in emphatic terms upon the objective character and the certainty of his results as compared with the a priori theorizing of his opponents. It is in this connection that he so forcibly protests that his principles are no mere hypotheses, but are rather certified facts. Thus in the General Scholium at the end of Book III of the *Principia* he tells us that universal gravitation is no "hypothesis": "gravity really does exist"; "I frame no hypotheses"; "hypotheses . . . have no place in experimental philosophy." It is accordingly quite in the spirit of Newton that Roger Cotes in his Preface to the second edition of the *Principia* (1713) insists that the "real existence" of gravity "is clearly demonstrated by observations," that "it is plain from the phenomena that such a virtue does really exist," and characterizes those who, "too much possessed with certain prejudices, are unwilling to assent to this new principle" as "ready to prefer uncertain notions to certain."

Such language, if unduly pressed or taken in too literal a sense, may very easily lead us into a serious misapprehension of Newton's true meaning—just how easily we may see from the case of his own contemporary disciples.

> The enthusiasm excited by the theory of gravitation, that of the tides, that of sound, that of colors, was an essentially dogmatic enthusiasm. As often happens in the history of the sciences, the pupils and admirers forced the words of the master, and replaced by brutal assertions truths that he had stated with reservations ... the contemporaries and the disciples of Newton, what formed at the end of the XVIIth century the Newtonian School, accepted the method of the *Principia* as an instrument possessing absolute value. With a boldness and a tenacity that contributed not a little to the success of the Newtonian doctrine, they affirmed that Newton alone was in possession of the true rules of experimentation, that Newton alone had known how to draw from them irrefragable conclusions, that he alone had set science on the road to success. [Bloch, pp. 465–466.]

They believed that the *Principia* in its methods and in its results had introduced into physics for the first time an absolute certainty equal to that of algebra or of arithmetic.

Newton himself neither supported nor disavowed these extreme interpreters of his work. Amid the polemics of the day they doubtless powerfully aided his cause. But we must not for all that suppose that he ever allowed them appreciably to affect his own thought. His own much more carefully qualified statement of the matter is to be found, for instance, in his Fourth Rule of Philosophizing:

> In experimental philosophy we are to look upon propositions collected by general induction from phenomena as accurately or very nearly true, notwithstanding any contrary hypotheses that may be imagined, till such time as other phenomena occur, by which they may either be made more accurate, or liable to exceptions. This rule we must follow, that the argument of induction may not be evaded by hypotheses. [*Principia*, III (Motte-Cajori, p. 400).]

Here it is very evident that Newton regards his conclusions not in the light of certain and finally demonstrated truths, but rather in the light of provisional approximations, possessed, no doubt, of a high degree of probability, but nevertheless open always to revision or correction as a result of further experience. And such is his real opinion throughout. Thus, in the *Opticks* he writes:

> As in mathematicks, so in natural philosophy, the investigation of difficult things by the method of analysis, ought ever to precede the method of composition. This analysis consists in making experiments and observations, and in drawing general conclusions from them by induction, and admitting of no objections against the conclusions, but such as are taken from experiments, or other certain truths. For hypotheses are not to be regarded in experimental philosophy. And although the arguing from

experiments and observations by induction be no demonstration of general conclusions; yet it is the best way of arguing which the nature of things admits of, and may be looked upon as so much the stronger, by how much the induction is more general. And if no exception occur from phaenomena, the conclusion may be pronounced generally. But if at any time afterwards any exception shall occur from experiments, it may then begin to be pronounced with such exceptions as occur. [Dover edition, p. 404.]

To the same point is the following passage:

In the last place, I should take notice of a casual expression, which intimates a greater certainty in these things, than I ever promised, *viz. the certainty of Mathematical Demonstrations.* I said, indeed, that the science of colors was mathematical, and as certain as any other part of Optics; but who knows not that Optics, and many other mathematical sciences, depend as well on physical sciences, as on mathematical demonstrations? And the absolute certainty of a science cannot exceed the certainty of its principles. Now the evidence, by which I asserted the propositions of colors, is in the next words expressed to be from experiments, and so but physical: whence the Propositions themselves can be esteemed no more than physical principles of a science. And if those principles be such, that on them a mathematician may determine all the phaenomena of colors, that can be caused by refractions, and that by disputing or demonstrating after what manner, and how much, those refractions do separate or mingle the rays, in which several colors are originally inherent; I suppose the science of colors will be granted mathematical, and as certain as any part of Optics. [Letter to Oldenburg, 1672.]

## 3. Newton On Hypotheses

But what then of Newton's frequently expressed contempt for "hypotheses"? It must already be clear that his attitude is by no means merely equivalent to that common seventeenth-century feeling that what is merely probable or provisional or approximate (no matter in how high a degree) has no place in a genuine science—which must, on the contrary, possess absolute certainty and finality. But it is by no means equally clear, at first glance, just what he does mean. His condemnatory statements are certainly very emphatic and seem to be expressed with a deep conviction of their truth and importance. Yet, on the other hand, we find that "hypotheses" are by no means entirely absent from his own work. We find him, for example, making use on occasion of the supposition that rays of light are really streams of solid particles. Yet at the same time he assures us that this is no fundamental presupposition of his system. It is merely a probable opinion, to the literal truth of which he by no means commits himself—an opinion, moreover, that forms no essential part of his teaching. In another passage he offers with similar reservations An Hypothesis Explaining the Properties of Light:

Were I to assume an hypothesis it should be this, if propounded more generally so as not to determine what light is, further than that it is something or other capable of exciting vibrations in the aether; for thus it will become so general and comprehensive of other hypotheses as to leave little room for new ones to be invented . . . and though I shall not assume either this or any other hypothesis, not thinking it necessary to concern myself whether the properties of light discovered by me be explained by this, or Mr. Hook's, or any other hypothesis capable of explaining them; yet while I am describing this, I shall sometimes, to avoid circumlocution and to present it more conveniently, speak of it as if I assumed it and propounded it to be believed. [Letter to Oldenburg, 1675–1676.]

Moreover, whatever his uncertainty with regard to the details of the hypothesis, "it never occurred to him to doubt the existence of a medium which at least performed the function of transmitting light. Amid all their disagreements Newton agreed with Hooke to this extent, that there existed an aether, and that it was a medium susceptible of vibrations" [E. A. Burtt, *The Metaphysical Foundations of Modern Physical Science*, Doubleday, Garden City, N.Y., p. 266]. In fact Newton propounds the hypothesis of an ether in another connection also. This time he is suggesting, again with some diffidence, a probable explanation of gravitation. And in this case also, despite uncertainty with regard to the details, he was unable, in view of his conviction of the impossibility of action at a distance, ever to relinquish the hypothesis, in some form or another, of an ethereal medium. More than this, he "never gave up hope that experimental evidence might eventually be secured which would establish or definitely overthrow some of these specific conjectures" concerning the nature of the ether. "It was in this spirit and to this purpose that he proposed many of the thirty-one queries attached to the *Opticks*. This judgment of Newton's ethereal hypothesis is interestingly confirmed by the last paragraph of the *Principia*" [Burtt, p. 278]. . . .

We may add to this the fact that Newton, on occasion, actually employs the term hypothesis to designate propositions that undoubtedly do form an integral part of his theory; to say nothing of his reference to the "Copernican Hypothesis," which he certainly does not reject or regard as superfluous. . . .

The truth of the matter is that Newton's polemic against hypotheses is directed not against any and every use of hypotheses, but rather against certain current forms of their abuse. Among these are the following:

1. In Newton's day many were accustomed to argue for the truth of a theory as follows. There are only a certain number of hypotheses that can possibly explain a given set of phenomena. Now in one way or another it may be possible to show that every one of these hypotheses is false—with one exception. This one exception *must* thereupon be accepted as constituting the true explanation.

Newton protests strongly against such an employment of hypotheses. He points out that this method of proof is extremely fallacious unless we are absolutely sure that we have really enumerated all the possibilities—and who can be altogether sure on such a point? No, the true method of investigating nature is the experimental. We must establish theories not merely by refuting all the suggested alternatives, but rather by positive and direct experimental confirmation. This is the teaching of the following passage:

> In the meanwhile give me leave, Sir, to insinuate, that I cannot think it effectual for determining truth, to examine the several ways by which the phaenomena may be explained, unless where there can be a perfect enumeration of all those ways. You know, the proper method for enquiring after the properties of things, is to deduce them from experiments. And I told you that the theory which I propounded was evinced to me, not by inferring, *it is thus, because it is not otherwise;* that is, not by deducing it only from a confutation of contrary suppositions, but by deriving it from experiments concluding positively and directly. The way therefore to examine it, is, by considering whether the experiments, which I propound, do prove those parts of the theory to which they are applied; or by prosecuting other experiments which the theory may suggest for its examination. [Letter to Oldenburg, 1672.]

2. Closely connected with this first misuse of hypothesis is the following. If the only way of proving the truth of a theory *were* really the indirect one of *disproving* all the conceivable alternatives, it would follow that no theory could be regarded as adequately established, no matter how good the direct experimental evidence for it, so long as any alternative whatsoever, however devoid of positive grounds, remained possible. Now Newton points out that, no matter how well established by experiment any given theory may be, it will always be relatively easy for an ingenious imagination to construct other hypothetical ways of accounting for the facts—and these hypotheses, however little plausible or probable, cannot be absolutely excluded as at least possible alternatives. But he insists that such considerations should never be allowed to affect our judgment in the least degree. If it were legitimate to reject well-founded theories on *such* grounds, it would forthwith become absolutely impossible for science to reach any results at all. His Fourth Rule of Philosophizing (quoted above) is plainly directed against such a use of hypotheses.

3. A third abuse of hypothesis Newton finds in the procedure of those who, like the Cartesians, having reached their physics by a priori construction, refuse thereupon to recognize the validity of any conclusion contrary to their system, even though it is derived by a legitimate induction from careful experimental investigation. This, in Newton's view, is utterly to invert the true order of things. The synthetic or deductive method can itself have no legitimate starting point that is not supplied by analysis and induction. He insists upon the priority, for all natural

science, of the latter process, and protests strongly against the rejection of its legitimate results merely because they conflict with dogmatic hypotheses.

The conclusion of Newton's critique of hypotheses is, therefore, in sum, that they are incapable of supplying adequate grounds either for the acceptance or for the rejection of any scientific theory, and that whosoever employs them for this purpose is guilty of an abuse. Scientific theories can be legitimately established by experimental evidence only, and they can be overthrown only (1) by showing the insufficiency of the evidence adduced in their favor or (2) by producing adverse experimental evidence.

We now pass to the consideration of Newton's view as to the *legitimate* use of hypothesis. We may perhaps best sum it up by saying that for him the true function of hypothesis is everywhere suggestive rather than dogmatic. Such, for example, is the utility of those hypotheses which find a place in the Queries of the *Opticks*, to which we have already referred. They serve to direct inquiry, to indicate new lines of investigation, and even to suggest new experiments by means of which science may be advanced. . . .

The mathematical laws of phenomena the scientist can hope to discover; but the ultimate natures of things, or the ultimate causes upon which these depend, may be made the subject of endless hypotheses among which it is impossible to decide by any available evidence. Newton declares repeatedly that it is not his intention to determine anything whatever with regard to these matters. Light, for example, is a "something" that is propagated in accordance with certain mathematical laws. That is all to which he will commit himself. Others may busy themselves with such speculations, if they so desire. It is easy to invent hypothetical explanations, and that, too, according to a variety of different principles. Some may even find such hypotheses valuable as furnishing imaginary representations by the aid of which their minds more readily grasp the relations of things. Newton, in fact, does not scruple to throw out frequent suggestions to this end, with appropriate warnings that they are not to be misunderstood. But for the most part Newton himself has very little interest in this sort of thing. He is occupied with more important matters. Why, after all, should we trouble to seek for more ultimate "causes" when the laws that we have discovered suffice to explain all the phenomena? . . .

Newton's objection to the "occult qualities" of the Scholastics on the ground that they "tell us nothing" reminds us of the similar objections of the Cartesians. . . .

Newton's objection, however, really goes further than this, for in his view the mechanistic explanations of the Cartesians are in no better case than are the qualities of the Scholastics. They, too, are "occult" rather than manifest, hypothetical entities lying behind phenomena rather than functional relationships discoverable within phenomena. . . .

In the passage from the *Opticks* dealing with occult qualities, Newton tells us that he employs in their stead "general laws of nature," i.e., formulas merely descriptive of certain relations discernible among phenomena—"their Truth appearing to us by Phaenomena." These, by contrast with occult qualities, are "manifest Qualities, and their Causes only are occult." Now these laws are also characterized as themselves "active Principles . . . by which the Things themselves are form'd" and by which "these Particles . . . are moved." Have we not here the clue to Newton's meaning? If so, the "true causes" of phenomena are determining principles or laws (like the law of gravity) which we can discover by observation and experiment to be actually at work in the world, as opposed to merely hypothetical qualities, or entities (like the Cartesian vortexes). It is at least noteworthy that this version of Newton's meaning seems to be that adopted by Cotes in his Preface to the Second Edition. The followers of the Newtonian philosophy, he there tells us, desire

> . . . to follow causes proved by phenomena, rather than causes only imagined, and not yet proved. The business of true philosophy is to derive the natures of things from causes truly existent. . . . Therefore if it be made clear that the attraction of all bodies is a property actually existing *in rerum natura*, and if it be also shown how the motions of the celestial bodies may be solved by that property, it would be very impertinent for any one to object that these motions ought to be accounted for by vortices.
>
> Those rather have recourse to occult causes who set imaginary vortices, of a matter entirely fictitious, and imperceptible to our senses, to direct these motions.

We are now in a position to understand more fully the true significance of the famous passage on hypothesis in the General Scholium at the end of Book III of the *Principia*:

> Hitherto we have explained the phaenomena of the heavens and of our sea by the power of gravity, but have not yet assigned the cause of this power. [. . .] But hitherto I have not been able to discover the cause of those properties of gravity from phaenomena, and I frame no hypotheses; for whatever is not deduced from the phaenomena is to be called an hypothesis; and hypotheses, whether metaphysical or physical, whether of occult causes or mechanical, have no place in experimental philosophy. In this philosophy particular propositions are inferred from the phaenomena, and afterwards rendered general by induction. Thus it was that the impenetrability, the mobility and the impulsive force of bodies, and the laws of motion and of gravitation were discovered. And to us it is enough that gravity really does exist, and acts according to the laws which we have

explained, and abundantly serves to account for all the motions of the celestial bodies, and of our sea. [Motte-Cajori, pp. 546–547.]

## SUMMARY OF POINTS FOR DISCUSSION

1. A *mechanist* should be able to make an inescapable case for the mathematical method in science; there is no arguing with success. He would have the greatest difficulty in showing this to be the *only* approach, or in showing that the approach is radically incompatible with a *qualitative* science. What, one might ask, is the value of an argument from *lack* of success?

2. An *Aristotelian* will be able to show that the success of a mechanical approach does not render a qualitative approach necessarily impossible or even unlikely. He will have difficulty, however, in showing how a quantitative science should ideally be related to his qualitative natural philosophy. (Historically, each side in the scholasticism versus Galilean science controversy argued that its results were more certain, thus implying a disparagement of the other view. Reconciling the views would require the elimination of any such disparagement.) How can quantitative and qualitative approaches be reconciled (if at all)?

3. A *positivist*, interpreting Newton outside his historical context, should be able to raise serious questions about the certainty of the results of the mathematical-experimental method. His difficulty would be the general difficulty faced by the positivist: How can he justify the results of the method as giving apparently universally valid predictions of the future which work in practice?

4. In some ideal debate, it seems that at least these conclusions would be acceptable to all three parties:

    *a.* The mathematical-experimental method yields unquestionable results.

    *b.* This method is not necessarily incompatible with a qualitative approach; during the late Middle Ages, historical research has shown that more lasting scientific achievements were made by a quantitative-qualitative combination than Galileo and his contemporaries were willing to admit.

    *c.* Nevertheless, the logical structure of the mathematical-experimental method (the so-called "hypothetico-deductive method") is *essentially* hypothetical, incapable *of itself* of producing certainty.

This last conclusion, when coupled with the preceding one, gives rise to a problem for Aristotelians, for whom it suggests one of two further questions: How can the hypothetical features of the experimental method be reconciled with the certainty of a "general science of nature"? or, How can a hypothetical method yield the *de facto* assurance (if not "certainty") that scientists give to many of their theories? The very statement of the question, in either form, would arouse vigorous dissent on the part of contemporary logical empiricists.

This will be the subject matter of the discussions of the next chapter.

# BIBLIOGRAPHY

### General

Works from which the last two selections were taken, i.e., Randall's *Career of Philosophy*, vol. I, and Madden's *Theories of Scientific Method*.

Burtt, E.: *The Metaphysical Foundations of Modern Physical Science*, Doubleday, Garden City, N.Y., 1954 (original edition 1924).

Crombie, A.: *Robert Grosseteste and the Origins of Experimental Science 1100–1700*, Clarendon Press, Oxford, 1953.

Crombie, A.: *Medieval and Early Modern Science*, 2 vols., Harvard, Cambridge, Mass., Doubleday, Garden City, N.Y., 1959.

### Medieval Aristotelians

Wallace, W.: *The Scientific Methodology of Theodoric of Freiberg*, University Press, Fribourg, Switzerland, 1959.

Weisheipl, J.: *The Development of Physical Theory in the Middle Ages*, Sheed & Ward, New York, 1959.

### Galileo

Galilei, Galileo: *Dialogues Concerning Two New Sciences*, H. Crew and A. de Salvio (trans.), McGraw-Hill, New York, 1963 (original edition 1914).

de Santillana, G.: *The Crime of Galileo*, University of Chicago Press, Chicago, 1955.

### Newton

Cohen, I.: "The Grand Design—A New Physics," *The Birth of a New Physics*, Doubleday, Garden City, N.Y., 1960, chap. 7.

Koyré, A.: *Newtonian Studies*, Harvard, Cambridge, Mass., 1965.

Thayer, H. (ed.): *Newton's Philosophy of Nature: Selections from His Writings*, Hafner, New York, 1953.

For reference to Newton's *Principia*, see p. 157.

# Chapter
# 3

# Mechanism,
# Naturalism, and
# Positivism:
# The Contemporary Scene

CONTROVERSIES ABOUT THE INTELLIGIBILITY of the world in which we live, first raised in the ancient world and continued down through the centuries, are still very much alive today. It can even be said, in fact, that the scientific version of these controversies, dealt with in the three chapters of this section, has come to something of a crucial stage in contemporary philosophical discussions. The discussions of this chapter, then, are the real focal point of Section 1. It is here that we return to the battleground for the conflicts that were mentioned in the Introduction—radical conflicts over the basic approach to science.

The most radical conflict in points of view is that between *positivists* and *realists*. The positivist, or his contemporary offspring the logical empiricist, denies that the world can be known as it really is; he will emphasize the provisional, cautious, tentative character of all scientific knowledge of the world. The realist—here represented by contemporary Aristotelians or Thomists made cautious by positivist critics—will not deny that a great deal of science is merely provisional, or even radically provisional. Yet he will stoutly maintain that some aspects of science do give us genuine knowledge of the world, and that this knowledge is not likely to be seriously challenged at any time in the future.

In the light of the previous discussion, in Chapter 2, this controversy can be restated in terms of the basic scientific method worked out by Galileo and Newton and progressively better understood up to our own time. It is now generally agreed, by realist as well as positivist, that the logical structure basic to scientific method is *hypothetical;* an alert Thomist or Aristotelian would agree that the best description of science is the somewhat crude but now quite common phrase, "hypothetico-deductive method." The realist would add, however, that there is something *more* to our knowledge of the world in which we live—either (1) scientific knowledge itself can be transformed into something that goes beyond the hypothetical to the real, or (2) at least there must be, in addition to science, a parallel philosophical interpretation of the data of science that tells us something about the real world. (The first of these views is represented by the Dominicans of the Albertus Magnus Lyceum in River Forest, Illinois; the second is that of such Thomistic philosophers as Jacques Maritain and Charles De Koninck.[1]) Either view would be strongly challenged by anyone with a positivist inclination—logical empiricists often do not like to admit that they are out-and-out positivists—and their claim would be that science itself and the best scientists support their view.

In this statement of the controversies in this chapter, it may be wondered just what has happened to the mechanistic view that showed up so strongly in Chapter 2. There positivism was barely visible; here it is mechanism that becomes difficult to see. The answer is that changes in science itself have made mechanism more and more difficult to maintain, at least in its simpler forms. These aspects of science will come up in later chapters, on the nature of matter and the structure of our world as known to contemporary physics. For the present it is sufficient to note that the revolutions of relativity and quantum mechanics in the early decades of this century made scientists extremely wary of the dogmatic mechanism-materialism of the late nineteenth century. Some of the reasons for this change will be referred to in a brief selection from Bertrand Russell in this chapter. Nevertheless, the simple intelligibility that is at the heart of mechanism, and which constitutes its chief psychological appeal, is still very much a dream of many scientists. This can be most clearly shown by one of the greatest of all scientific minds, Albert Einstein:

> In our scientific expectations we have progressed toward antipodes. You believe in the dice-playing god, and I in the perfect rule of law in a world of something objectively existing. (Letter to Max Born, November 7, 1944.)
> I cannot substantiate my attitude to physics in such a manner that you would find it in any way rational. I see of course that the statistical

---

[1] There are, of course, other Thomistic interpretations of science, many of which are more sophisticated than those mentioned. The best known (and also the most difficult) of these is Bernard Lonergan's, in *Insight*, Philosophical Library, New York, 1957.

interpretation . . . has a considerable content of truth. Yet I cannot seriously believe it because the theory is inconsistent with the principle that physics has to represent a reality in space and time. . . . I am absolutely convinced that one will eventually arrive at a theory in which the objects connected by laws are not probabilities, but conceived facts. (Letter to Born, December 3, 1947; both letters in Max Born, *Natural Philosophy of Cause and Chance*, Dover, New York, 1964, pp. 122–123.)

This dream or hope of what science *ought* to be like, which is here viewed as a quasi-mechanistic longing for simplicity, is represented, in the selections that follow, by Feigl's article on unitary science, completed by brief selections from two philosophers who are widely held to be materialists, Bertrand Russell and J. J. C. Smart.

However, the most fundamental conflict here is concerned with the question whether or not there is anything *certain or absolute* in science—if there is not, then it is very difficult to sustain the realist view that the objects of science can be known, at least in part, as they really are. To the question, our present-day would-be mechanist has to answer that in the present state of knowledge science can offer no absolutes, though in some *ideal* (and perhaps future) state it should, and these absolutes would have the *full determinateness* of classical mechanics. The positivist or positivistically inclined logical empiricist would give a *simple negative* answer: There are no absolutes in science and there cannot be. Finally, the Aristotelian realist would give a very much *qualified affirmative* answer: There are a limited number of theories in science that do tell us something about the real world, and which are not likely to be overturned in the future. The best of these realist responses would side with contemporary researches in the history of science and attempt to show historically that there are in fact unchallenged principles in science, without which science as we know it would be simply impossible.

In the selections, these last two positions are represented by William Wallace, arguing for some final answers in science, and Ernest Nagel, offering a strong logical critique of the Aristotelian canons of proof as applied to science.

## UNITY OF SCIENCE AND UNITARY SCIENCE[1]

*Herbert Feigl (1902–    )*

In order to clear up much current confusion *three* meanings of the term "unity of science" (and of "physicalism") should be distinguished.

The first meaning, adopted by Carnap, Neurath, and others is the *unity of the language of science* which is also the basic idea of the En-

[1] From H. Feigl and M. Brodbeck (eds.), *Readings in the Philosophy of Science*, pp. 382–384. Copyright, 1953, by Appleton-Century-Crofts, Inc. Reprinted by permission of Appleton-Century-Crofts, Division of Meredith Publishing Company.

cyclopedia of Unified Science. This idea can be considered as a logically revised and refined formulation of the essential thesis of empiricism and operationism (on an inter-subjective basis).

The *second* meaning is the thesis of *naturalism*. It is hardly possible to give even a moderately definite and precise formulation of this so frequently debated but so poorly defined point of view. Approximately it seems to amount to the belief (or, in a more adequate formulation, the heuristic program) according to which the explanatory constructs of all sciences will not need to go beyond the spatio-temporal-causal frame. This program excludes not only metaphysical entities ("absolutes," "entelechies," etc.)—as does the weaker first thesis of empiricism—but rules out also certain logically conceivable and empirically meaningful forms of hypotheses. Only certain "normal" forms of spatio-temporal frames and causal (or statistical) laws are considered necessary for an explanation of the observed phenomena. One somewhat vague aspect of this naturalistic doctrine lies in certain (implicit) postulates concerning the continuity of causal influences. Naturalism of this form leaves open, but does not positively affirm, the reducibility of biological, psychological, and sociological laws to physical laws. Even if irreducibility is assumed (emergentist), naturalism would still differ from vitalistic and animistic doctrines which assert this irreducibility on entirely different grounds.

The thesis which I wish to clarify and whose present value I wish to appraise is the *third* one: *physicalism in the strict sense*, postulating the potential derivability of *all* scientific laws from the laws of physics. This is the most radical and therefore also the most problematic of the three theses. As it is an open question as to whether biology, psychology, and the social sciences are ultimately reducible to physical theory, we cannot afford to be dogmatic—one way or the other. It is also expressly admitted that speculation in the direction of this sort of unification may in many fields be premature and therefore possibly harmful to scientific progress. The success of biological, psychological, and sociological theories formulated in their own specific terms indicates that a temporary disregard for farther reaching reductions can be of great heuristic value. It will, however, always be of paramount logical and general scientific interest to determine whether the facts as known and scientific method, being what it is at a given stage of development, exclude, leave open, or even make plausible the thesis (prognosis) of radical physicalism.

The main motivation of the following defense of this thesis lies in the need to refute the more and more frequent misconceptions concerning it —exemplified in their extreme form by the confusion of physicalism with "mechanistic materialism." This designation spreads generally a rather repellent odor and is used by many writers as a weapon of aggression and disparagement even against scientific trends which are completely free from the metaphysical nonsense in traditional materialism and the factual inadequacies of the mechanistic world view. But if we bring up to date that which, scientifically and methodologically, was always valuable in materialism, we merely pursue the program of the unity of science (in the first, second, and as far as possible, in the third sense).

There is a good deal of historical, experimental, and theoretical evidence in favor of strict physicalism. A parallel study of the *levels of explanation* (i.e., of the levels of description, empirical laws, and theories of two or three orders) in the various branches of science reveals an impressive *convergence of theories toward a unitary scheme*. Mechanics, astronomy, acoustics, thermodynamics, optics, electricity, magnetics, and chemistry are integratively united (at least to an astounding extent) in the theories of relativity and quanta. Biology, through biophysics and biochemistry, psychology, through neuro-physiology, seem to follow in the same direction.

The notoriously most recalcitrant problems for such a radical reduction are the explanation of *"purposiveness"* in all organic life and the facts of *"consciousness," "meaning," "freedom," "value,"* and *"creativity"* in mental life. The central difficulty here, as well as in the reduction of the social sciences seems to lie in a clear definition of *"emergence"* and in the problem of the predictability of emergent wholes and their features. Logical analysis of these difficulties seems to indicate that the customary philosophical arguments against physicalistic reducibility are either logically faulty (metaphysically confused) or rest on a deficient understanding of the meaning and methods of modern physical science. Constructively, it can be shown that the empirical translations (first thesis) of the *"recalcitrant"* facts makes it at least plausible that physical explanations (third thesis) are not logically inconceivable— much as the enormous technical difficulties must be admitted.

There is an empirical formulation of purposiveness as a characteristic of certain types of dynamic systems; there is the behavioristic analysis of consciousness and the logical demonstration of the pseudo-character of the traditional mind-body difficulty (i.e., the dualism is of linguistic, not of factual nature); the semiotic meaning-relation can be accounted for on the basis of rule-controlled symbolic behavior. Similarly the terms *"right"* and *"wrong"*—whether they refer to formal or factual truth, to esthetic, ethical, or legal objects of evaluation—indicate conformity or non-conformity to accepted standards or rules whose origin, acceptance, evaluation, modification, or abolition in turn can be subjected to scientific study. There is the account of freedom as a special form of causation (i.e., the situation in which the person as a whole, more than the momentary environment, is the condition of action) and there are behavioristic, gestaltist, psychoanalytic approaches to the problems of cognitive and artistic creativity. Finally, an analysis of the concept "emergent novelty" does away with the ontological mysteries and enables us to define its empirical nucleus as a special form of configurational order, not necessarily beyond the possibility of prediction on the basis of more elementary laws. In view of the ever-changing theoretical structure of physics it must be admitted that "radical physicalism" also does not have any very precise meaning. It seems that only through fairly arbitrary decision can "physical" laws be delimited from "nonphysical" ones. A more definite meaning may be suggested by formulating the thesis of physicalism in the following way: The set of physical laws which enables us to deduce the facts of chemistry will also be sufficient for biology and psychology.

A presentation such as this is likely to evoke the suspicion that it aims impatiently at a solution of the "riddles of the universe." I hope, however, that it is sufficiently clear that I have tried only to survey some major issues in order to analyze and assess the logical possibility of physicalism and thus to counteract a certain philosophical defeatism now again greatly in fashion. I also do not in the least wish to belittle scientific theorizing on its given autonomous levels of research. Only such actual scientific work will finally show either that the physicalistic synthesis is hopeless or that (and how) it can be achieved.

**Editor's Note:** Because Feigl's position does not represent a genuine and unambiguous modern mechanism—he explicitly repudiates such a characterization in the text—two other brief selections are added. In the first, Bertrand Russell shows why strict mechanistic materialism is difficult to maintain in our day, then proceeds to favor it as a hypothesis which, while not "metaphysically true," is most beneficial as a "practical maxim of scientific method" and a goal to be striven for. In the course of his discussion, Russell mentions the extension of mechanism into the psychological realm; in the other brief selection added here, J. J. C. Smart argues rather strongly for the view that man is in fact an elaborate machine, not in principle incapable of being reproduced by an elaborate computer or robot. Both these views are in fact widespread among certain scientists, and philosophically speaking, they represent the closest approximations in our own day to a mechanistic view of science.

## MATERIALISM, PAST AND PRESENT

*Bertrand Russell (1872–    )*

The two dogmas that constitute the essence of materialism are: First, the sole reality of matter; secondly, the reign of law. The belief that matter alone is real will not survive the sceptical arguments derived from the physiological mechanism of sensation. But it has received recently another blow, from the quarter whence it was least to be expected, namely,

[1] Originally an introduction to F. Lange, *A History of Materialism*, 1950. Used by permission of Humanities Press, Inc., New York, and Routledge & Kegan Paul Ltd., London.

from physics. The theory of relativity, by merging time into space-time, has damaged the traditional notion of substance more than all the arguments of philosophers. Matter, for common sense, is something which persists in time and moves in space. But for modern relativity-physics this view is no longer tenable. A piece of matter has become, not a persistent thing with varying states, but a system of inter-related events. The old solidity is gone, and with it the characteristics that, to the materialist, made matter seem more real than fleeting thoughts. Nothing is permanent, nothing endures; the prejudice that the real is the persistent must be abandoned. . . .

In the present condition of human knowledge . . . either to assert or to deny the universal reign of law is a mark of prejudice; the rational man will regard the question as open. All perennial controversies, such as that between determinists and believers in free will, spring from a conflict between opposing passions, both widespread, but one stronger in one man and the other in another. In this case, the conflict is between the passion for power and the passion for safety, because if the external world behaves according to law, we can adapt ourselves to it. We desire the reign of law for the sake of safety, and freedom for the sake of power. Common sense assumes that law governs inanimate nature and one's neighbours, while freedom is reserved for oneself. In this way both passions are gratified to the full. But philosophy demands some more subtle reconciliation, and is therefore never weary of inventing new ways of combining freedom with determination. The sceptic can merely observe this struggle with detachment, and he is fortunate if his detachment does not degenerate into cynicism. . . .

In our own time, the old battle of materialism persists chiefly in biology and physiology. Some men of science maintain that the phenomena of living organisms cannot be explained solely in terms of chemistry and physics; others maintain that such explanation is always theoretically possible. Professor J. S. Haldane may be regarded, in this country, as the leading exponent of the former view; in Germany it is associated with Driesch. One of the most effective champions of the mechanistic view was Jacques Loeb, who showed (*inter alia*) that a sea-urchin could have a pin for its father, and afterwards extended this result to animals much higher in the scale. The controversy may be expected to last for a long time, since, even if the mechanists are in the right, they are not likely soon to find explanations of all vital phenomena of the sort that their theory postulates. It will be a severe blow to the vitalists when protoplasm is manufactured in the laboratory, but they will probably take refuge in saying that their theories only apply to multi-cellular organisms. Later, they will confine vitalism to vertebrates, then to mammals, then to men, and last of all to white men—or perhaps it will be yellow men by that time. Ordinary scientific probability suggests, however, that the sphere of mechanistic explanation in regard to vital phenomena is likely to be indefinitely extended by the progress of biological knowledge.

Psychology, which might have been expected to be more opposed to materialism than any other science, has, on the contrary, shown decided leanings in that direction. The behaviourist school maintains that psychology should only concern itself with what can be seen by external observation, and denies totally that introspection is an independent source of scientific knowledge. This view would make all the phenomena with which psychology is concerned physical phenomena, thereby conceding to materialism the utmost of its claims. . . .

The conclusion of the above discussion would seem to be that, as a practical maxim of scientific method, materialism may be accepted if it means that the goal of every science is to be merged in physics. But it must be added that physics itself is not materialistic in the old sense, since it no longer assumes matter as permanent substance. And it must also be remembered that there is no good reason to suppose materialism metaphysically true: it is a point of view which has hitherto proved useful in research, and is likely to continue useful wherever new scientific laws are being discovered, but which may well not cover the whole field, and cannot be regarded as definitely true without a wholly unwarranted dogmatism.

## PHILOSOPHY AND SCIENTIFIC REALISM[1]

*J. J. C. Smart (1920–    )*

Descartes thought that while animals were mere machines, men were machines with souls. As Ryle has put it, according to Descartes, man is a ghost in a machine. At first sight the mere fact of consciousness seems to prove Descartes' point. For it would seem that however complicated we made an electronic computer, for example, it would not be conscious. It would appear therefore that man differs from a physical mechanism in some very fundamental way. However, if my conclusions in the last chapter are correct, these appearances are deceptive. There would seem to be no reason why a sufficiently complex electronic gadget should not be conscious or have experiences. If consciousness is a brain process, then presumably it could also be an electronic process. Provided the electronic process were of the same pattern as the appropriate neural process, it also would be a conscious experience.

[1] From J. J. C. Smart, *Philosophy and Scientific Realism*, Humanities Press, New York, 1963, pp. 106–107. Used by permission of Humanities Press, Inc. and Routledge & Kegan Paul Ltd., London.

According to Ryle, Descartes is wrong on another count as well. Not only is it incorrect to think of man as a ghost in a machine, it is also incorrect to think of man as a machine at all, even a ghostless one. I think that Ryle must here be thinking of rather simple mechanisms: the reasons he gives for saying that we are not machines turn on the peculiar purposefulness, appropriateness, and adaptiveness of human, and indeed animal, behaviour. To say that we have a mind is to say that we behave intelligently, not that we have a soul or "ghost." But is there any reason why a machine should not have the sort of purposefulness, appropriateness, and adaptiveness that is characteristic of human beings? I shall contend that we have no reason for thinking that a machine could not have the human sort of intelligence, and therefore that the antecedent scientific plausibility of physicalism should lead us to espouse the view that men are physical mechanisms. The hypothesis that I shall put forward is an old one in that it goes back at least to LaMettrie's *L'Homme Machine*, but it has been enormously strengthened by recent developments in cybernetics, the theory of self-regulating mechanisms.

## A THOMISTIC PROPOSAL[1]

*W. A. Wallace (1918–    )*

Aquinas' answer [to the question of physical proof] is still the one to which the practicing scientist implicitly subscribes. We maintain that the essential contribution of Einstein is to cancel out the excessive mathematical realism of Galileo, while still leaving open the possibility of a type of physical certainty and proof such as conceived by Thomas Aquinas.

A justification for this view may perhaps be seen with the aid of a simple example. Rather than discuss the reality of elementary particles, which could involve us in advanced science, we prefer to discuss a problem that can be understood even in a medieval thought context. We shall analyze the scientific evidence currently adduced to prove (1) that the earth is approximately an oblate spheroid in shape, and (2) that it rotates on its polar axis once every twenty-four hours.

In the interests of rigor, and to facilitate discussion of the central issue, we shall (a) frame both arguments in the form of a syllogism. Then we shall (b) answer an objection that is commonly encountered against each argument, and with that draw some inferences about the current status of physical proof in modern science.

1 From W. A. Wallace, *Einstein, Galileo, and Aquinas: Three Views of Scientific Method*, Thomist, Washington, D. C., 1963, pp. 19–24.

## (a) Two Arguments

The first argument may be stated as follows:

*A body on which a freely swinging pendulum of fixed length has periods of oscillation which decrease slightly with increasing latitude from the equator to both poles is an oblate spheroid slightly flattened at the poles.*

But *the earth is a body on which a freely swinging pendulum of fixed length has periods of oscillation which decrease slightly with increasing latitude from the equator to both poles.*

Therefore *the earth is an oblate spheroid slightly flattened at the poles.*

The second argument then reads:

*A body on which a freely swinging pendulum deviates at the rate of one revolution per twenty-four hours at the poles, decreasing according to the sine of the latitude to zero deviation at the equator is rotating on its polar axis once every twenty-four hours.*

But *the earth is a body on which a freely swinging pendulum deviates at the rate of one revolution per twenty-four hours at the poles, decreasing according to the sine of the latitude to zero deviation at the equator.*

Therefore *the earth is rotating on its polar axis once every twenty-four hours.*

Were we to investigate the connection between these two conclusions, we would further find that the flattening at the poles is actually *caused* by the centrifugal force of the earth's daily rotation. The behavior of the pendulum, in both cases, is causally connected with both the earth's shape and its rotation, which explains why it can serve as middle term in both *a posteriori* demonstrations. But apart from this, the earth's shape is also causally connected with the daily rotation—a dependence on which we shall have more to say when discussing objections against the two proofs.

## (b) Two Objections

### (i) From non-Euclidean geometry

Some will object against the first argument—the one concluding to the shape of the earth—that this was regarded as valid in the pre-Einstein period, when it was thought that Euclidean geometry was uniquely applicable to the physical universe. But in the present day, when non-Euclidean geometries have proved to be remarkably fruitful in explaining physical phenomena, one cannot say for *sure* that the earth is a sphere or an oblate spheroid; in another geometry it might be another mathematical figure, and thus the argument no longer truly demonstrates.

To this objection we answer that, if relativity theory has shown anything, it has shown that the geometry used by the physicist to describe the shape of the earth is basically immaterial. For dimensions as small as those of the earth, it is of no physical importance whatsoever whether the geometry is Euclidean, or Riemannian, or Lobatchewskian. But the very objection reveals one thing that is quite important, namely, that the objector is a mathematical realist who conceives pure mathematical form as objectively existing in, and determining, the universe to a particular geometry.

As has been shown earlier, this is not the Thomistic concept: physical quantity is much too irregular, it is much too perturbed by physical factors—such as matter and motion and time, and their means of measurement—to yield pure geometrical form, except through a process of mathematical abstraction. Thus, when the physicist says that the earth is an oblate spheroid, just as he prescinds from the mountains and valleys and other physical irregularities, so he prescinds from the slight differences associated with alternative *pure* geometries, to say something that is physically meaningful about the shape of the earth.

### (ii) From the general theory of relativity

The second argument also seems to be vulnerable—this time to an objection drawn from the general theory of relativity. We have argued that it is possible to *demonstrate* that the earth is actually rotating on its axis once every twenty-four hours. Now Einstein, and before him the great German physicist, Ernst Mach—who undoubtedly gave inspiration to Einstein's new theories—have held that it is impossible to detect an *absolute* rotation in the universe. Thus they would argue that the cause assigned above for the deviation of the pendulum on the earth's surface (or for the bulge at the equator) need not be the rotation of the earth. The same effect can be correlated mathematically with the apparent motion of the "fixed" stars, and thus one cannot be absolutely sure that the earth's rotation is causing the pendulum phenomena or the bulge at the center, since these *might* be caused by other forces connected with the diurnal motion of the stars.

A Thomistic answer to this difficulty is suggested by a statement of the English astronomer and commentator on general relativity theory, Sir A. S. Eddington. He writes in this connection:

> I doubt whether anyone will persuade himself that the stars have anything to do with the phenomenon. We do not believe that if the heavenly bodies were all annihilated it would upset the gyrocompass. In any case, precise calculation shows that the centrifugal force could not be produced by the motion of the stars, so far as they are known. [*Space, Time, and Gravitation*, Harper & Row, New York, 1959 (original edition 1920), p. 153.]

As for the search for some unknown force that *might* explain the phenomenon, Eddington becomes more caustic:

> As we go further into space to look for a cause, the centrifugal force becomes greater and greater, so that the more we defer the debt the heavier the payment demanded in the end. Our present theory is like the debtor who does not mind how big an obligation accumulates, satisfied that he can always put off the payment.

In this matter, Thomas Aquinas, we may be reasonably sure, would be content with a physical explanation of the motion of the pendulum or of the bulge at the equator in terms of known causes, and would be quite unhappy with an explanation, or a methodology, that would remove a hypothetical cause to infinity.

As to the mathematical correlation with the fixed stars mentioned by Mach and Einstein, this would not disturb him. He would say—as we have pointed out above—that *mathematically* it makes no difference which one, the earth or the fixed stars, is conceived as moving. But once he saw the physical evidence available today to show that the plane of oscillation of a pendulum is independent of the motion of its support, that it is determined uniquely by its point of suspension, the center of gravity of its bob, and the center of gravity of the local region; or once he conceived himself that there are centrifugal forces connected with every rotation that *we* initiate, he would not look in the remote depths of space for a causal explanation to account for the deviation of a pendulum on the earth's surface, or for the observed bulge in the earth's contour at the equator. He would conclude, as do most modern scientists, that these are caused by the rotation of the earth, and that the earth therefore is actually spinning on its axis.

## EPISTEMIC REQUIREMENTS FOR EXPLANATIONS[1]

*Ernest Nagel (1901–     )*

The requirements for explanations considered thus far have been almost exclusively logical conditions. But it is obvious that other requirements must also be recognized. If, for example, an initial condition in a proposed explanation for the occurrence of an individual event were known to be false, the proposal would be immediately rejected as unsatisfactory. Let us therefore turn briefly to some epistemic[2] requirements for adequate explanations.

In discussing this question, Aristotle maintained that the premises in a deductive explanation must among other things be true, that they must be known to be true, and that they must be "better known" than the explicandum [*Posterior Analytics*, book I, chap. 2]. We shall examine these conditions in turn and discuss some related ones as well.

[1] From Ernest Nagel, *The Structure of Science*, © 1961, by Harcourt, Brace & World, Inc., New York, pp. 42–46, and reprinted with their permission.

[2] Having to do with knowledge (usually true knowledge). Nagel is here making a sharp distinction between *logic* and *actual knowledge* (which need not proceed logically).

1. Any evaluation of the suggestion that the premises of an explanation must be true is complicated by an important circumstance. There frequently occur among the explicit premises of scientific explanations universal statements which are part of some comprehensive scientific theory. However, competent thinkers are divided on the issue whether such statements (and indeed, whether any scientific theory) can be appropriately characterized as either true or false. Accordingly, anyone who subscribes to the view that these characterizations are misapplied when used in connection with such statements will automatically reject the requirement that the explicit premises in a satisfactory explanation must be true. The rejection of this requirement thus hinges on the way the issue mentioned is resolved. The issue will occupy us later. For the present, however, we shall assume that every statement which may appear as a premise in an explanation is either true or false.

If this assumption is made, the requirement that the premises in a satisfactory explanation must be true seems inescapable. It is always relatively easy to invent an arbitrary set of premises which satisfy the logical conditions for deductive explanations; and unless further restrictions were placed on the premises, only a moderate logical and mathematical ability would be required for explaining any fact in the universe without leaving one's armchair. In point of fact, however, all such arbitrarily constructed explanations would be dismissed as inadequate if any of the premises were known to be false. The truth of the premises is undoubtedly a desirable condition for satisfactory explanations.

2. However, this requirement does not carry us far in judging the worth of a proposed explanation if we are not in a position to say whether or not the premises are false. The Aristotelian requirement that the premises must be *known* to be true thus provides an apparently effective criterion for eliminating many proposed explanations as unsatisfactory. But this requirement is much too strong. Were it adopted, few if any of the explanations given by modern science could be accepted as satisfactory. For in point of fact, we do *not* know whether the unrestrictedly universal premises assumed in the explanations of the empirical sciences are indeed true; and, were the requirement adopted, most of the widely accepted explanations in current science would have to be rejected as unsatisfactory. This is in effect a *reductio ad absurdum* of the requirement. In practice it would lead simply to the introduction of another term, perhaps freshly coined for the purpose, for distinguishing those explanations that are judged to have merit by the scientific community—despite their nominal "unsatisfactory" character under the requirement—from those explanations that are judged differently. There is therefore no point in adopting the strong Aristotelian requirements for the adequacy of explanations.

Nevertheless, a stipulation of some kind, though weaker than this

Aristotelian one, is needed concerning the cognitive status of explanatory premises. A reasonable candidate for such a weaker condition is the requirement that the explanatory premises be compatible with established empirical facts and be in addition "adequately supported" (or made "probable") by evidence based on data other than the observational data upon which the acceptance of the explicandum is based. The first part of this requirement is simply the demand that there should be no grounds for regarding the premises as false. The second part seeks not only to exclude so-called *ad hoc* premises for which there is no evidence whatsoever. It also seeks, among other things, to eliminate explanations that are in a sense circular and therefore trivial because one or more of the premises is established (and perhaps can be established) only by way of the evidence used to establish the explicandum. Suppose, for example, that we undertook to explain the explosive noises known as static which issued from a radio on a given day; and suppose that one of the explanatory premises stated the initial condition that on this day there were violent magnetic storms on the sun. However, if the sole evidence for the occurrence of these storms were the static on the radio, the explanation would suffer from a species of circularity and would generally be regarded as defective. In this example, however, evidence for the instantial premise could in point of fact be obtained independently of the noises issuing from the radio. The explanation would have doubtful merit if no such independent evidence could be given.[3]

The weaker condition concerning the cognitive status of premises in explanations is undoubtedly vague. For at present no precise and generally accepted standard is available for judging whether an assumption is indeed "adequately supported" by given evidence. Despite this vagueness, however, those who acquire competence in some field of inquiry often are in good agreement as to the adequacy of the supporting evidence for a definite assumption. In actual practice, at any rate, the use of the weaker condition results in a fair consensus concerning the worth of a proposed explanation. The objection may nevertheless be raised against this condition that, since the evidence for a supposed universal law does not remain constant in time, an explanation that includes the law in its premises and that is satisfactory at one time may cease to be satisfactory when unfavorable evidence for the law is discovered. But the objection is not a disturbing one, unless the dubious assumption is made that in judging an explanation to be satisfactory a timeless property is being predicated of the explanation. It does not seem unreasonable, therefore, to adopt the condition as an epistemic requirement for adequate explanations.

---

[3] At this point Nagel gives a long footnote reference to C. Hempel and P. Oppenheim, "Studies in the Logic of Explanation," *Philosophy of Science*, vol. XV, pp. 135–175, 1948.

3. The Aristotelian requirement, that the premises in a scientific explanation must be "better known" than the explicandum, is intimately related to Aristotle's conception of what constitutes the proper object of scientific knowledge; the requirement was intended by him to apply exclusively to the explanation of scientific laws. On this conception genuine scientific knowledge is possible only of what cannot be otherwise than it is. Accordingly, there can be no scientific knowledge of particular events; and universal laws concerning some area of nature, when they are not immediately recognized as inherently "necessary," must be explained by exhibiting them as the consequences of the "first principles" for that area which can be directly grasped as possessing such necessity. These first principles are therefore the ultimate premises in scientific explanations; and they are "better known" than any of the explicanda because their necessity is intrinsic and transparent to the intellect. The branch of knowledge that undoubtedly served as the model for this conception of science is demonstrative geometry. For according to the view widely held about geometry until fairly recently, each of its theorems states what must be the case universally; and while neither this necessity nor this universality may be immediately evident, both are established when a theorem is deduced from the more general axioms or first principles whose universality is "self-evident." In maintaining that the premises in an explanation must be "better known" than the explicandum, Aristotle was thus simply making explicit his conception of the nature of science.

This conception is true of nothing that can be identified as part of the asserted content of modern empirical science. Accordingly, Aristotle's requirement that the explanatory premises be better known than the explicandum is entirely irrelevant as a condition for anything that would today be regarded as an adequate scientific explanation. On the other hand, various psychologized versions of the Aristotelian requirement have enjoyed wide currency and have frequently been advanced by distinguished men of science as essential conditions for satisfactory explanations. The substance of these suggested conditions is that, since what normally requires explanation is something strange and unexpected, an explanation will yield genuine intellectual satisfaction only if it makes what is unfamiliar intelligible in terms of what is familiar. For example, an eminent contemporary physicist maintains that an "Explanation consists merely in analyzing our complicated systems into simpler systems in such a way that we recognize in the complicated system the interplay of elements already so familiar to us that we accept them as not needing explanation" [P. Bridgman: *The Nature of Physical Theory*, Princeton, Prnceton, N.J., 1936, p. 63]. And he argues that, since current quantum theory does not show how the physical systems falling into its province are the resultants of familiar modes of action between familiar kinds of constituents, the theory does not give us a sense of explaining anything, despite its admittedly remarkable systematizing achievements. Similar views have been expressed by many other thinkers, in the natural as well as in the social sciences.

It would be flying into the teeth of the evidence to deny that important developments in the history of science have been controlled by the desire to explain new domains of fact in terms of something already familiar. One need only recall the persistent use of familiar mechanical models in constructing explanations for the phenomena of heat, light, electricity, and even human behavior in order to recognize the influence of this conception of explanation. Nevertheless, explanations are not invariably judged to be unsatisfactory unless they effect a reduction of the familiar to the unfamiliar. When the bleaching effect of sunlight on colored materials is explained in terms of physical and chemical assumptions about the composition of light and of colored substances, the explanation is not rejected as unsatisfactory, even though it is the familiar which is being accounted for in terms of what to most men is quite unfamiliar. Moreover, the conception of explanation under discussion is in patent disaccord with the fact that throughout the history of science explanatory hypotheses have frequently been introduced which postulate modes of interrelation between assumed elements, where the interrelations and elements are initially strange and occasionally even seemingly paradoxical.

Nevertheless, two brief points should be noted. If an explanation satisfies the epistemic condition previously discussed, then, even though its explanatory premises may at one time have been unfamiliar, they must have finally achieved the status of assumptions well-supported by evidence. Accordingly, even if the explanation does not reduce the unfamiliar to what was initially familiar, it is an acceptable explanation because the premises are firmly grounded in evidence that has ceased to be unfamiliar to some part of the scientific community. In the second place, though explanatory premises may make use of quite unfamiliar ideas, such ideas often exhibit important analogies with notions employed in connection with already familiar subject matters. The analogies help to assimilate the new to the old, and prevent novel explanatory premises from being radically unfamiliar.

## SUMMARY OF POINTS FOR DISCUSSION

*1.* If there were a modern-day defender of strict *mechanism*, he should be able to show the appeal of simple, clear, reductive explanations in science. This appeal will be seen at its clearest in Chapter 5, in the discussion of atomism; there L. L. Whyte argues that atomism "has a powerful psychological appeal, for it suggests a limited task with high rewards. If there really exist ultimate units, we have only to discover their laws and all their possible combinations, and we shall be all-knowing." Similarly, Einstein with his belief in "the perfect rule of law in a world of something objectively existing" expresses a widespread feeling of scientists, which must say something profound about science. Why would such views be so appealing if there were nothing to them?

2. A modern-day *Aristotelian* should not have too great a difficulty in showing that there are, in fact, theories in science that are undoubted. He should also be able to show that his defense of certitude with respect to these theories does not involve *absolute* certainty, or certainty in the sense in which it is found in mathematics or logic, and also that it does not require a retreat to "metaphysical insight." He will have difficulty, however, considering the prevalence of opposed views, in convincing the modern mind that there is any kind of certainty other than the mathematical variety. What would a "limited" or "physical certainty" mean in logical terms, and is there a reasonable process by which the scientist's lack of doubt with respect to some theories can be justified?

3. A *positivist* or logical empiricist will be able to show to all but the most unreconstructed intuitionist that the hypothetico-deductive method, of itself, cannot produce certainty. He will also be able to demonstrate the virtual ubiquity of the method in science. Where he will have difficulty is in explaining the fact of undoubted theories in science. Is the attitude, on the part of scientists, simply unscientific? If so, is it to be explained in terms of hidden metaphysical assumptions, sociological or psychological factors, etc?

4. From all this, and to an extent from the discussions of the two previous chapters, there appears some sort of overall solution:

a. A yearning for simple, quasi-mechanical explanations has an important role to play in science.

b. The hypothetico-deductive method can never satisfy this yearning, if it is interpreted as saying the simple model really exists, without doubt, in the world around us.

c. The fact that some theories in science are undoubted must, then, be explained either as a psychological "filling in" in response to the quasi-mechanical yearning, or as an implicit proof having the limited sort of certitude proposed by Aristotelians.

5. However, an ultimate resolution—if one is possible—of the problem of the intelligibility of the sensible world must be reserved for some meta-science (epistemology, metaphysics, etc.), and it will depend to a great extent on the resolution of other problems, such as the classical "problem of causality" and "problem of induction."

## BIBLIOGRAPHY

**Editor's Note:** This Bibliography will depart from the pattern of the bibliographies in the first two chapters, where references were given for each of the views presented in the chapter, as well as a general orientation. The reason is that here we return to the matter of the

Introduction, where the general background is sketched in some detail and in which a bibliography can be found. In addition, there would be no particular point in trying to give references for the kind of yearning expressed in the contemporary quasi-mechanist view. Hence references will be given here only for the Aristotelian position and, to a more limited extent, for the empiricist position. For a fuller bibliography of the empiricist point of view, the student is also referred to that given in the Introduction; here a classic logical-empiricist text is supplemented by a view growing directly out of a historical context (Holton and Roller) and one that professes to be in direct contact with working scientists (Nash).

**Views that deemphasize "final proofs" in the knowledge of the world**

Holton, G., and D. Roller: *Foundations of Modern Physical Science*, Addison-Wesley, Reading, Mass., 1958, chaps. 8 and 13–15.

Nagel, Ernest: *The Structure of Science*, Harcourt, Brace & World, New York, 1961, chaps. 2 and 3.

Nash, L.: *The Nature of the Natural Sciences*, Little, Brown, Boston, 1963.

**Views that emphasize "final proofs" in varying degrees**

Ashley, B.: "Does Natural Science Attain Nature or Only the Phenomena?" in V. Smith (ed.), *The Philosophy of Physics*, St. John's University Studies, Philosophical Series no. 2, New York, 1961.

De Koninck, C.: "Natural Science as Philosophy," *Culture*, vol. XX, pp. 245–267, 1959; and *The Hollow Universe*, Oxford, Fair Lawn, N.J., 1960.

Maritain, J.: *The Degrees of Knowledge*, G. Phelan (trans.), Scribner's, New York, 1959; and *Philosophy of Nature*, Philosophical Library, New York, 1951.

Smith, V.: *The General Science of Nature*, Bruce, Milwaukee, 1958; and *Science and Philosophy*, Bruce, Milwaukee, 1965.

Wallace, W.: "Some Demonstrations in the Science of Nature," in *The Thomist Reader 1957*, Thomist, Washington, D.C., 1957, pp. 90–118.

# 2

# CONTINUITY
# AND DISCONTINUITY
# IN THE STRUCTURE
# OF MATTER

AN APPROACH TO THE INTELLIGIBILITY of the world can be mechanistic, realistic, positivistic. But what about the world itself that is being approached? The most fundamental aspect of this world, as an object of science and the philosophy of science, is *matter*. What is it? What are its components? How does it act, if at all? How is it structured, interrelated, locked together to form a world that can, because of it, be called "material"?

The best introduction to these ideas today is a brief summary of the state of physics in its understanding of matter. No longer is matter thought of by the physicist in terms of atoms or even elementary particles in simple conjunction with one another. The very model of the atom itself has undergone profound modifications in this century, beginning with the simple planetary model of Nils Bohr, with which every high school chemistry student is familiar. This was soon followed by still picturable "wave" models of the atom, most often associated with the name of Erwin Schrödinger; but even this promptly gave way to the abstract mathematics of the "matrix-mechanics" model of the atom of Werner Heisenberg. All these models still have their usefulness in science, even the largely superseded planetary model. It is still the easiest to imagine and most useful in introductory teaching.

Complications still greater are at hand, however, in the understanding of the myriad of elementary particles that have been found inside the atom (or at least as results of its disintegration through one means or another). Most intriguing of these features of the study of matter are Heisenberg's "principle of uncertainty" and Bohr's "principle of complementarity"—the first required in calculations of the energy states of elementary particle systems, the other referring to an overall approach to elementary particles which allows the scientist pragmatically to use either particle or wave interpretations, whichever works best in the experiment at hand. A little more about each of these will come up in the pages that follow; here the point is simply that the study of matter is vastly more complex than it once seemed.

Two final complications need to be mentioned. Calculations made today in the study of elementary particles (and other areas of physics as well) are based on what is called "quantum mechanics." This is an esoteric world indeed for the nonscientist; even for the science major, who will find it more intelligible, it is by no means easy. Quantum theories offer intriguing challenges to the philosopher, but for the most part they are beyond the scope of the beginner. However, there is an area of equal sophistication which can be outlined with more confidence; it is the application of relativity ideas to the world of the very small, of elementary particles and their structure. For purposes of this section—the matter will come up again in discussions of space and space-time—the most interesting of these applications is the one to which Einstein devoted the greater part of the energy of his last years—the so-called "unified field theory." This is an attempt to integrate all the forces at work in the world to bind matter together in a single mathematical formulation. Fundamental to this effort, which has so far proved ineffective (and which many scientists are ready to write off as misguided), is a conception of the world in radically anti-atomist terms: not that atomic theory would be overturned, but it would be derivative as a *discontinuity* from a more basic model of the world as one vast wave structure of continuity.

It is this last aspect of contemporary theorizing that has once again made respectable Aristotle's basically continuity-oriented view of matter. The first of the two chapters in this section (Chapter 4) is devoted to that theory and the opposition to it and misconceptions of it down through the centuries; Chapter 5 then turns to a more direct discussion of continuity and discontinuity as these come up in contemporary views of the nature of matter.

# Chapter
# 4

# Primary Matter:
# Concept or
# Reality?

IN THE INTRODUCTION, IN THE BRIEF OUTLINE of an Aristotelian realist approach to the understanding of science, two basic points were made with respect to Aristotle's conception of primary matter. (1) It is best defined as "the condition of the possibility of substantial change" (which is therefore found in reality in things *if* they can change substantially). And (2) the conception of primary matter has little direct bearing on modern scientific theories. It may well be implicit, as was also mentioned there, in certain distinctions made in science, but of itself it necessarily belongs to a qualitative and not a quantitative science. Nevertheless, this does not mean that primary matter is of no significance at all in the interpretation of science—it is the root of the entire Aristotelian conception of the world in terms of *continuity*. And it is for this reason that it is worth considering now.

The question of substantial change, the other basic point with respect to primary matter, is also one that does not greatly trouble the scientific mind. In this respect, most scientists are implicit mechanistic atomists; they presume that atoms enter into the composition of molecules and larger macroscopic structures whole and intact. Such a view, if pressed philosophically, would lead inevitably to the conclusion that all changes in the world are to be accounted for by the rearrangement of atoms (or more fundamental elementary particles). The way in which these changes would be accounted for would, naturally, be much more sophisticated than that proposed by the ancient atomists. It would involve symmetry principles, conservation laws, etc. But if the account did not recognize the difference between the *ontological status* of, say, free hydrogen and hydrogen as *part* of a water molecule, it would be reducible to a kind of mechanistic atomism. Not a very important point scientifically, perhaps, since science is concerned primarily not with the ontological status of anything but with its measurable and theory-related aspects. Yet it is a very important point for the *realist* interpretation of science. And it could be potentially important for the ultimate intelligibility of the world in terms of continuity should science ever resolve the continuity-discontinuity question.

In this chapter the existence of substantial change will be assumed; for a defense of the mechanistic denial of substantial change, the student is referred either to ancient atomism in Chapter 1 or else to the defense of an atomistic ideal in Chapter 5.

What is substantial change? That needs to be answered first. Without going into details of the Aristotelian doctrine on substance and accidents, it is sufficient to indicate that substantial change is said to differ *fundamentally* from accidental changes—changes in place, quality, and size (including expansion and growth). The way in which it differs is by being *more fundamental;* these changes all leave the basic nature of the matter undergoing the change intact. On the other hand, any change that to common experience does not leave the basic nature intact would be classified by Aristotle as substantial— the change from wood to smoke and ashes, from living to dead matter, or even the generation of a new living offspring by an animal or man. The point of the Aristotelian doctrine is that, in principle, any substance in the universe can under appropriate conditions (including lapse of time and intervening series of changes) be converted into any other. (As Heisenberg notes in the selection from his work below, the present state of scientific knowledge supports Aristotle in this presumption; however, this is not the point—Aristotle is talking about a possibility *in principle,* based on the experience of some substantial changes but not requiring the verification of universal transmutability.)

The structure of this chapter is somewhat complicated, because of the nature of the subject matter and especially the intrinsic difficulty for the student in grasping what Aristotle means by primary matter and its defining (lack of) quality—pure potentiality. The first selection is taken from Aristotle himself and outlines his basic argument for the existence of a *primary* matter, together with the basic intimation of its nature. This is followed by the only real controversy or matter for discussion in the chapter—the alternative Aristotelian interpretations of primary matter as *concept* or *reality,* represented here by Ernan McMullin and Norbert Luyten, respectively. Since Luyten's view seems closer to that of Aristotle himself, and since it involves the very difficult notion of (pure) *potentiality*, a selection from Heisenberg has been added to show that this kind of reality is not totally alien to the modern mind; Heisenberg's argument is not philosophically sophisticated, but it does make a valid point about potentiality as a possible explanatory principle in contemporary particle physics. Finally, the chapter is brought to a close with a very difficult selection from Norwood Russell Hanson. The Hanson selection is included, in spite of its difficulty, because it makes two very excellent points about the nature of matter: (1) It shows convincingly that very few discussions of matter in the history of thought have been talking about anything like Aristotle's notion of potentiality, and (2) it argues persuasively for a sophistication in such discussions—for a use of categories as difficult and nonmechanistic as Aristotle's potentiality—that has been notably lacking in the past (and perhaps was not possible, historically, before the advent of Bohr's complementarity).

## THE PRIMARY SUBSTRATUM[1]

*Aristotle (384–322 B.C.)*

We will now give our own account, approaching the question first with reference to becoming in its widest sense: for we shall be following the natural order of inquiry if we speak first of common characteristics, and then investigate the characteristics of special cases.

We say that one thing comes to be from another thing, and one sort of thing from another sort of thing, both in the case of simple and of complex things. I mean the following. We can say (1) the "man becomes musical," (2) what is "not-musical becomes musical," or (3) the "not-musical man becomes a musical man." Now what becomes in (1) and (2) —"man" and "not musical"—I call *simple*, and what each becomes— "musical"—simple also. But when (3) we say the "not-musical man becomes a musical man," both what becomes and what it becomes are *complex*.

As regards one of these simple "things that become" we say not only "this becomes so-and-so," but also "from being this, comes to be so-and-so," as "from being not-musical comes to be musical"; as regards

---

[1] *Physics*, book I, chap. 7. This selection, though it contains all the principal elements in Aristotle's doctrine, at least implicitly, needs to be filled out with references to the *Metaphysics*. There, especially in book VIII, Aristotle spells out in explicit detail the most important features of primary matter: its potentiality (chap. 1), the matter proper to each species of being (chap. 4), the clear distinction between matter and its actualization on which the idea of *pure* potentiality is based (chap. 5), and the composition of actuality and potentiality, form and matter, which requires pure potentiality *in* things composed of form and matter (chap. 6). From *The Oxford Translation of Aristotle*, by permission of the Clarendon Press, Oxford, pp. 189b30–191a23.

the other we do not say this in all cases, as we do not say (1) "from being a man he came to be musical" but only "the man became musical."

When a "simple" thing is said to become something, in one case (1) it survives through the process, in the other (2) it does not. For the man remains a man and is such even when he becomes musical, whereas what is not musical or is unmusical does not continue to exist, either simply or combined with the subject.

These distinctions drawn, one can gather from surveying the various cases of becoming in the way we are describing that, as we say, there must always be an underlying something, namely that which becomes, and that this, though always one numerically, in form at least is not one.[2] (By that I mean that it can be described in different ways.) For "to be man" is not the same as "to be unmusical." One part survives, the other does not: what is not an opposite survives (for "man" survives), but "not-musical" or "unmusical" does not survive, nor does the compound of the two, namely "unmusical man."

We speak of "becoming that from this" instead of "this becoming that" more in the case of what does not survive the change—"becoming musical from unmusical," not "from man"—but there are exceptions, as we sometimes use the latter form of expression even of what survives; we speak of "a statue coming to be from bronze," not of the "bronze becoming a statue."[3] The change, however, from an opposite which does not survive is described indifferently in both ways, "becoming that from this" or "this becoming that." We say both that "the unmusical becomes musical," and that "from unmusical he becomes musical." And so both forms are used of the complex, "becoming a musical man from an unmusical man," and "an unmusical man becoming a musical man."

But there are different senses of "coming to be." In some cases we do not use the expression "come to be," but "come to be so-and-so." Only substances are said to "come to be" in the unqualified sense.

Now in all cases other than substance it is plain that there must be some subject, namely, that which becomes. For we know that when a thing comes to be of such a quantity or quality or in such a relation, time, or place, a subject is always presupposed, since substance alone is not predicated of another subject, but everything else of substance.

But that substances too, and anything else that can be said "to be" without qualification, come to be from some substratum, will appear on examination. For we find in every case something that underlies from which proceeds that which comes to be; for instance, animals and plants from seed.

Generally things which come to be, come to be in different ways: (1)

---

[2] Though it is (in some sense) one, it has two aspects.

[3] A very poor example in English, where the latter expression would be unremarkable, perhaps even customary.

by change of shape, as a statue; (2) by addition, as things which grow; (3) by taking away, as the Hermes from the stone; (4) by putting together, as a house; (5) by alteration, as things which "turn" in respect of their material substance.

It is plain that these are all cases of coming to be from a substratum.

Thus, clearly, from what has been said, whatever comes to be is always complex. There is, on the one hand, (a) something which comes into existence, and again (b) something which becomes that—the latter (b) in two senses, either the subject or the opposite. By the "opposite" I mean the "unmusical," by the "subject" "man," and similarly I call the absence of shape or form or order the "opposite," and the bronze or stone or gold the "subject."

Plainly then, if there are conditions and principles which constitute natural objects and from which they primarily are or have come to be— have come to be, I mean, what each is said to be in its essential nature, not what each is in respect of a concomitant attribute—plainly, I say, everything comes to be from both subject and form. For "musical man" is composed (in a way) of "man" and "musical": you can analyse it into the definitions of its elements. It is clear then that what comes to be will come to be from these elements.

Now the subject is one numerically, though it is two in form.[4] (For it is the man, the gold—the "matter" generally—that is counted, for it is more of the nature of a "this," and what comes to be does not come from it in virtue of a concomitant attribute; the privation, on the other hand, and the contrary *are* incidental in the process.) And the positive form is one—the order, the acquired art of music, or any similar predicate.

There is a sense, therefore, in which we must declare the principles to be two, and a sense in which they are three; a sense in which the contraries are the principles—say for example the musical and the unmusical, the hot and the cold, the tuned and the untuned—and a sense in which they are not, since it is impossible for the contraries to be acted on by each other. But this difficulty also is solved by the fact that the substratum is different from the contraries, for it is itself not a contrary. The principles therefore are, in a way, not more in number than the contraries, but as it were two, nor yet precisely two, since there is a difference of essential nature, but three. For "to be man" is different from "to be unmusical," and "to be unformed" from "to be bronze."

We have now stated the number of the principles of natural objects which are subject to generation, and how the number is reached: and it is clear that there must be a substratum for the contraries, and that the contraries must be two. (Yet in another way of putting it this is not

4 Has two aspects.

necessary, as one of the contraries will serve to effect the change by its successive absence and presence.)

The underlying nature is an object of scientific knowledge, by an analogy.[5] For as the bronze is to the statue, the wood to the bed, or the matter and the formless before receiving form to any thing which has form, so is the underlying nature to substance, i.e., the "this" or existent.

This then is one principle (though not one or existent in the same sense as the "this"), and the definition was one as we agreed; then further there is its contrary, the privation. . . . Whether the form or the substratum is the essential nature of a physical object is not yet clear. But that the principles are three, and in what sense, and the way in which each is a principle, is clear.

So much then for the question of the number and nature of the principles.

5 This is the key paragraph in the selection and absolutely essential to an understanding of primary matter.

## PURE POTENCY: CONCEPT OR REALITY?[1]

*Norbert Luyten (1909–    ) and Ernan McMullin (1924–    )*

### Aristotle's Position (Luyten)

This was exactly the problem Aristotle discussed in his criticism of his Ionian predecessors. He blames them for having limited their considerations to the material cause alone, in other words for their having reduced everything to matter. But this criticism does not mean that Aristotle rejects the whole of Ionian speculation as worthless. In a way he reaffirms the most fundamental idea in it: that of a basic kinship between things in our universe. What is more, he agrees on calling the ultimate foundation of this commonness, "matter." But, rejecting the identification between matter and *physis,* he restores the true character of potency attached to the genuine notion of matter. To identify matter with the true nature of things, means to admit a materialistic monism of a sort which contradicts our most immediate experience. To reduce all the rich variety of things to a mere superficial change of a unique permanent substance is to ignore the real nature of things. What things are we know through their manifestations, which indicate different, distinct realities. We have to take these indications seriously, and therefore must see them as mani-

1 Selections from Norbert Luyten, "Matter as Potency" and comment on it by Ernan Mc-Mullin, in E. McMullin (ed.), *The Concept of Matter,* University of Notre Dame Press, Notre Dame, Ind., 1963, pp. 125–126 and 134–135.

festing different natures. There is not just one nature; the unique "physis" of the Ionians is broken up into a multitude of different natures, each manifesting itself in a different form. So nature no longer can be considered as a unique substance. We have to admit as many substances as there are different "forms." This leads Aristotle to hold the "form" as the more adequate expression of the true nature—the *physis*—of things. "Form" here no longer means the external shape or quality, but the substantial principle, the intrinsic "nature" underlying and "causing" the exterior appearances. Does this mean that for Aristotle the universe is split up into a multitude of distinct, unrelated "natures," juxtaposed without any connexion? As we pointed out before, Aristotle acknowledges the value of the Ionian intuition: the fact that one thing changes into another indicates a profound community. And as our experience shows us that this fact of change—which in Aristotle's perspective is a substantial change—rather than being an exception, is in fact a general feature of reality, we have to admit a universal community between things. The question is now, what makes this community? Not the *physis* as form because this is distinct in different beings. On the other hand, it must be something intrinsic to things, and in this way, it must belong to their nature.

The only way to explain this seemingly contradictory situation is to admit that the root of the above-mentioned community is intrinsic to the very nature of things. From this it follows that the "physis" in each reality is no longer something simple: it is not only the reason why this latter is different from all others, it is at the same time the reason why it is in communion with them. But it could not be both under the same aspect. Yet one reality can only have one *physis*, one essence. The only solution to this difficulty is to admit a "composition" in the *physis* itself. The reason for the distinctness cannot simply coincide and be strictly identical with the reason for the community. The first—the form—being the reason for the determination of the thing, the other must represent its determinability, its possibility of being determined in some other way (manifested by the fact of transmutation or substantial change). This brings us back to the notion of matter as possibility or potency. But whereas in the earlier context matter appeared mainly as possibility in the context of an agent who produces something from it, in the present perspective its "possibility" relates explicitly to different determined modes of being, to different forms. This brings us to the famous duality of matter and form, terminologically specified in the Aristotelian tradition as primary matter and substantial form.

With this notion of primary matter, the identification of matter and potency is complete. Every aspect of determination in the nature (*physis*) of things is referred to the form. Matter no longer appears as the true (determined) essence of things. It belongs to the essence in a rather negative way. The Aristotelian definition, characterizing matter by its lack of every determined content, sufficiently expresses this negative aspect. As a matter of fact, it is so thoroughly negative that from Aristotle to our own day many philosophers have rejected it as a mere conception of the mind, a logical extrapolation without any value in reality.

### Comment (McMullin)[2]

Dr. Luyten's paper gives an exceptionally clear exposition of the topic, so clear that some awkward points of juncture in the argument show up much more evidently than they do in customary textbook treatments. . . .

The second difficulty is in the context of the notion of *pure* potency. I have some difficulty in knowing what exactly this means and in justifying it. You indicate that because matter is potentiality in the line of substance it must be "pure" potency. I am not sure if I understand this. Are you implying that any given object can in principle become any other object? Would you not agree that there are only certain things a table can become? The restrictions here come from the form, of course, but if one looks at this *particular* table and speaks about the composition of matter and form within it, the matter-principle here regarded as a real co-principle of the table can scarcely be regarded as a principle of pure potency, can it? Even though the limitations on what the table can become proceed from the form, we do not seem to have the right to claim that there is a principle of pure indetermination or pure potency here in the first place. The indeterminacy or "purity" of the potency seem to be properties of the *concept* of prime matter, i.e. of the notion of prime matter abstracting from any particular occurrence or instance of it in a concrete object. If one looks at the totality of material changes, one might want to say that, in general, there is an unspecified series of things into which material objects can change, but the lack of specification here comes from the fact that we are abstracting from the conditions of the *particular* change. It does not seem to come from the ontological character of the matter-principle itself, considered in a concrete instance. If one looks at a material object, then, and claims that there is within it a *real* distinction between matter and form, the "matter" in this instance does not seem to be the principle of pure potency of which you speak but rather a principle of limited potency, the limitation, in this case, proceeding from the quantity, that is, from the form. I suspect that you are using the notion of "principle" or the notion of

---

2 This brief presentation is intended more for discussional purposes than as representing McMullin's opinion; for that, see his article, "Matter as a Principle" (pp. 169–208), in the same volume.

"pure" potency in a way which is slightly different from mine, one which very likely would allow you to respond to this difficulty easily.

## QUANTUM THEORY AND THE STRUCTURE OF MATTER[1]

*Werner Heisenberg (1901– )*

The concept of matter has undergone a great number of changes in the history of human thinking. Different interpretations have been given in different philosophical systems. All these different meanings of the word are still present in a greater or lesser degree in what we conceive in our time as the word "matter."

The early Greek philosophy from Thales to the Atomists, in seeking the unifying principle in the universal mutability of all things, had formed the concept of cosmic matter, a world substance which experiences all these transformations, from which all individual things arise and into which they become again transformed. This matter was partly identified with some specific matter like water or air or fire; only partly, because it has no other attribute but to be the material from which all things are made.

Later, in the philosophy of Aristotle, matter was thought of in the relation between form and matter. All that we perceive in the world of phenomena around us is formed matter. Matter is in itself not a reality but only a possibility, a "potentia"; it exists only by means of form. In the natural process the "essence," as Aristotle calls it, passes over from mere possibility through form into actuality. The matter of Aristotle is certainly not a specific matter like water or air, nor is it simply empty space; it is a kind of indefinite corporeal substratum, embodying the possibility of passing over into actuality by means of the form. The typical examples of this relation between matter and form in the philosophy of Aristotle are the biological processes in which matter is formed to become the living organism, and the building and forming activity of man. The statue is potentially in the marble before it is cut out by the sculptor.

Then, much later, starting from the philosophy of Descartes, matter was primarily thought of as opposed to mind. There were the two complementary aspects of the world, "matter" and "mind," or, as Descartes put it, the "res extensa" and the "res cogitans." Since the new methodical principles of natural science, especially of mechanics, excluded all tracing of corporeal phenomena back to spiritual forces, matter could

[1] From Werner Heisenberg, *Physics and Philosophy*, pp. 147–160 and 166. Copyright © 1958 by Werner Heisenberg. Reprinted by permission of Harper & Row, Publishers.

be considered as a reality of its own independent of the mind and of any supernatural powers. The "matter" of this period is "formed matter," the process of formation being interpreted as a causal chain of mechanical interactions; it has lost its connection with the vegetative soul of Aristotelian philosophy, and therefore the dualism between matter and form is no longer relevant. It is this concept of matter which constitutes by far the strongest component in our present use of the word "matter."

Finally, in the natural science of the nineteenth century another dualism has played some role, the dualism between matter and force. Matter is that on which forces can act; or matter can produce forces. Matter, for instance, produces the force of gravity, and this force acts on matter. Matter and force are two distinctly different aspects of the corporeal world. In so far as the forces may be formative forces, this distinction comes closer to the Aristotelian distinction of matter and form. On the other hand, in the most recent development of modern physics, this distinction between matter and force is completely lost, since every field of force contains energy and in so far constitutes matter. To every field of force there belongs a specific kind of elementary particles with essentially the same properties as all other atomic units of matter.

When natural science investigates the problem of matter it can do so only through a study of the forms of matter. The infinite variety and mutability of the forms of matter must be the immediate object of the investigation and the efforts must be directed toward finding some natural laws, some unifying principles that can serve as a guide through this immense field. Therefore, natural science—and especially physics— has concentrated its interest for a long period on an analysis of the structure of matter and of the forces responsible for this structure.

Since the time of Galileo the fundamental method of natural science had been the experiment. This method made it possible to pass from general experience to specific experience, to single out characteristic events in nature from which its "laws" could be studied more directly than from general experience. If one wanted to study the structure of matter one had to do experiments with matter. One had to expose matter to extreme conditions in order to study its transmutations there, in the hope of finding the fundamental features of matter which persist under all apparent changes.

In the early days of modern natural science this was the object of chemistry, and this endeavor led rather early to the concept of the chemical element. A substance that could not be further dissolved or disintegrated by any of the means at the disposal of the chemist— boiling, burning, dissolving, mixing with other substances, etc.—was called an element. The introduction of this concept was a first and most important step toward an understanding of the structure of matter. The enormous variety of substances was at least reduced to a comparatively small number of more fundamental substances, the "elements," and thereby some order could be established among the various phenomena of chemistry. The word "atom" was consequently used to designate the smallest unit of matter belonging to a chemical element, and the smallest particle of a chemical compound could be pictured as a small group of different atoms. The smallest particle of the element iron, e.g., was an iron atom, and the smallest particle of water, the water molecule, consisted of one oxygen atom and two hydrogen atoms.

The next and almost equally important step was the discovery of the conservation of mass in the chemical process. For instance, when the element carbon is burned into carbon dioxide, the mass of the carbon dioxide is equal to the sum of the masses of the carbon and the oxygen before the process. It was this discovery that gave a quantitative meaning to the concept of matter: independent of its chemical properties matter could be measured by its mass.

During the following period, mainly the nineteenth century, a number of new chemical elements were discovered; in our time this number has reached one hundred. This development showed quite clearly that the concept of the chemical element had not yet reached the point where one could understand the unity of matter. It was not satisfactory to believe that there are very many kinds of matter, qualitatively different and without any connection between one another.

In the beginning of the nineteenth century some evidence for a connection between the different elements was found in the fact that the atomic weights of different elements frequently seemed to be integer multiples of a smallest unit near to the atomic weight of hydrogen. The similarity in the chemical behavior of some elements was another hint leading in the same direction. But only the discovery of forces much stronger than those applied in chemical processes could really establish the connection between the different elements and thereby lead to a closer unification of matter.

These forces were actually found in the radioactive process discovered in 1896 by Becquerel. Successive investigations by Curie, Rutherford and others revealed the transmutation of elements in the radioactive process. The $\alpha$-particles are emitted in these processes as fragments of the atoms with an energy about a million times greater than the energy of a single atomic particle in a chemical process. Therefore, these particles could be used as new tools for investigating the inner structure of the atom. The result of Rutherford's experiments on the scattering of $\alpha$-rays was the nuclear model of the atom in 1911. The most important feature of this well-known model was the separation of the atom into two distinctly different parts, the atomic nucleus and the surrounding electronic shells. The nucleus in the middle of the atom occupies only an extremely small fraction of the space filled by the atom (its radius is about a hundred thousand times smaller than that of the atom), but contains almost its entire mass. Its positive electric charge, which is an integer multiple of the so-called elementary charge, determines the number of the surrounding electrons—the atom as a whole must be electrically neutral—and the shapes of their orbits.

This distinction between the atomic nucleus and the electronic shells at once gave a proper explanation of the fact that for chemistry the chemical elements are the last units of matter and that very much stronger forces are required to change the elements into each other. The chemical bond between neighboring atoms is due to an interaction of the electronic shells, and the energies of this interaction are comparatively small. An electron that is accelerated in a discharge tube by a potential of only several volts has sufficient energy to excite the electronic shells to the emission of radiation, or to destroy the chemical bond in a molecule. But the chemical behavior of the atom, though it consists of the behavior of its electronic shells, is determined by the charge of the nucleus. One has to change the nucleus if one wants to change the chemical properties, and this requires energies about a million times greater.

The nuclear model of the atom, however, if it is thought of as a system obeying Newton's mechanics, could not explain the stability of the atom. As has been pointed out in an earlier chapter, only the application of quantum theory to this model through the work of Bohr could account for the fact that, for example, a carbon atom after having been in interaction with other atoms or after having emitted radiation always finally remains a carbon atom with the same electronic shells as before. This stability could be explained simply by those features of quantum theory that prevent a simple objective description in space and time of the structure of the atom.

In this way one finally had a first basis for the understanding of matter. The chemical and other properties of the atoms could be accounted for by applying the mathematical scheme of quantum theory to the electronic shells. From this basis one could try to extend the analysis of the structure of matter in two opposite directions. One could either study the interaction of atoms, their relation to larger units like molecules or crystals or biological objects; or one could try through the investigation of the atomic nucleus and its components to penetrate to the final unity of matter. Research has proceeded on both lines during the past decades and we shall in the following pages be concerned with the role of quantum theory in these two fields.

The forces between neighboring atoms are primarily electric forces, the attraction of opposite and the repulsion of equal charges; the electrons are attracted by the nuclei and repelled from each other. But these forces act not according to the laws of Newtonian mechanics but those of quantum mechanics.

This leads to two different types of binding between atoms. In the one type the electron of one atom passes over to the other one, for example, to fill up a nearly closed electronic shell. In this case both atoms are finally charged and form what the physicist calls ions, and since their charges are opposite, they attract each other.

In the second type one electron belongs in a way characteristic of quantum theory to both atoms. Using the picture of the electronic orbit, one might say that the electron goes around both nuclei spending a comparable amount of time in the one and in the other atom. This second type of binding corresponds to what the chemists call a valency bond.

These two types of forces, which may occur in any mixture, cause the formation of various groupings of atoms and seem to be ultimately responsible for all the complicated structures of matter in bulk that are studied in physics and chemistry. The formation of chemical compounds takes place through the formation of small closed groups of different atoms, each group being one molecule of the compound. The formation of crystals is due to the arrangement of the atoms in regular lattices. Metals are formed when the atoms are so tightly packed that their outer electrons can leave their shells and wander through the whole crystal. Magnetism is due to the spinning motion of the electron, and so on.

In all these cases the dualism between matter and force can still be retained, since one may consider nuclei and electrons as the fragments of matter that are kept together by means of the electromagnetic forces.

While in this way physics and chemistry have come to an almost complete union in their relations to the structure of matter, biology deals with structures of a more complicated and somewhat different type. It is true that in spite of the wholeness of the living organism a sharp distinction between animate and inanimate matter can certainly not be made. The development of biology has supplied us with a great number of examples where one can see that specific biological functions are carried by special large molecules or groups or chains of such molecules, and there has been an increasing tendency in modern biology to explain biological processes as consequences of the laws of physics and chemistry. But the kind of stability that is displayed by the living organism is of a nature somewhat different from the stability of atoms or crystals. It is a stability of process or function rather than a stability of form. There can be no doubt that the laws of quantum theory play a very important role in the biological phenomena. For instance, those specific quantum-theoretical forces that can be described only inaccurately by the concept of chemical valency are essential for the understanding of the big organic molecules and their various geometrical patterns; the experiments on biological mutations produced by radiation show both the relevance of the statistical quantum-theoretical laws and the existence of amplifying mechanisms. The close analogy between the working of our nervous system and the functioning of modern electronic computers stresses again the importance of single elementary processes in the living organism. Still all this does not prove that physics and chemistry will, together with the concept of evolution, someday offer a complete description of the living organism. The biological processes must be handled by the experimenting scientist with greater caution than processes of physics and chemistry. As Bohr has pointed out, it may well be that a description of the living organism that could be called complete from the standpoint of the physicist cannot be given, since it would require experiments that interfere too strongly with the biological functions. Bohr has described this situation by saying that in biology we are concerned with manifestations of possibilities in that nature to which we belong rather than with outcomes of experiments which we can ourselves perform. The situation of complementarity to which this formulation alludes is represented as a tendency in the methods of modern biological research which, on the one hand, makes full use of all the methods and results of physics and chemistry and, on the other hand, is based on concepts referring to those features of organic nature that are not contained in physics or chemistry, like the concept of life itself.

So far we have followed the analysis of the structure of matter in one direction: from the atom to the more complicated structures consisting of many atoms; from atomic physics to the physics of solid bodies, to chemistry and to biology. Now we have to turn to the opposite direction and follow the line of research from the outer parts of the atom to the inner parts and from the nucleus to the elementary particles. It is this line which will possibly lead to an understanding of the unity of matter. Here we need not be afraid of destroying characteristic structures by our experiments. When the task is set to test the final unity of matter we may expose matter to the strongest possible forces, to the most extreme conditions, in order to see whether any matter can ultimately be transmuted into any other matter.

The first step in this direction was the experimental analysis of the atomic nucleus. In the initial period of these studies, which filled approximately the first three decades of our century, the only tools available for experiments on the nucleus were the $\alpha$-particles emitted from radioactive bodies. With the help of these particles Rutherford succeeded in 1919 in transmuting nuclei of light elements; he could, for instance, transmute a nitrogen nucleus into an oxygen nucleus by adding the

$\alpha$-particle to the nitrogen nucleus and at the same time knocking out one proton. This was the first example of processes on a nuclear scale that reminded one of chemical processes, but led to the artificial transmutation of elements. The next substantial progress was, as is well known, the artificial acceleration of protons by means of high-tension equipment to energies sufficient to cause nuclear transmutation. Voltages of roughly one million volts are required for this purpose and Cockcroft and Walton in their first decisive experiment succeeded in transmuting nuclei of the element lithium into those of helium. This discovery opened up an entirely new line of research, which may be called nuclear physics in the proper sense and which very soon led to a qualitative understanding of the structure of the atomic nucleus.

The structure of the nucleus was indeed very simple. The atomic nucleus consists of only two kinds of elementary particles. The one is the proton which is at the same time simply the hydrogen nucleus; the other is called neutron, a particle which has roughly the mass of the proton but is electrically neutral. Every nucleus can be characterized by the number of protons and neutrons of which it consists. The normal carbon nucleus, for instance, consists of 6 protons and 6 neutrons. There are other carbon nuclei, less frequent in number (called isotopic to the first ones), that consist of 6 protons and 7 neutrons, etc. So one had finally reached a description of matter in which, instead of the many different chemical elements, only three fundamental units occurred: the proton, the neutron and the electron. All matter consists of atoms and therefore is constructed from these three fundamental building stones. This was not yet the unity of matter, but certainly a great step toward unification and—perhaps still more important—simplification. There was of course still a long way to go from the knowledge of the two building stones of the nucleus to a complete understanding of its structure. The problem here was somewhat different from the corresponding problem in the outer atomic shells that had been solved in the middle of the twenties. In the electronic shells the forces between the particles were known with great accuracy, but the dynamic laws had to be found, and were found in quantum mechanics. In the nucleus the dynamic laws could well be supposed to be just those of quantum mechanics, but the forces between the particles were not known beforehand; they had to be derived from the experimental properties of the nuclei. This problem has not yet been completely solved. The forces have probably not such a simple form as the electrostatic forces in the electronic shells and therefore the mathematical difficulty of computing the properties from complicated forces and the inaccuracy of the experiments make progress difficult. But a qualitative understanding of the structure of the nucleus has definitely been reached.

Then there remained the final problem, the unity of matter. Are these fundamental building stones—proton, neutron and electron—final indestructible units of matter, atoms in the sense of Democritus, without any relation except for the forces that act between them or are they just different forms of the same kind of matter? Can they again be transmuted into each other and possibly into other forms of matter as well? An experimental attack on this problem requires forces and energies concentrated on atomic particles much larger than those that have been necessary to investigate the atomic nucleus. Since the energies stored up in atomic nuclei are not big enough to provide us with a tool for such experiments, the physicists have to rely either on the forces in cosmic dimensions or on the ingenuity and skill of the engineers.

Actually, progress has been made on both lines. In the first case the physicists make use of the so-called cosmic radiation. The electromagnetic fields on the surface of stars extending over huge spaces are under certain circumstances able to accelerate charged atomic particles, electrons and nuclei. The nuclei, owing to their greater inertia, seem to have a better chance of remaining in the accelerating field for a long distance, and finally when they leave the surface of the star into empty space they have already traveled through potentials of several thousand million volts. There may be a further acceleration in the magnetic fields between the stars; in any case the nuclei seem to be kept within the space of the galaxy for a long time by varying magnetic fields, and finally they fill this space with what one calls cosmic radiation. This radiation reaches the earth from the outside and consists of nuclei of practically all kinds, hydrogen and helium and many heavier elements, having energies from roughly a hundred or a thousand million electron volts to, again in rare cases, a million times this amount. When the particles of this cosmic radiation penetrate into the atmosphere of the earth they hit the nitrogen atoms or oxygen atoms of the atmosphere or may hit the atoms in any experimental equipment exposed to the radiation.

The other line of research was the construction of big accelerating machines, the prototype of which was the so-called cyclotron constructed by Lawrence in California in the early thirties. The underlying idea of these machines is to keep by means of a big magnetic field the charged particles going round in circles a great number of times so that they can be pushed again and again by electric fields on their way around. Machines reaching up to energies of several hundred million electron volts are in use in Great Britain, and through the co-operation of twelve European countries a very big machine of this type is now being constructed in Geneva which we hope will reach up to energies of 25,000 million electron volts. The experiments carried out by means of cosmic radiation or of the big accelerators have revealed new interesting features of matter. Besides the three fundamental building stones of matter—electron, proton and neutron—new elementary particles have been found which can be created in these processes of highest energies and disappear again after a short time. The new particles have similar properties as the old ones except for their instability. Even the most stable ones have lifetimes of roughly only a millionth part of a second, and the lifetimes of others are even a thousand times smaller. At the present time about twenty-five different new elementary particles are known; the most recent one is the negative proton.

These results seem at first sight to lead away from the idea of the unity of matter, since the number of fundamental units of matter seems to have again increased to values comparable to the number of different chemical elements. But this would not be a proper interpretation. The experiments have at the same time shown that the particles can be created from other particles or simply from the kinetic energy of such particles, and they can again disintegrate into other particles. Actually the experiments have shown the complete mutability of matter. All the elementary particles can, at sufficiently high energies, be transmuted into other particles, or they can simply be created from kinetic energy and can be annihilated into energy, for instance into radiation. Therefore, we have here actually the final proof for the unity of matter. All the elementary particles are made of the same substance, which we may call energy or universal matter; they are just different forms in which matter can appear.

If we compare this situation with the Aristotelian concepts of matter and form, we can say that the matter of Aristotle, which is mere "potentia," should be compared to our concept of energy, which gets into "actuality" by means of the form, when the elementary particle is created.

Modern physics is of course not satisfied with only qualitative description of the fundamental structure of matter; it must try on the basis of careful experimental investigations to get a mathematical formulation of those natural laws that determine the "forms" of matter, the elementary particles and their forces. A clear distinction between matter and force can no longer be made in this part of physics, since each elementary particle not only is producing some forces and is acted upon by forces, but it is at the same time representing a certain field of force. The quantum-theoretical dualism of waves and particles makes the same entity appear both as matter and as force. . . .

But all these problems will be a matter of future research in atomic physics. One may hope that the combined effort of experiments in the high energy region and of mathematical analysis will someday lead to a complete understanding of the unity of matter. The term "complete understanding" would mean that the forms of matter in the sense of Aristotelian philosophy would appear as results, as solutions of a closed mathematical scheme representing the natural laws for matter.

## THE DEMATERIALIZATION OF MATTER[1]

*Norwood Russell Hanson (1924–1967)*

### Primary and Secondary Qualities

William Whewell wrote in 1834:

> ... If we in our thoughts attempt to divest matter of its powers of resisting and moving, it ceases to be matter, according to our conceptions, and we can no longer reason upon it with any distinctness. And yet ... the properties of matter ... do not obtain by any absolute necessity.... [*Astronomy and General Physics* (1834), pp. 211–212.]

Within the subsequent century the matter-concept underwent radical changes. Let us explore these changes and note how they relate to the distinction between primary and secondary properties.

Determining the essence of the matter-concept was a problem already familiar to Democritus:

> A thing merely appears to have color; it merely appears to be sweet or bitter. Only atoms and empty space have a real existence. [Cf. K. Freeman, *Ancilla to the Pre-Socratic Philosophers*, Blackwell, Oxford, 1948, p. 93.]

Compare Plato:

> Properties such as hard, warm, and whatever their names may be, are nothing in themselves.... [*Theaetetus*, 156e.]

Galileo joined this chorus:

> White or red, bitter or sweet, noisy or silent, fragrant or malodorous [...] are names for certain effects upon the sense organs. [*Il Saggiatore.*]

Locke gives the distinction its classic shape:

> The qualities then that are in bodies, rightly considered, are ...: First, the bulk, figure, number, situation, and motion or rest of their solid parts. Those are in them, whether we perceive them or not; and when they are of that size that we can discover them, we have by these an idea of the thing as it is in itself; as is plain in artificial things. These I call *primary qualities*. Secondly, the power that is in any body, by reason of its insen-

[1] Reprinted from *Philosophy of Science*, vol. XXIX, pp. 27–32, 34–36, 1962, with permission of the editors. The article is also reprinted in E. McMullin (ed.), *The Concept of Matter*, University of Notre Dame Press, Notre Dame, Ind., 1963, pp. 549–554, 556–559.

sible primary qualities, to operate after a peculiar manner any of our senses, and thereby produce in *us* the different ideas of several colors, sounds, smells, tastes, etc. These are usually called *sensible qualities*. . . . The first of these . . . may be properly called real, original, or primary qualities; because they are in the things themselves, whether they are perceived or not: and upon their different modifications it is that the secondary qualities depend. [*Essay Concerning Human Understanding*, book II, chap. 8, sec. 23.]

Thus on the one hand there are the properties matter *really has;* these are geometrical, statical, and dynamical. Shape, mass, motion and impact —these are a body's primary properties. However, its apparent color in ultra-violet light—or daylight—its taste, its tone, its fragrance; these are the body's secondary properties. Our appreciation of these latter varies with the state of our senses; secondary properties result from interaction between percipient and perceived. The primary qualities, however, seem "in the bodies themselves." Hence, they are the very properties of matter itself.

As historians know, the primary-secondary distinction dissolved in George Berkeley's inkwell. Knowing a body's shape seemed to the Bishop as much the result of interaction as any secondary property. (18th-century psychologists knew that a given mass could generate variable perceptions in subjects differently conditioned.) Berkeley's epistemology, therefore, erased any distinction in principle between primary and secondary properties. Either the two were equally weak, or equally strong—depending on how one interprets Berkeley. Either secondary properties are just as basic to matter as the primaries, or the primaries give no more indication of matter "as it really is" than the secondaries. The latter seems more like Berkeley; hence I adopt it here.

Berkeley's analyses, however, seemed *merely* philosophical. Distinctions between primaries and secondaries may indeed fail under strict analysis. But Berkeley's scientific contemporaries still treated the distinction as fundamental, philosophers nothwithstanding. Scientists were concerned with the physical properties of objects, not their "real" properties. We shall return to this distinction.

Consider now Heisenberg's insight into the history of atomism and the manner in which it reflects the primary-secondary contrast:

It is impossible to explain . . . qualities of matter except by tracing these back to the behavior of entities which themselves no longer possess these qualities. If atoms are really to explain the origin of color and smell of visible material bodies, then they cannot possess properties like color and smell. . . . Atomic theory consistently denies the atom any such perceptible qualities. [W. Heisenberg, "Ideas of the Natural Philosophy of Ancient Times in Modern Physics," *Philosophic Problems of Nuclear Science*, F. Hayes (trans.), Pantheon, New York, 1952, p. 61; originally published in the German journal *Die Antike*, vol. XIII.]

Boyle is making a similar point:

> Matter being in its own nature but one, the diversity we see in bodies must necessarily arise from somewhat else than the matter they consist of. [*Works* (1744), vol. 3, p. 15.]

Lucretius' atoms were colorless; an aggregate's color depended on the size, shape, and interrelations of its constituent atoms. His atoms were without heat, sound, taste or smell [cf. *On the Nature of Things*, book II, line 842].

And Bacon wrote:

> Bodies entirely even in the particles which affect vision are transparent, bodies simply uneven are white, bodies uneven and in a compound yet regular texture are all colors except black; while bodies uneven and in a compound, irregular, and confused texture are black. [*Novum Organum*, book II, aph. 23.]

Birch writes of Newton:

> The atoms ... were themselves, he thought, transparent; opacity was caused by "the multitude of reflections caused in their internal parts." [*History of the Royal Society* (1756–1757), vol. 3, p. 247.]

Thus the atomic hypothesis, and its intricate history, would crumble unless the ancient distinction between primary and secondary qualities braced it. No classical atomist thought atoms to be colored, fragrant, hot, or tasteable; the basic function of atoms was to explain away such properties as but the molar manifestations of the atom's primary properties and geometrical configurations.

Not every atomist stressed the same atomic primary properties, although all agreed that, whatever they were, the atom's properties were necessarily primary, an argument to which we shall return. The atom's primaries usually included things like position, shape, motions, etc.

Position was paramount for Democritus, but it was *shape* for Epicurus and Lucretius. Newton fixed on the *motions* of atoms. Gassendi remarked their *combinatory properties*; this already constitutes an extension of the Lockean notion. But doubtless combinatory capacity would have been accepted by all as a primary property, although not every atomist would have stressed it *à la* Gassendi. Henceforth, the term "primary" will be used in this extended way. Atomic *irresolvability* attracted Boyle, but this is virtually tautological, since "*atomos*" means just this. For Lavoisier, Richter, and Dalton, *mass* was basic. Berzelius stressed their *binding force* (again this falls within our extended class of primaries). Further properties were stressed by Faraday, Weber, Maxwell, Boltzmann, Clausius, Mayer, Loschmidt, and Hittorf. But, by all, the atoms were characterized by some cluster of primary properties, on a selected one of which further theoretical constructions were founded.

The exception is Stumpf,[2] who could not imagine atoms as spatial bodies lacking color. But he is the exception proving the rule—by which is meant "probing the rule": we know what is generally true when we note how a counter-instance deviates.

The predominant sentiment of the Scientific Revolution was expressed by Newton:

> I ... suspect that [the phenomena of nature] may all depend upon certain forces by which the particles or bodies ... are either mutually impelled towards one another and cohere in regular figures, or are repelled and recede from one another. [*Principia* (Motte-Cajori), p. xviii.]

Here is a yet wider extension of Locke's use of "primary." But forces which impel and repel would surely be on the primary side of the ancient fence.

The degree to which the primary-secondary distinction remained scientifically fundamental, despite Berkeley's leveling analysis, is illustrated by Euler:

> The whole of natural science consists in showing in what state the bodies were when this or that change took place, and that ... just that change had to take place which actually occurred. [*Anleitung zur Naturlehre*, sec. 50.]

Helmholtz is as direct:

> The task of physical science is to reduce all phenomena of nature to forces of attraction and repulsion, the intensity of which is dependent only upon the mutual distance of material bodies. Only if this problem is solved are we sure that nature is conceivable. [*Uber die Erhaltung der Kraft* (On the conservation of force).]

These sentiments reflect a spectrum of related attitudes: the mechanical philosophy, theoretical determinism, the reduction of all science to physics. These are generable only from an implicit atomism. Historically, this devolves into something resembling the classical distinction between primary and secondary properties.

"Resembling" is the operative word. Berkeley speculated about the *real* properties of matter. He felt the classical primary-secondary distinction to be unsound. These properties were on the same epistemic level so far as knowing "reality" was concerned. One of the Bishop's scientific contemporaries could grant this, however, and yet preserve the same distinction at a different level—that concerned not with matter's *real* properties (a philosopher's inquiry at most), but with its *physical* properties. This latter is a scientist's inquiry at least.

Berkeley's "Thou shalt not speak of primary properties as philosophically real" is hence distinguishable from a prohibition heard in this century: "Thou shalt not speak of primary properties as physically real." In

2 German philosopher-psychologist (1848–1936).

the 18th century, a scientist could have accepted the first and rejected the second. Now he may very well accept the second, whatever may be his attitude towards the first.

Hence, so far as one is concerned with distinguishing primary properties (which were real and in matter itself) from secondary properties (which were merely produced in us)—Berkeley's epistemic criticism was devastating. Still, the distinction remained viable in natural philosophy, the province not of philosophically real, but of physically real properties. Physically real properties contrast with mere appearances (intersubjectively understood). That a submerged stick is really straight contrasts with its bent appearance, and that the solidified $CO_2$ is really cold contrasts with our impression of it as blisteringly hot. But concern with the philosophically real undercuts these scientific inquiries altogether. The latter concern stable, permanent properties of objects as contrasted with those which are evanescent, contextually dependent, and accrue to them via special conditions of observation, e.g. ultra-violet illumination, intoxicated observers. Berkeley's inquiry is concerned with the philosophical extension of this scientific contrast, as signalled by the question: "And which of these kinds of properties does matter *really have?*" The scientist's use of the primary-secondary distinction is restricted to delineating the contrast "observed under all conditions" vs. "observed only under special conditions." The philosopher asks the more pervasive question, which Berkeley answers by a denial: to wit, there are no better grounds for supposing matter really has properties we regularly observe it to have, than there are for thinking its properties are those we irregularly observe.

Within the class of physically real properties scientists did distinguish primaries from secondaries. They had to do so to sustain an intelligible atomism. But Berkeley's objectives were not scientific; he dismissed the distinction as philosophically untenable. Physical science is only now undergoing its Berkeleyan self-criticism. When Whewell wrote, it had not. He spoke of conceptual constraints against tinkering with our ideas of the primary physical properties of matter. These constraints are no longer as binding as in the 19th century. Indeed, our understanding of elementary matter, of electrons, cannot proceed within a classical conception of primary physical properties.

For a theory of electrons to succeed now, the electron-idea must be divested of its classical conceptions of resisting and moving. This is what Whewell claimed we could not do:

> Divest matter of its powers of resisting and moving ... and we can no longer reason upon it with any distinctness.

But electrons can be reasoned upon with distinctness, although, it may be granted, they remain unfamiliar material objects. . . .

## Dematerialization

Matter has been dematerialized, not just as a concept of the philosophically real, but now as an idea of modern physics. Matter can be analyzed down to the level of fundamental particles. But at that depth the direction of the analysis changes, and this constitutes a major conceptual surprise in the history of science. The things which for Newton typified matter—e.g., an exactly determinable state, a point shape, absolute solidity—these are now the properties electrons do not, because theoretically they cannot, have.

Matter has been dematerialized, but now more radically than with Berkeley. He showed that, despite ancient epistemic dogmas, primary and secondary properties were in the same conceptual boat. One of his scientific contemporaries could have inferred from the Bishop's analyses that therefore primary properties were just as weak as were the secondaries as indicators of the real properties of matter. He could have concluded this and still continued to do consistent physics. For Berkeley's criticism was abstractly philosophical. It concerned our knowledge of the "real" properties of matter, as opposed to its physical properties. It left Newtonian mechanics intact and unscathed. Similarly, perplexities of contemporary epistemology have no effect on today's mechanical engineers.

The dematerialization of matter encountered in this century, however, has rocked mechanics at its foundations. As an intra-physical revolution in ideas, this compares with the intra-mathematical revolution initiated by Gödel. Some scientists still think of electrons as point-masses with most of the properties of minute billiard balls—just as some mathematicians still have formalist (i.e. Hilbertian) hankerings. But how unclear such physicists can be when questioned about the nature of things like $\beta$-beam interference patterns. Either they say nothing at all, or nothing at all intelligible (usually capped with some remark like "I am an empiricist"). In the 18th century one could have accepted Berkeley's demonstration of the inadequacy of primary properties as indicators of "real" matter, and still do consistent physics; much as today a psychologist can grant there are philosophical problems about other minds, and still rely on the verbal responses of his subjects. But the 20th century's dematerialization of matter has made it conceptually impossible to accept a Newtonian picture of the properties of matter and still do consistent physics.

Some will assent to much I have said here, and yet will qualify my conclusion. They may grant that the ancient distinction between primary and secondary properties, like philosophy itself, branched into the natural philosophy of the 17th century, and the pure philosophy of the 18th century—the latter as typified in Berkeley. And an intimate historical connection between the successful growth of atomism in science and the correlative dependence of scientists on some version of the primary-secondary distinction might also be granted. Perhaps it will even be conceded that Berkeley's challenge to this distinction affected only the epistemological branch of the conceptual tree, not its scientific branch. The latter has been affected only by *contemporary* matter theory, wherein any correspondence between the properties matter (e.g. electrons) is now known to have, and the classical "primary" properties, is at best analogical, and at worst non-existent.

These are my theses thus far. From them, however, some will not conclude as I do, that modern physics has destroyed our intra-scientific version of the primary-secondary distinction just as Berkeley destroyed its intra-philosophical version. . . .

. . . But since there is in this criticism no challenge to the historical point that *our* ideas about the primary properties of particles are different from those of the tradition concerned with primary properties (despite Whewell's contention that no such change could occur), nor any challenge to the further point that Berkeley's attack on the primary-secondary distinction left physicists free to exploit the distinction in their atomistic theories of the 18th and 19th centuries, whereas they are no longer free to do this in the old way—since these main points are unaffected by the contention that the objectifiability-non-objectifiability contrast *is* the same as primary-secondary contrast (with the property-values left unspecified), I will back off with only the grumble that even this contention could be demonstrated as indefensible. But the demonstration must await another occasion.

## SUMMARY OF POINTS FOR DISCUSSION

*1.* A strict Aristotelian should be able to show without difficulty that if anyone admits the existence of genuine substantial change, he must also accept the reality of the *condition of the possibility* of such change. This requires a real substrate in things, but also one which is completely without substantial determinations, without any qualification whatsoever that would explain *what* a substantial being *is* (in the formal sense). However, this very conception—which amounts to the same thing as "pure potentiality" as a reality and not just a concept—involves all sorts of difficulties in knowing what type of reality such an indeterminate substrate could have. The concept of potentiality is difficult enough in itself, and it is obviously going to be more difficult to explain *pure* potentiality. In addition, the scientist might well ask, "Does such a difficult conception have any utility in science?"

*2.* Anyone who, like McMullin, would want to view primary matter as merely a concept or theoretical entity would concentrate his attention on the conceptual difficulties involved in primary matter. The view also serves to highlight better than Aristotle himself the *limitation* on primary matter consequent upon its mode of existence (i.e., only in its determinations)—namely, that the substantial changes of which it is the condition are not dependent solely on matter, but also on the substantial principle or form, and thus these substantial changes must follow one another in a strictly limited way in an orderly universe. (This would be an Aristotelian justification of conservation laws in science.) However, on the debit side, it can be asked whether the view can sustain the existence of true substantial change (as McMullin would want to do) without in fact ending up with an explanation identical to the strict Aristotelian position.

3. A mechanist would be able to show the lack of utility of the conception of pure potentiality in a purely quantitative science; he would, however, have difficulty in defending his own mechanical outlook in the present state of physical science.

4. Positivists in general would be uninterested in the debate, because it deals with something on the ontological level, but in general, insofar as they might be drawn into the discussion, they would most likely side with McMullin.

5. Finally, it is worth noting that discussions of matter, down through the centuries, have often been concerned with fundamentally different realities and problems. Certainly few thinkers after the advent of modern science have been talking about anything even remotely like Aristotle's pure potentiality. Hanson's selection would tend to say that, at the present state of knowledge in physics, scientists and philosophers of science should *rethink* these old discussions, but as the debates were carried out, historically, they did not involve terms as complicated as those of Aristotle.

## BIBLIOGRAPHY

**General**

The two most useful references are McMullin's *The Concept of Matter* and Heisenberg's *Physics and Philosophy*, from which the selections were taken. These can be supplemented by the references in the next chapter, on continuity and discontinuity in the structure of matter.

**Aristotle**

Solmsen, F.: *Aristotle's System of the Physical World*, Cornell, Ithaca, N.Y., 1960.

**The history of quantitative concepts of matter**

Jammer, M.: *Concepts of Mass in Classical and Modern Physics*, Harvard, Cambridge, Mass., 1961.

# Chapter

# 5 *

# Continuity and
# Discontinuity in the
# Structure of Matter

MATTER IS AGAIN OUR SUBJECT, but this time the emphasis is on the interpretation of modern scientific theories about the structure of matter. The main
philosophical point at issue is whether matter is fundamentally *discrete* or
*continuous*—atomic and particulate, or made up of modifications of some
basic "stuff." In terms appropriate to ancient times or the Middle Ages, it
is a question of atomism against Aristotelian anti-atomism; in a contemporary
discussion the question is better stated in mathematical terms of continuity
and discontinuity. Are particles and particle theories merely singular solutions
of a fundamental wave equation? Or are waves, energy, and interactions functions of discrete unit particles existing in otherwise empty space?

The discussion can be introduced very well by means of the following selection from Lancelot Law Whyte. His preference, as stated in the final pages of
his little book, is for an "ideal fusion of discontinuous and continuous
aspects." He cites P. W. Bridgman to the effect that, "Today the thesis of the
atomic constitution of matter is universally accepted with no reservations
whatever by every competent physicist." But Whyte then notes that the universal acceptance may refer only to a certain level of theorizing (that of
chemical molecules and atoms at normal energies), and one may also add
that such acceptance by physicists does not rule out further philosophical
reflection about continuity and discontinuity *on the ontological plane.*

Finally, Whyte notes the real issue:

> A relativistic field theoretician ... may hold that the primary phe-
> nomenon is a relational field of energy and that apparent discreteness is
> a secondary and transitory effect arising only in special circumstances.
> *The open question is whether the field or its sources is theoretically*
> *primary. (Essay on Atomism, p. 102; italics added.)*

And if the question is open on the level of physical theory, it is all the
more open on the level of philosophical discussion.

## ATOMISM[1]

*Lancelot Law Whyte (1896–    )*

In the broadest sense, atomism means the reduction of complex phenomena to fixed unit factors. This includes *epistemological* atomism, or
the doctrine of units of perception; *linguistic* atomism, the use of an
alphabet; *logical* atomism, the postulation of unit propositions; *biological*
atomism, the assumption of discrete cells, genes, etc.; and various kinds
of *social, economic,* and *psychological,* as well as *physical* atomism,
which is our concern here. Atomic methods can be applied even where
the units are not isolated entities randomly arranged, but components in
an ordered system, as are the genes in the genetic system. Some kind of
atomism, or use of constant irreducible units, is probably indispensable
in the systematic ordering of complex facts of any kind. Unit factor
statistical analysis is an atomic method applicable in many fields. Even
the use of coordinates and differential equations—often regarded as the
characteristic expression of continuity—depends on the availability of
atomic systems providing invariant quantitative units or measures of
length, time, etc. Moreover, atomism is often latent where it is not explicit, as in the application of group theory to symmetrical arrangements.
For symmetry can be studied without explicitly considering the nature of
the units whose regular arrangement forms the symmetrical pattern.

This analytical procedure, the reduction of complexity to units, comes
naturally to the Western mind, and appears to be the only policy for
intellectual exploration discovered so far which can be pursued sys-
temically, as a *method.* Atomism is the pre-eminent intellectual method.
If a better one lies ahead, it must grow out of, and must subsume, the
achievements of atomism in physics and elsewhere.

[1] Lancelot Law Whyte, *Essay on Atomism*, Wesleyan University Press, Middletown, Conn.,
1961, pp. 12–15, 21–27. Copyright © 1961 by Wesleyan University. Reprinted by permission of Wesleyan University Press.

The structure of mental processes is as yet little understood, but the rational conscious intellect, as developed in the West, is basically analytical, in the sense that it moves by definite operations or steps from one more or less isolable stepping stone (image, idea, or word) to the next. It seeks discreteness and permanence in these stepping stones, and infers such properties whenever possible. The unconscious mind may not proceed by indivisible steps, but reason must when it seeks clear discriminations. And where appropriate it simplifies matters for the intellect if the stepping stones can be treated as identical with one another— that is, as intrinsically equivalent units.

Thus discontinuity of its linguistic and logical *terms* is for the conscious analytical intellect psychologically and logically prior to notions of continuity. The intellect pays attention to and thinks about the stones *before* it becomes aware of the steps between them. This functional priority of substantive units may not have been reflected in the history of the development of reason in all human communities. For example, early Chinese thought may have reflected continuity of process more directly. But it is relevant for the West that the Pythagoreans, with their discrete integers and point patterns, came before Euclid, with his continuous metrical geometry, and that physical atomism as a speculative philosophy preceded by some two thousand years the conception of a continuous physical medium with properties of its own. Moreover, the counting of time was a commonplace before the sophisticated idea of a continuous temporal quantitative magnitude was developed. During the centuries of the Middle Ages in Europe, when the Greek atoms were almost forgotten, the Latin word *atomus* stood for the smallest unit of time: "the twinkling of an eye." Quanta of process, and their numbers, come naturally to minds which themselves move by steps, but first come the stepping stones. Thus the two atomicities of the XXth century—the discreteness of the material constituents of physical systems, the discontinuity of process and interactions—directly reflect the dual discreteness of the operation of the intellect: the stepping stones and the steps; but they may be none the less objective for that.

This being so, it is not surprising that the history of physical atomism has been one of the most important and exciting adventures of the human mind. Whatever the limitations of atomism, and however profoundly it may be modified in the future, it is here that the ordering intellect has come most closely to grips with the objective structure which, I believe, existed before there were men and will survive them. Hence the unique prestige of atomic physics; hence nuclear power; and hence also the greatest dangers confronting mankind.

But physical atomism is more than logical analysis. It is the assumption that there is a quantitative limit to division, that small ultimate units exist, and that large-scale phenomena are to be accounted for in terms of the small and therefore in terms of these ultimate units. This is the essence of atomism: the view that physical structure is not infinitely complex and that there exists a limit to research into smaller regions. Atomism has rightly been described as a policy for research; it can never be proved that the ultimate units have actually been reached, though at some stage it may become unnecessary to assume the existence of any finer structure or further complexity.

The atomic assumption has much in its favour. A survey of the *prima facie* evidence for the discrete construction of matter would cover a great part of physics, from the everyday properties of expansion and contraction, dispersion, and so on, to the subtleties of optical, stereochemical, and crystalline properties. Perhaps the most striking direct evidences of discrete structure are the Brownian motion, the close agreement of the values of Avogadro's number obtained by different methods, radioactive properties, the X-ray diffraction patterns produced by crystals, and the photographs of particle tracks. Though these phenomena do not prove that *ultimate* structure has been reached, they point unmistakably to discreteness of structure in nuclei, atoms, and molecules.

But atomism is not merely a policy or method which has proved brilliantly effective at certain levels of material analysis; it is also a positive assumption regarding ultimate structure. This assumption has a powerful psychological appeal, for it suggests a limited task with high rewards. If there really exist ultimate units, we have only to discover their laws and all their possible combinations, and we shall be all-knowing and all-powerful, like gods. So it seems. . . .

In 1892 W. W. Rouse Ball of Trinity College, Cambridge, who was well informed on competent opinion—J. J. Thomson was also at Trinity —wrote: "The popular view is that every atom of any particular kind is a minute indivisible article possessing definite qualities, everlasting in its properties, and infinitely hard." Rouse Ball wisely added descriptions of two rival atomic doctrines: Boscovich's point centres, and another based on twists in an elastic solid aether.

Four years later the hard everlasting atom began its rapid exit from physics. In 1896 Becquerel discovered the radioactivity of uranium; in 1898 the Curies found the same property in thorium and radium; and in 1902–1903 Rutherford and Soddy proposed the transformation hypothesis. The "popular view" barely survived a decade.

One might define as "atomic" *any theory based on the changing spatial relations of a finite number of separate indivisible entities of as few kinds as possible.* But what is an entity? How permanent must it be? Are quantized fields "separate indivisible entities"?

Another tempting definition is: *Any theory is atomic which assumes that a finite number of ultimate entities are present in any finite system.* This stresses the spatially finite character of the relations of the particles, but it solves no problems and leaves the status of quantum mechanics obscure. Fertile theories often elude supposedly clear definitions.

It is more profitable not to attempt a general definition and instead to consider what conceptions of atomic particles have been most fertile and have had the widest applications. There have been only three basically distinct and widely successful conceptions. They present striking contrasts.

*A. Democritan-Newtonian hard atoms*    Newton (c. 1686–1720), following the Greek atomists, adopted as most appropriate the view that the ultimate constituents of matter are themselves minute, hard, permanent, indivisible bits of matter of definite sizes and shapes. They occupy parts of space and move through the empty spaces between them. Occupied and empty space are sharply distinguished. Many scientists still think like this.

*B. Boscovichian point centres*    Boscovich (1758) proposed a substitute having several advantages. The smallest units are not extended pieces of matter, but persisting physical points evidenced as centres of interaction. Only the spatial relations of these physical points enter physics, and every pair of such points are in interaction.

*C. De Broglie-Schrödinger wave-particles*    De Broglie (1923–1924) and Schrödinger (1926) introduced a third, more powerful, conception: that in certain circumstances the ultimate particles possess wave as well as particle properties. This idea, though substantially modified in statistical quantum mechanics, is the most comprehensive of the three and provides the basis of current atomic physics. The wave theory of light had long presented a challenging contrast to atomism; here the waves seem to have beaten the particles.

"*A*" is familiar but mathematically awkward, involving discontinuity at the surface of the atoms. It is also inescapably associated with the idea that "matter cannot act where it is not." Even Newton believed that all genuine physical action was by material contact, though he saw no way of using this to account for his law of gravitation.

"*B*" is ideal for many purposes, and mathematically convenient. It implies that each point atom pervades space, acting everywhere except where it is itself. A valuable emphasis is thus placed on interactions, or changes of relative velocity. But this idea has proved too restricted, at least as Boscovich presented it.

"*C*" is the most successful so far, but it lacks both visual immediacy and mathematical simplicity. Moreover, recent mathematical modifications have made its physical basis obscure. This has led to many different interpretations being offered, of varying degrees of "orthodoxy."

To these three primary ideas must be added various special conceptions of less value: vortex rings and other rotating units, twists in a rotationally elastic jelly, dislocations or holes in a close packing of spheres, negative atoms of various kinds, and so on. There is also Eddington's ghost-particle, from which he excluded all vestiges of materiality, so that it became merely a "carrier of variants" or "a conceptional unity whose probability function" is specified by certain wave vectors. Finally, recent work has suggested that what marks a "fundamental" particle is not its physical indivisibility, but the possession of a definite set of *fixed parameters* (mass, charge, spin, etc.) and no internal *variables* that might represent changes of inner structure. For a fundamental particle must be incapable of internal modification.

"C" is the most recent and certainly the most successful, but in many respects it represents a departure from the classical atomic tradition. Moreover, the high-energy wave-particles discovered since 1930 are intuitively felt not to be true "constituents" of material systems. Underlying this judgment lies a criterion which has seldom been made explicit: A true constituent of physical systems must possess characteristic properties which are *not* functions of position (relatively to other particles) or of time (relatively to events in its neighbourhood). This criterion of genuine constituents corresponds to Epicurus' "impassibility" of the atoms, the property of not being affected by anything. Any particle whose properties, for example, its times of appearance and disappearance, are functions of its space-time position relatively to the experimental system may be called *virtual* in the sense that it behaves in certain respects like a constituent particle, though not actually one. It seems that many of the recently discovered particles are virtual in this sense; they possess variable properties which are functions of their environment.

Particles which are unstable are not less "real" or "important" than true particle constituents, and they are certainly more interesting, just because they are less understood. But they lack one important feature of the constituents of an ideal classical particle theory: the determination of a unique continuity through time of localization in space, which was provided in classical theories by the persisting identity of a particular particle following a precisely determined spatial path.

The necessity in classical physics for this type of temporal continuity of spatial localization was made explicit by Hertz, who developed (1890) a system of classical mechanics in which he defined a *material particle* (for the purpose of a *macroscopic* theory) as "a characteristic by which we associate without ambiguity a given point in space at a given time with a given point in space at any other time." Boscovich's permanent point-particles were an attempt to provide the same property in a *micro* or atomic theory.

Quantum mechanics and quantum experiments have eliminated this stabilizing feature by undermining exact determinism, localisation, particle identity, and permanence. Only a certain probability remains of a one-to-one association of any spatial feature *now* with a similar feature *a moment later*. It is sheer luck, in a sense, that any physical apparatus stays put, for the laws of quantum mechanics allow it a finite, though small, probability of dispersing while one is not looking, or even while one is. A continuous particle-track and a stable apparatus possess a finite probability and no more. For the high-energy quantum physicist, the classical particle has vanished irretrievably—or so it seems.

However, this disruption of the classical particle is not solely the responsibility of recent quantum theory and experiment, for a difficulty had arisen earlier in relativity theory. Einstein's aim was a comprehensive relativistic theory, and he knew that classical particles were alien bodies which should be represented, if possible, as unique regions in a relativistic energy field. But it was unlikely that such virtual particles or field foci could be permanent. Indeed it seems that at any time after, say, 1910 or 1915 (when it became clear that negatively and positively charged particles had definite radii associated with them) Einstein might have predicted the existence of unstable particles by using the following syllogism:

1. The laws express, in terms of intervals, the properties of relativistic space-time fields.
2. Experiments have shown that some electrical particles have an effective finite radius.
3. Therefore some electrical particles must have an effectively finite lifetime.

Or, in dimensional terms: since $l_0$ enters electrical particle theory, $t_0 = l_0/c$ must enter relativistic particle theory as a life-period (since the interpretation of $t_0$ as the reciprocal of a frequency was not possible in this context).

Behind this line of reasoning lies the assumption that particles are quasi-localized semipermanent forms of relativistic field energy, their radii, lives, and masses being properties of temporary energy distributions which for undiscovered reasons are centred at points and which appear therefore as "unstable particles." There is much evidence for this basically anti-atomistic view, in which there are no truly discrete entities but only a continuum of transformations. The power of the energy concept, of relativisitic methods, and the discovery of many unstable particles, all speak in its favour.

Yet there is a snag. However much the field physicist tries to inhibit unique points, they haunt him like a naughty remnant of particle manners. Can physics do without the sharp localization in space of centres of action which persist and form stable patterns? If everything is an energy flux, why should any definite forms exist? If the universe is a mingling of probability clouds spread through a cosmic eternity of space-time, how is there as much order, persistence, and coherent transformation as there is? Physics has little use for a pointless world.

The point-centre conception of atomic particles is suitable for a particle theory, but in a field theory it gives rise to mathematical troubles, for the field becomes infinite at the point-centre. But field theory has not yet found any adequate substitute for these unique points.

**Editor's Note:** In the selection just completed, Whyte, whose own preference is clearly for a particulate view of matter, nevertheless gives an excellent argument for an interpretation of the structure of matter in terms of *continuity*. In the following selection just the opposite will be true. Milic Capek is an outspoken defender of continuity; his *The Philosophical Impact of Contemporary Physics*, from which the selection is taken, has no other aim than to combat lingering elements of classical, particulate physics in the thought of contemporary physicists and philosophers of science. Even so, Capek's presentation of the atomic views against which he is fighting could not be more apt, succinct, and accurate.

## THE MAIN FEATURES OF THE CORPUSCULAR-KINETIC VIEW OF NATURE[1]

*Milic Capek (1909–    )*

The mechanical scheme of nature may be summarized in the following five propositions:

1. Matter, which is discontinuous in its structure, that is, made of absolutely rigid and compact units, moves through space according to the strict laws of mechanics.
2. All apparently qualitative differences in nature are due to the differences in configuration or motion of these basic units or their aggregates.
3. All apparently qualitative changes are merely surface effects of the displacement of the elementary units or their aggregates.
4. All interaction between the basic corpuscles is due exclusively to their direct impact. Action at a distance is a mere figure of speech.
5. Qualitative variety as well as qualitative transformation are *psychic additions* of the perceiving human mind; they do not belong to the nature of things.

It is important to emphasize at once in order to prevent a possible misunderstanding that this scheme represented only an *ideal limit* which

[1] From Milic Capek, *The Philosophical Impact of Contemporary Physics*, Van Nostrand, Princeton, N.J., 1961, pp. 79–83.

physics was continuously striving to approach and which it never completely attained. New discoveries again and again imposed new modifications and corrections. These spoiled the beauty and rigor of the consistent mechanical scheme, but they were unavoidable if a close contact with physical experience was to be preserved. But in spite of all compromises and repeated failures to attain the ideal kinetic explanation in its unspoiled self-consistent purity, the tendency to move in this direction was, for the majority of physicists, irresistible. The superiority of the mechanistic explanation was so overwhelming that no failure to apply it consistently to a certain specific group of facts was ever regarded as final and definitive; on the contrary, it was always hoped that the further progress of science would make a strict mechanistic explanation possible. Again and again this hope was fulfilled. There is no place here for even a brief historical sketch of the development of classical science; a few typical instances should suffice to demonstrate that classical physics and the mechanical view of nature, contained in the five propositions above, were identical.

It is clear that the propositions listed above are not logically independent. The last proposition, which was usually tacitly assumed by physicists, but explicitly stressed by philosophers of the classical period, was a mere consequence of Propositions 2 and 3; for qualitative change and diversity must have some ontological status, and if they do not belong to the "nature of things," they must take a refuge in the perceiving human mind. But even Propositions 2 and 3 are not independent assumptions; they both follow from the basic claim of the homogeneity and constancy of matter; from the homogeneity of the basic material units followed the denial of qualitative differences in nature, while from their immutability followed the denial of any change other than *that of position*. Thus both statements are simple corollaries of atomism.

It is true that the Aristotelian idea of qualitatively diversified and qualitatively changing nature was dying hard. We have already mentioned that when the concept of natural place was given up, the idea of four different elements was virtually doomed; with the discovery of the infinity and homogeneity of space, the unity and homogeneity of matter was implicitly asserted. Yet, in spite of this, it is amazing to see how the Aristotelian elements in a disguised form obstinately persisted in the minds of scientists. Chemistry did not get rid of the idea of phlogiston until the times of Lavoisier; a whole century after the discovery of Newton's law of gravitation the idea of a substance without weight or even possessing a negative weight was still regarded as a respectable hypothesis, although its affinity with the old Aristotelian concept of the intrinsically light element, whether air or fire, is quite obvious. It was also Lavoisier who had to disprove experimentally that the alleged qualitative conversion of water into earth does not occur; in 1770 he proved that the total weight of the closed glass vessel and of the water which had been boiling in it remained the same, but that the weight of the "earth" deposited on the bottom of the vessel was exactly equivalent to the loss of the weight of the vessel; consequently that the "earth" came not from the water, but from the glass [E. von Meyer, *A History of Chemistry from Earliest Times to the Present Day*, Macmillan, London, 1891, p. 152]. The alleged qualitative transformation of a lighter substance into a heavier one was thus nothing but a *displacement* of different masses whose total weight remained the same. Yet, in spite of his successful effort to free the incipient science of chemistry from the remnants of disguised Aristotelian ideas, Lavoisier's mind was not completely free of them. He retained the idea of *caloricum*, a mysterious fluid postulated for the explanation of the phenomena of heat, without apparently realizing the close kinship of this substance with phlogiston; to us it is now clear that the caloric is, epistemologically speaking, nothing but an objectified sensation of warmth, and Lavoisier in this respect hardly went beyond Aristotle [H. Metzger, *La Philosophie de la matière chez Lavoisier*, Paris, 1935, pp. 38–44].

Even in the nineteenth century, when the kinetic theory of heat as a mode of motion removed this particular remnant of Aristotelianism and when the atomistic theory was brought by John Dalton from the heights of philosophical speculation down to the solid ground of experiment, physics and chemistry were still far from the ideal of mechanical explanation described above. A striking feature of Dalton's atomism was its *qualitative* character; its philosophic ancestor was Anaxagoras rather than Democritus. In this respect the qualitative atomism of Dalton, in insisting on the irreducible qualitative diversity of the atoms of different elements, sharply contrasted with the basic tenet of philosophical atomism which from Democritus to Gassendi repeatedly claimed that all qualitative differences in nature were purely phenomenal. From the strictly mechanical point of view it was intolerable to admit that the physical and chemical differences between, for instance, hydrogen and oxygen, were ultimate and irreducible data. But mechanistic philosophers as well as philosophically minded scientists never gave up the hope that the qualitative differences between the atoms of chemical elements are not irreducible and ultimate, but are due in the last analysis to differences in configuration of more minute and more basic particles.

Thus Robert Boyle, who first clearly formulated the concept of chemical element, and who also insisted on the persistence of the elements in the compounds, believed nevertheless that the smallest particles of the elements (such as gold and mercury) are still *corpora manifeste mixta* (clearly mixed bodies) [*Chemista scepticus*, Geneva, 1680, p. 15; *The*

*Sceptical Chymist,* Dent, London, 1911, p. 32], that is, composed of the truly elementary and qualitatively homogeneous atoms strongly cohering together. Boyle thus two centuries before the discovery of radioactivity anticipated the complexity of the chemical atom and the possibility of the transmutation of the elements! In the nineteenth century the same idea was held by various philosophers and scientists like Dalton's contemporary Prout and later by Bertholet, Gibbs, Lotze, Wundt, and Herbert Spencer [von Meyer, pp. 189–191; cf. J. B. Stallo, *Concepts and Theories of Modern Physics,* Appleton-Century-Crofts, New York, 1882, chap. 3; E. Meyerson, *Identité et réalité,* Paris, 1908, pp. 266–269].

What is remarkable is that these hopes and expectations, which were motivated exclusively by philosophical reasons, were *almost* fulfilled by the empirically established electron theory. Although this theory belongs to the modern era of physics, in a certain sense it may be regarded as a culmination of the classical tendencies, since it apparently succeeded in reducing nearly all qualitative differences in nature to the differences of complexity and aggregation of the homogeneous basic corpuscles. The simplest element, hydrogen, was pictured as made up of two elementary particles—the *electron* and the central *proton* around which it revolved. By increasing gradually the number of the peripheral electrons and the number of the nuclear particles, all ninety-two elements then known could be obtained. By combining these elements into compounds and the resulting compounds into minerals, there arose all the apparently inexhaustible variety of inorganic nature. Similarly, organic compounds were results of the association of the atoms of carbon (each of which is nothing but a system of six electrons revolving around the complex nucleus), with other elements, and in this way the apparently miraculous complexity of organic bodies was successfully explained.

It would be an enthusiastic overstatement to claim the Democritean ideal of explanation could not have been realized more fully and successfully; but nevertheless its success was spectacular enough to justify the optimistic hopes that the remaining gaps in the mechanistic picture of the world would eventually be filled. These gaps were represented by the irreducible polarity of electric charges as well as by the duality of matter and electricity; after so many brilliant successes of mechanistic explanation it was natural to hope that these last vestiges of qualitative diversity would be resolved in the all-embracing unity of aether. It is true that the simultaneous emergence of the theory of relativity and of the theory of quanta represented a jarring note which considerably cooled down the optimism of the mechanistic model makers. . . . It remains true that the last triumph of the corpuscular-kinetic explanation of nature as embodied in the early electron theory of matter was the most spectacular and most impressive.

# EDITOR'S NOTE ON AN ARISTOTELIAN VIEW OF THE STRUCTURE OF MATTER

In this passage Capek mentions that Aristotelian antimechanist ideas "obstinately persisted" through centuries of the rise of mechanism. In a later section of the book, while discussing the transformation of the concept of motion in relativity physics, he returns to Aristotle once again. "Does [this interpretation] mean that contemporary physics returns by a roundabout way to the Aristotelian concept of motion? This is true to a certain extent, and Hermann Weyl did not fail to notice the affinity between modern field theory and the Aristotelian concept."[1] Though Capek goes on to say the return is only partial—"There are no simple returns in the development of science"— the remark is interesting as a suggestion that an Aristotelian *could* have something to say on the interpretation of atomic structure in contemporary physics.

Such an Aristotelian view would have to take as its inspiration the ancient four-element theory of Aristotle himself, however jarring this might sound to the modern ear. The reason is not an anachronistic yearning for the simplicity of only four elements. It is that it was on this basis that Aristotelians formed their idea of the "virtual presence" of elements in what they called "mixtures," and this idea of *virtual* presence of atoms in compounds is what the modern Aristotelian would say is permanently valid in Aristotle's doctrine. For the Aristotelian, elements in a compound are not the same as atoms in the free state; their properties, though they help to explain the properties of the compound, remain operative only in an altered state. As Capek suggests— and as was seen in the selection from Whyte—it is field-theory interpretations of particles that suggest a return to conceptions of atomic structure in terms of "virtual parts." This is even clearer on the level of subatomic particles, where the transitional, almost anomalous status of many of the particles suggests most clearly that they belong, radically and fundamentally, to a structural environment. The Aristotelian term for such beings is "substantial parts."

Substantial parts can be understood best in the complicated structures of living organisms. There the complicated hydrocarbons—which already show subordination of parts for functional purposes—necessarily play a further functional role if the organism is to carry out the intricate operations un-covered in biochemistry and molecular biology. "Function in a system" is the key, and the point here is that such interactions are as true of inorganic matter, especially in field theories, as they are of organic matter. Substantial parts, whether in organic or inorganic matter, have the following character-istics:

[1] Capek, *op. cit.*, p. 272.

1. They pertain to the *integrity* of a substance, not to its essence. A vital organ, for instance, can be removed from a living being without killing it; or if this is not so, when the organ is an essential one, it is still true that the part removed is already of a specific kind appropriate to the being in question.
2. When removed, substantial parts can continue to exist for a long time; modern medicine offers dozens of examples in the area of living things.
3. Such parts are material with respect to the being as a whole, and they must be quantified or extended. The function of such parts is to serve as substrate for the properties of the substance, especially its dynamic or active properties.

Carrying this analysis over to the atom and its structure, it is obvious that atoms in molecules and subatomic particles in atoms have roles to play that can only be interpreted as functional interactions in closed systems. There is within the atom a structure of heterogeneous parts functionally maintaining a relative equilibrium similar to that of atoms in molecules and of macromolecules in living organisms. In an Aristotelian interpretation, (1) these parts on various levels would *not* constitute *the essence* of the whole, (2) they could *exist apart*—for instance as ions, radiation, etc.—and (3) within the structure of the whole they would serve a *functional role* as substrates or "organs" for the properties of the whole. (To give a really complete Aristotelian picture, it would have to be added that individual bodies are then functionally related to one another in ever larger systems, ending up with a completely relative or relational universe—this will be seen in the next chapter, on space.)

No selection will be given here to represent this Aristotelian view of the structure of matter, but some references can be given that allow a more complete picture. Two excellent articles are "The Reality of Elementary Particles"[2] and "Elementarity and Reality in Particle Physics,"[3] both by William A. Wallace. In addition, process philosophers, who find the best confirmation of their views in contemporary field theories in physics, argue for a "unification of the physical world" that can only be interpreted as a sort of neo-Aristotelian functionalist interpretation of matter; for this, see the introduction to Chapter 8, on space-time, where several quotations are given from Errol Harris.

Thus the opposing views—(ontological) continuity or atomism, reality as field or particle. Another view is possible, however, and is in fact the pragmatic view most used by the physicists themselves.[4] It is called "complementarity,"

---

[2] *Proceedings of the American Catholic Philosophical Association,* vol. XXXVIII, pp. 154–166, 1964.

[3] M. Wartofsky and R. Cohen (eds.), *Boston Studies in the Philosophy of Science,* vol. 3, Humanities Press, New York, 1967, pp. 236–263.

[4] N. R. Hanson, "The Copenhagen Interpretation of Quantum Theory," in A. Danto and S. Morgenbesser (eds.), *Philosophy of Science,* Meridian paperback, New York, 1960, pp. 450–470 (esp. p. 455).

following Nils Bohr, and it means simply that the physicist uses wave (field) theories in contexts where they work, and particle views where they work. In Bohr's conception this is meant to be a profound philosophical view; in many physicists it is merely a matter of pragmatic utility; and among popular interpreters of science it is intended as a statement about a "wave-particle" structure of matter. All these views become grist for the mill of the *positivist* interpreter of science, who claims that we simply do not know what the structure of matter is—it is merely a matter of more or less useful theories or hypotheses, neither truer than the other and both useful.

The following selection is intended to display this positivist interpretation. The basic selection is from Edward Madden, and it is completed by a quotation from Hans Reichenbach, whose views Madden is commenting on.

## PHILOSOPHICAL PROBLEMS OF PHYSICS

*Edward H. Madden (1925–      ) and Hans Reichenbach (1891–1953)*

### Introduction[1] (Madden)

The main difficulty in quantum theory is that there are two rival hypotheses about, or physical models of, the nature of matter, neither one of which can fit all the facts nor be combined with the other into a more general hypothesis. . . .

Early in the history of physics the atomic, or particle, hypothesis and the wave hypothesis came into conflict in explaining the nature of light. Newton suggested an atomic theory of light because if one assumes that light consists of small particles, or "corpuscles," which are propagated in straight lines, then he can explain simple facts like shadow casting and many other complex ones. Huygens and Young . . . promoted the wave theory because if one assumes light is a wave, in an ether medium, then he can explain, among other things, what the atomic theory cannot, namely light interference. But in 1924 Louis de Broglie produced a mathematical theory which, he believed, allowed one not only to interpret light as both particle and wave but to interpret matter, too, as particles accompanied by waves, thus inaugurating a dual interpretation in mechanics itself. However, this particle and wave interpretation broke down, and Erwin Schrödinger suggested instead that matter itself consists only of waves. For example, "When a stone is dropped into a still pond a circular group of waves spreads out from the central disturbance. If a narrow ditch opens into the pond, a narrow section of the circular

[1] From Edward H. Madden (ed.), *The Structure of Scientific Thought*, Houghton Mifflin, Boston, 1960, pp. 63–64.

waves will travel up the ditch acting much like a particle moving along the water surface. Here we have a wave group acting like a particle." [M. Walker, "An Orientation toward Modern Physical Theory," *Scientific Monthly*, vol. LXXXI, p. 34, 1955.] But this interpretation, too, runs into trouble. The mathematical system which Schrödinger interpreted as a physical wave predicts the *probability*, or percentage-spread, that point events will occur in some specified region of space. But, then, "if we say that these 'waves of probability' are 'real' we use the word 'wave' in the same sense that it is used in expressions like 'wave of suicides' or 'wave of disease,' etc. To speak of a 'wave of flu' as a 'real wave' would be an unusual use of the word 'real.'" [P. Frank, *Philosophy of Science*, Prentice-Hall, Englewood Cliffs, N.J., 1957, p. 244.] Consequently Max Born, Werner Heisenberg, and others interpret matter to be only particles. But these particles, they say, are *indeterminate*, because one cannot specify at one moment both their position and their momentum. Moreover, their behavior is not orderly or causally understandable since their paths do not appear to be continuous! Hence the claim of the breakdown of causality in modern quantum mechanics. But what sense, after all, does it make to interpret matter as particles when these assumed particles do not act like particles should act from what we know of the macroscopic behavior of things?

Nils Bohr, seeing the difficulties of all these views, concludes, in what he calls the "principle of complementarity," that it is possible to interpret waves as real or particles as real, but not both. Moreover, we cannot decide between these interpretations because, due to the indeterminate nature of the alleged particles, no crucial experiment is possible.

### Duality of Interpretations (Reichenbach)[2]

The controversy between the adherents of the wave and the corpuscle interpretation has been transformed into a duality of interpretations. Whether the constituents of matter are waves or particles is a question concerning unobservables; and the unobservables of atomic dimensions, unlike those of the world at large, cannot be uniquely determined by the postulate of a normal system—because there exists no such system. . . .

It is this characteristic feature of quantum-mechanical occurrences which I would regard as the deeper meaning of Bohr's principle of complementarity. When he calls the wave and the particle description complementary, this means that for questions where one is an adequate interpretation the other is not, and vice versa. For instance, considering the interference pattern on a screen we shall refer to the wave in-

2 From Hans Reichenbach, The Rise of Scientific Philosophy, University of California Press, Berkeley, Calif., 1951, pp. 186, 188, and 189–190.

terpretation; but in face of observations with Geiger counters, which show us individual and localized impacts, we shall use the particle interpretation. . . .

It was a long way from Democritus' atoms to the duality of waves and corpuscles. The substance of the universe—in the physicist's sense and not in the metaphoric connotation of the philosopher who identified it with reason—has turned out to be of a rather dubious nature, if compared with the solid particles in which both the philosopher and the scientist believed for some two thousand years. The conception of a corporeal substance, similar to the palpable substance shown by the bodies of our daily environment, has been recognized as an extrapolation from sensual experience. What appeared to the philosophy of rationalism as a requirement of reason—Kant called the concept of substance synthetic a priori—has been revealed as being the product of a conditioning through environment. The experiences offered by atomic phenomena make it necessary to abandon the idea of a corporeal substance and require a revision of the form of the description by means of which we portray physical reality. With the corporeal substance goes the two-valued character of language, and even the fundamentals of logic are shown to be the product of an adaptation to the simple environment into which human beings were born. Speculative philosophy has never exhibited a power of imagination equal to the ingenuity which scientific philosophy has displayed under the guidance of scientific experiments and mathematical analysis. The path of truth is paved with the errors of a philosophy too narrow to envisage the variety of possible experiences.

## SUMMARY OF POINTS FOR DISCUSSION

The subject matter of this chapter does not lend itself to discussion as well as that of other chapters. The experimental method has proved marvelously effective in getting us where we are in the understanding of the structure of matter, and it thus seems only reasonable to go on trusting a method that has proved effective. This is not to say that philosophers have no business discussing the nature of matter. Nor does it imply that there are not genuine philosophical disagreements between field- and particle-theory supporters, and between both of these and positivists who make an ideal of the pragmatic attitude of complementarity. Yet all these thinkers, presumably, would bow to an experimental solution of the problem of matter, if one were forthcoming.

In this situation it seems best to propose a series of questions which are pertinent to an experimental solution and which have something of the philosophical flavor of the different points of view:

1. To what extent is the problem of the structure of matter an experimental one, and to what extent philosophical?

2. N. R. Hanson, in his defense of complementarity mentioned earlier, asks the question: "Should philosophers discontinue attempts to develop proposals which counter the Cophenhagen interpretation?" His answer is "no," as it should be. But just what is the purpose and value of philosophical speculation on an issue like the structure of matter? Can it supply new insights, new theories, new experimental directions?

3. Does it not seem that the present state of scientific knowledge in physics strongly supports field rather than particle theories? If this is so, does the evidence allow one to predict with any assurance what some future state of science will be?

4. What value is there in a philosophical stance that would raise the pragmatic dualism of the physicist's complementarity to the level of a philosophical statement about the (unknowability of the) structure of reality? Or, conversely, what can really be said about the structure of matter if it presents itself, experimentally, as describable in terms of incompatible sets of theories, wave and particle?

These questions are suggestive—no more than that. What they suggest perhaps more than anything else is that philosophical consideration of the whole scientific enterprise is still today very much in order. Though particle physics has yielded fantastic results, synthesis eludes the grasp of the physicist; while relativity and quantum mechanics are mathematically and (to some) esthetically pleasing, their large-scale applications encounter extraordinary difficulties. If such is the case with physics, then surely science as a whole still very much needs the assistance of speculation on the grand scale.

## BIBLIOGRAPHY

### General

Boorse, H. and L. Motz (eds.): The World of the Atom, 2 vols., Basic Books, New York, 1966.

Ford, K.: The World of Elementary Particles, Blaisdell, New York, 1963.

Jammer, M.: Concepts of Mass in Classical and Modern Physics, Harvard, Cambridge, Mass., 1961, and The Conceptual Development of Quantum Mechanics, McGraw-Hill, New York, 1966, esp. chaps. 4, "The Transition to Quantum Mechanics," and 7, "The Copenhagen Interpretation."

### Leading Scientists on the Structure of Matter

Born, M.: Natural Philosophy of Cause and Chance, Dover, New York, 1964 (original edition, Oxford, 1949).

de Broglie, L.: Physics and Microphysics, Pantheon, New York, 1955.

Dirac, P.: "The Evolution of the Physicist's Picture of Nature," Scientific American, vol. 208, pp. 45–53, May, 1963.

Heisenberg, W.: Physics and Philosophy, Harper & Row, New York, 1958.

Planck, M.: *The Universe in the Light of Modern Physics*, Norton, New York, 1931.

Schrödinger, E.: *Science and the Human Temperament*, Norton, New York, 1935.

## Philosophical Interpretations

Bohm, D.: *Causality and Chance in Modern Physics*, Van Nostrand, Princeton, N.J., 1957.

Frank, P.: *Philosophy of Science*, Prentice-Hall, Englewood Cliffs, N.J., 1957.

Hanson, N.: "The Copenhagen Interpretation of Quantum Theory," in A. Danto and S. Morgenbesser (eds.), *Philosophy of Science*, Meridian paperback, New York, 1960, pp. 450–470.

Harris, E.: *The Foundations of Metaphysics in Science*, Humanities Press, New York, 1965, part I.

Reichenbach, H.: *The Rise of Scientific Philosophy*, University of California Press, Berkeley, Calif., 1951.

Wallace, W.: "The Reality of Elementary Particles," *Proceedings of the American Catholic Philosophical Association*, vol. XXXVIII, pp. 154–166, 1964; and "Elementarity and Reality in Particle Physics," in M. Wartofsky and R. Cohen (eds.), *Boston Studies in the Philosophy of Science*, vol. 3, Humanities Press, New York, 1967, pp. 236–263.

## Complementarity

Gamow, G.: *Thirty Years That Shook Physics*, Doubleday, Garden City, N.Y., 1966; account of Bohr-Einstein encounter at 6th Solvay Congress (1930), pp. 114–116.

Moore, R.: *Niels Bohr: The Man, His Science, and the World They Changed*, Knopf, New York, 1966, esp. chaps. 9–10.

Schilpp, P. (ed.): *Albert Einstein: Philosopher-Scientist*, Tudor, New York, 1949, esp. pp. 199–241 (Bohr) and 666–676 (Einstein's reply).

# Part 2

# PRINCIPLES
# OF MEASUREMENT
# IN SCIENCE

MEASUREMENT IS A FOUNDATION STONE of the edifice of modern science, along with the experimentation so often necessary for exact measurement. It was exact measurement that made the difference between Galileo and the Aristotelians of his day; his "new sciences" were distinctive precisely insofar as they gave preeminence to mathematical-measureable effects. Again, the claim has been made that "a quantitative precision strikingly better than its older competitor" is one of the hallmarks of nearly every revolutionary advance in the history of science (Thomas S. Kuhn, *The Structure of Scientific Revolutions*, University of Chicago Press, Phoenix Books, Chicago, 1964, p. 152). However, the point really needs no proof. Modern science is nothing if not dedicated to exact measurement.

What do we mean by the term "measure"? What can classify as a "measurement" in science? To answer the first question first, an excellent definition of the term "measure" was already part of the Aristotelian tradition before the advent of modern science. St. Thomas Aquinas writes:

> The term "measure" is used properly in reference to quantities, for we call that a measure by which the quantity of a thing is known. The reference is to a smallest unit [*minimum*] within the category of quantity: either simply, as in numbers, which are measured by unity, the smallest unit simply speaking; or a smallest unit by human designation, as in extensive quantities [*continuis*], where there is no smallest unit simply, for which reason we designate a "span" [*palmam*] as a smallest unit for measuring cloth, or a "stadium" for the measurement of a road. From this the term "measure" is carried over into all categories. [*Commentum in I librum Sententiarum*, dist. 8, q. 4, a. 2, ad 3.]

A briefer presentation of basically the same definition is given in St. Thomas's *Commentary on the Metaphysics of Aristotle*, Book X, lesson 2. In addition, we should also note that for the Aristotelians measurement had one primary property, that "the measure must be homogeneous with the thing measured" (St. Thomas Aquinas, *Commentary on the Posterior Analytics*, book I, lesson 36).

The basic ideas in this definition of measurement and its chief property have not been superseded. However, the terminology is not that of modern thought, nor does it answer the second question, about what measurement means in modern science. (For an Aristotelian treatment of measurement in science, cf. W. A. Wallace, "The Measurement and Definition of

Sensible Qualities, *New Scholasticism*, vol. xxix, pp. 1–26, 1965.) Hence, before turning to the three great measuring systems of science—space, time, and space-time—it will be worthwhile to present a selection that has become something of a classic on the logical nature of measurement. It is with the application of the basic ideas in this selection that we shall be dealing in the three chapters of Part 2.

## MEASUREMENT[1]

*M. R. Cohen (1880–1947) and Ernest Nagel (1901–    )*

Comparisons based upon counting . . . depend on our ability to distinguish clearly between different groups or different characters. Frequently, however, characters cannot be sharply distinguished because they form a continuous series with one another. Thus we may wish to distinguish different knives on the basis of their "sharpness," different woods on the basis of their "hardness," different children on the basis of their "alertness." For some purposes it is sufficient to know that one piece of wood is harder than another, employing such rough criteria of the hardness of a wood as the ease with which we can drive a nail into it. But we often want to know just how hard one piece of wood is as compared with any other kind of wood, and we then require a more certain and uniform criterion than the one suggested. We wish, if possible, to assign numbers to indicate the different *degrees* of hardness; and we often do so. The numbers so assigned are said to *measure* the varying degrees of the quality. What principles must we observe in using numbers to denote such differences in qualities?

We must be on guard against a common error. It is often believed that because we can assign numbers to different degrees of a quality, the different degrees always bear to each other the same ratio as do the numbers we have assigned to them. This is a serious mistake, and arises because it is supposed that measurement requires nothing more than the assigning of numbers. As we shall see, not all qualities can be "measured" in the same sense. Thus when we say that one tank contains 100 quarts of water and another 50 quarts, it is legitimate to say, as we shall soon find, that the first tank contains *twice as much* water as the second. In this case, the ratio of the volumes is the same as the ratio of the numbers. But when we say that the temperature one day is 100° and on another 50°, is it permissible to say that the temperature on the first day was *twice as much* as on the second? Or when we find that one student

[1] From M. R. Cohen and Ernest Nagel, *An Introduction to Logic and Scientific Method*, copyright, 1934, by Harcourt, Brace & World, New York, pp. 293–297. Copyright, 1962, by Ernest Nagel and Leonora Cohen Rosenfield. Reprinted by permission of the publishers.

has an I.Q. of 100 and another an I.Q. of 50, is it correct to say that the first student is *twice as intelligent* as the second? An analysis of the conditions of measurement will show that the last two assertions are strictly without meaning.

We must note that numbers may have at least three distinct uses: (1) as tags, or identification marks; (2) as signs to indicate the *position* of the degree of a quality in a *series* of degrees; and (3) as signs indicating the *quantitative* relations between qualities. On some occasions numbers may fulfill all three functions at once.

1. The numbers given to prisoners or railroad cars serve only as convenient ways of *naming* these objects. Numbers are more convenient than verbal names, because a "name" can be found for any new individual brought into the group by simply taking the number one greater than the last number that has been so employed. When numbers are used for this purpose, most people recognize that no relation between the objects numbered corresponds to the numerical relation between the numbers assigned. The prisoner numbered 500 is not five times as dangerous or wicked as the one numbered 100. It is not even always true that Convict No. 500 entered the prison later than Convict No. 100, since the same number can be assigned several times without confusion.

2. A scientifically more important use of numbers is when the *order* of numerical magniture is the same as the *order* of the position of the character studied in a scale or ladder of qualities. Suppose we wish to distinguish bodies from one another with respect to their being harder or softer. We may then accept the following definition of what it means for one body to be harder than another: Diamond is harder than glass if diamond can scratch glass but glass cannot scratch diamond; and one body will be said to be just as hard as a second body if neither can scratch nor be scratched by the other. We may then arrange bodies in a scale of hardness if we can show experimentally that relations like the following hold between every triplet of unequally hard bodies: Diamond is harder than glass, glass is harder than pine wood, diamond is harder than pine wood. The relational property of "being harder than" is then shown to be asymmetrical (if $B_1$ is harder than $B_2$, $B_2$ is not harder than $B_1$); and transitive (if $B_1$ is harder than $B_2$, and $B_2$ is harder than $B_3$, then $B_1$ is harder than $B_3$). We can then arrange bodies in a linear series of hardness and thus get a scale or "ladder" of this quality.

Suppose now we have 100 different unequally hard bodies $B_1, B_2, \ldots$ $B_{100}$ arranged so that $B_1$ is the hardest and $B_{100}$ is the softest body, in conformity with the above conditions. We may wish to assign numbers to them to indicate their relative hardness in such a way that the order of numerical magnitude is the same as the order of relative degrees of hardness. (This can be done, since the relation of magnitude of numbers is asymmetrical and transitive.) But what number shall we assign to body $B_1$? We may decide to assign to it the number 0, or 1, or 25, or in fact any number we please. Suppose we decide on 1 for $B_1$, and also on 100 for $B_{100}$, and agree moreover to designate 2 as the hardness of $B_2$, 3 as the hardness of $B_3$, and so on.

These choices, however, were in no way forced upon us. We may have decided on 1 for $B_1$, 5 for $B_2$, 10 for $B_3$, and so on. *In terms of the procedure* we have followed in arranging the bodies in a scale of hardness, no meaning can be attached, therefore, to the statement that $B_{50}$ is *twice as soft* as $B_{25}$. This statement has no meaning because the only relations we have defined, in arranging the bodies in the scale, are the relations of transitivity and asymmetry with respect to being capable of scratching. The statement falsely suggests that because one body is "higher up" on the scale than another, it "contains more" of something called "hardness." And it falsely suggests, because one body is supposed to contain more of this something, that it contains a unit amount of it *a certain number of times.* Both of these suggestions must be ruthlessly eliminated. They arise from the mistaken idea that hardness is something which can be *added.* But there is nothing in the process of constructing the scale which can justify this. Hardness and softness, like temperature, shape, density, intelligence, courtesy, are *non-additive* qualities. Such qualities are frequently called *intensive.* They can be "measured" only in the sense that the different degrees of the quality may be arranged in a *series.* Concerning them, questions of *how much* or *how many times* are meaningless.

3. We turn to the third use of numbers. They can sometimes be employed to measure quantitative relations in the strict sense, so that answers to the questions, "How much?" and "How many?" can be given in terms of them. Suppose we consider a set of bodies and that we wish to measure their weights. In order to do this, we must be able, in the first place, to construct a scale or ladder of weights in a manner similar to establishing a scale of hardness. We will agree, for example, that one body, $R$, is heavier than another body, $S$, if when $R$ and $S$ are placed in the opposite pans of a beam balance, the pan containing $R$ sinks. We must then establish experimentally that the relation of "heavier than" is transitive and asymmetrical. We will also agree that body $R$ is *equal in weight to* (or is as heavy as) $R'$ if $R$ is not heavier than $R'$ and $R'$ is not heavier than $R$; this means that neither pan of the balance will sink when $R$ and $R'$ are placed in opposite pans.

We are able not only to construct a scale of degrees of weights. We can also find an interpretation *in terms of some operation upon bodies* for such a statement as that one body is three times another in weight. An interpretation is possible because weights can be *added.* The physical process of addition is *the placing of two or more weights together* in the same pan of the balance. Let us now find three bodies, *B*, *B'*, *B''*, which are equally heavy, and place them in one pan; place another body, *C*, in the other pan so that the beam will balance. The body *C* is then as heavy as the three bodies *B*, *B'*, *B''* combined, and is *three times* as heavy as any one of them. This procedure can be extended to define a series of standard weights. In terms of this procedure it becomes significant to say that one object is *n* times as heavy or 1/*n*th as heavy as another.

But we have not yet done enough to be sure that numbers assigned by such a process have all their familiar meanings. We have shown that weight is an additive property as contrasted with hardness, which is not. We must also show, again by experiment, that the numbers so assigned to weights are consistent with themselves. We must make sure that we do not allow *different* numbers to be assigned to the same object. Thus suppose the weight of object *A* is regarded as the unit or 1, and that we can assign weights to other objects by this process so that $A_2$ will have weight 2, $A_4$ weight 4, and $A_6$ weight 6. Can we be sure that $A_2$ and $A_4$ placed together in one pan will just balance $A_6$ placed in the other? It is very important to note that we cannot be certain of this until we per-form the experiment. The proposition that $2 + 4 = 6$ can be demon-strated in *pure arithmetic* without experiment. But until we perform the proper experiments we cannot be certain that the *physical operation* of addition of weights does conform to the familiar properties of pure arithmetical addition. The physical operation of addition of weight pos-sesses the usual formal properties of arithmetical addition only in *some* cases, not in *all*: the beam balance must be well constructed, its arms must be of equal length, and so on.

The method of measuring weights can be employed to measure other properties as well. Lengths, time intervals, areas, angles, electric current, electric resistance, can be measured in the same way. These properties are additive: we can find a process such that combining two objects having a property we obtain an object with an increased degree of that property. Properties which are additive are frequently called *extensive*. They can be measured in accordance with the processes indicated in this section. Such measurement we shall call *fundamental*.

# Chapter

# 6

# Absolute Space:
# Newton
# and his Critics

THE FIRST OF THE THREE GREAT MEASUREMENT SYSTEMS of modern science is the *absolute space* of Newton. Its counterpart, absolute time, will be taken up in Chapter 7, after which will follow a consideration of the most recent general system, Einstein's space-time, which is a rival of both absolute space and absolute time.

That space is an intrinsic element in the measurements of science is not the question here. Rather, the question is whether or not space is a reality. In our day, when it has become as customary to talk about "space travel" as it once was to speak of traveling across country, it may seem to the general reader absurd to ask whether space is real. If it is not, what are those astronauts traveling in? However, it is merely a sign of how long it takes ideas to spread among even literate readers that such a question could be raised today, for since the early part of this century no physicist would seriously think that travel in "empty space" is a real possibility. What space travelers travel in is a highly rarified gas, not empty space.

In fact, the philosophical issue at stake in this chapter is whether or not there is any such thing as *empty space*. Historically, philosophical conflicts about space have centered around problems of *full* or *empty* space, *absolute* or *relative* (relational) space. Is space something absolute that exists apart from the bodies located in it? Or is space merely a relation between bodies in a universe that is full, that is without any emptiness between bodies which are all in immediate contact with one another? An excellent introduction to these questions is given by Albert Einstein in the following brief selection.


## CONCEPTS OF SPACE[1]

*Albert Einstein (1879–1955)*

If two different authors use the words "red," "hard," or "disappointed," no one doubts that they mean approximately the same thing, because these words are connected with elementary experiences in a manner which is difficult to misinterpret. But in the case of words such as "place" or "space," whose relation with psychological experience is less direct, there exists a far-reaching uncertainty of interpretation. The historian attempts to overcome such uncertainty by comparison of the texts, and by taking into account the picture, constructed from literature, of the cultural stock of the epoch in question. The scientist of the present, however, is not primarily trained or oriented as a historian; he is not capable of forming nor willing to form his views on the origin of the fundamental concepts in this manner. He is more inclined to allow his views on the manner in which the relevant concepts might have been formed, to arise intuitively from his rudimentary knowledge of the achievements of science in the different epochs of history. He will, however, be grateful to the historian if the latter can convincingly correct such views of purely intuitive origin.

Now as to the concept of space, it seems that this was preceded by the psychologically simpler concept of place. Place is first of all a (small) portion of the earth's surface identified by a name. The thing whose "place" is being specified is a "material object" or body. Simple analysis shows "place" also to be a group of material objects. Does the word "place" have a meaning independent of this one, or can one assign such a meaning to it? If one has to give a negative answer to this question, then one is led to the view that space (or place) is a sort of order of material objects and nothing else. If the concept of space is formed and limited in this fashion, then to speak of empty space has no meaning. And because the formation of concepts has always been ruled by instinctive striving for economy, one is led quite naturally to reject the concept of empty space.

It is also possible, however, to think in a different way. Into a certain box we can place a definite number of grains of rice or of cherries, etc.

[1] Reprinted by permission of the publishers from the Foreword to Max Jammer, *Concepts of Space*, Cambridge, Mass.: Harvard University Press, copyright, 1954, by the President and Fellows of Harvard College, pp. xiii–xvi.

It is here a question of a property of the material object "box," which property must be considered "real" in the same sense as the box itself. One can call this property the "space" of the box. There may be other boxes which in this sense have an equally large "space." This concept "space" thus achieves a meaning which is freed from any connection with a particular material object. In this way by a natural extension of "box space" one can arrive at the concept of an independent (absolute) space, unlimited in extent, in which all material objects are contained. Then a material object not situated in space is simply inconceivable; on the other hand, in the framework of this concept formation it is quite conceivable that an empty space may exist.

These two concepts of space may be contrasted as follows: (a) space as positional quality of the world of material objects; (b) space as container of all material objects. In case (a), space without a material object is inconceivable. In case (b), a material object can only be conceived as existing in space; space then appears as a reality which in a certain sense is superior to the material world. Both space concepts are free creations of the human imagination, means devised for easier comprehension of our sense experience.

These schematic considerations concern the nature of space from the geometric and from the kinematic point of view, respectively. They are in a sense reconciled with each other by Descartes' introduction of the coördinate system, although this already presupposes the logically more daring space concept (b).

The concept of space was enriched and complicated by Galileo and Newton, in that space must be introduced as the independent cause of the inertial behavior of bodies if one wishes to give the classical principle of inertia (and therewith the classical law of motion) an exact meaning. To have realized this fully and clearly is in my opinion one of Newton's greatest achievements. In contrast with Leibniz and Huygens, it was clear to Newton that the space concept (a) was not sufficient to serve as the foundation for the inertia principle and the law of motion. He came to this decision even though he actively shared the uneasiness which was the cause of the opposition of the other two: space is not only introduced as an independent thing apart from material objects, but also is assigned an absolute role in the whole causal structure of the theory. This role is absolute in the sense that space (as an inertial system) acts on all material objects, while these do not in turn exert any reaction on space.

The fruitfulness of Newton's system silenced these scruples for several centuries. Space of type (b) was generally accepted by scientists in the precise form of the inertial system, encompassing time as well. Today one would say about that memorable discussion: Newton's decision was, in the contemporary state of science, the only possible one, and particularly the only fruitful one. But the subsequent development of the problems, proceeding in a roundabout way which no one then could possibly foresee, has shown that the resistance of Leibniz and Huygens, intuitively well founded but supported by inadequate arguments, was actually justified.

It required a severe struggle to arrive at the concept of independent and absolute space, indispensable for the development of theory. It has required no less strenuous exertions subsequently to overcome this concept—a process which is probably by no means as yet completed. . . .

The victory over the concept of absolute space or over that of the inertial system became possible only because the concept of the material object was gradually replaced as the fundamental concept of physics by that of the field. Under the influence of the ideas of Faraday and Maxwell, the notion developed that the whole of physical reality could perhaps be represented as a field whose components depend on four space-time parameters. If the laws of this field are in general co-variant, that is, are not dependent on a particular choice of coördinate system, then the introduction of an independent (absolute) space is no longer necessary. That which constitutes the spatial character of reality is then simply the four-dimensionality of the field. There is then no "empty" space, that is, there is no space without a field.

## EDITOR'S NOTE ON ARISTOTLE'S CONCEPTION OF PLACE AND LATER DEVELOPMENTS

Einstein's review of the problems of space is from his Foreword to Jammer's *Concepts of Space*. Jammer's work is an outstanding introduction to the history of concepts of space down through the centuries from the early Greeks to the present time. A brief survey of that history, here, will be a good introduction to the discussions of this chapter. The survey leans heavily on Jammer's *Concepts of Space*.

In general, it can be said that up to the fourteenth century there were only two basic conceptions of the location of bodies, that of Aristotle for whom bodies are in "place," and that of the atomists for whom they are in "space" (though not exactly in the modern sense of the term). The one major variation in the ancient world was Lucretius's expansion of the atomist notion into an infinite space, and both this conception and its forerunner had a remote beginning in Plato's ideas on bodies as delimited parts of geometrical space or pure extension.

Aristotle's doctrine of "place" starts from the idea of the condition of the possibility of local motion, without which, he says, the notion of place would never have arisen. His definition of place is "the innermost motionless boundary of what contains" a given body. This can be restated as "the unchanging surface of the surrounding physical environment in immediate contact with a body." Aristotle further holds that all bodies in the universe, except the universe itself as a whole, are surrounded by other bodies and are thus "in place." This implies the rejection of any void or empty spaces, of the kind upheld in his day by the atomists, and leads to or at least is tied in with Aristotle's conception of "natural places." For Aristotle the world is an inter-related system of concentric spheres all in contact with one another; on the sphere of the earth the natural place of heavy and inactive elements is the center, that of the lighter elements further and further from the center in accord with their relative activity ("lightness").

This conception was set up in conscious opposition to the ideas of Plato and the atomists. It was taken up by some of the ancient philosophers, while others preferred one of the opposing views—especially the infinite space of Lucretius. In the Middle Ages Aristotle's ideas tended to dominate among the Scholastics, as would be expected, but it was among Aristotelians dissatisfied in one way or another with Aristotle's formulation that the rejection of place in favor of space began. It was the revival of atomism, with its implicit rejection of the space dynamism of natural places, that completed the movement from place to space as the basic measuring system for modern science.

After the advent of relativity, several authors (among them Einstein himself in the selection above) noticed the similarity between modern field theories and the Aristotelian idea of natural place. However, too much should not be made of this resemblance: field theories are just that, *theories* in the context of elaborate hypothetico-deductive systems of laws; Aristotle's conception was intended not as a theory, but as a description of *reality* as it is. Nevertheless, Aristotle's place concept is still useful: For one thing, many measurements are still made by surrounding one body with another (marked off in unchanging units), and field theories make it preferable to locate physical bodies relative to the nearest frame of reference rather than to an assumed absolute space.

Against this background it is possible to set up the discussions of this chapter, which center around Newton's absolute space. The basic philosophical question is, "Does absolute space exist?" Is it a reality or merely a mathematical abstraction?

Newton himself seems to have given an *affirmative* answer—absolute space exists. However, the selection given here is from the *Principia*, is the basic postulate of absolute space (and absolute time), and could be interpreted *either* as a statement about reality *or* as only a theoretical requirement of Newton's system of the world. To the Newton selection is added one from Adolf Grünbaum, emphasizing Newton's antirelational view and the high degree of sophistication of that view.

The most outspoken *negative* answer, in Newton's own time, was that of

Leibniz. He rejected Newton's absolute space as something introduced without sufficient reason, something therefore scientifically useless.

Similar to Leibniz' negative answer is that of Ernst Mach, for whom absolute space must be rejected, not on metaphysical grounds like those of Leibniz, but because it is unobservable. The Mach selection in its turn is accompanied by another selection from Grünbaum (the most prolific contemporary philosopher of space and time), which shows the limitations of the idea that relativity has finally eliminated absolute space. Grünbaum's selection is difficult, but by that very fact it serves to show the technical difficulties involved in the discussion of space; it also serves as a transition to the ideas of Chapter 8, on space-time.

Finally, two other views on space should be referred to: Aristotelians, in accord with the ideas outlined above, would reject absolute space as a reality, though there is no reason they should not accept it as a useful system of measurement; Immanuel Kant, on the other hand, who is being slighted by not being represented in this chapter, would accept the basic idea of absolute space, but make it a mental category rather than a physical reality.

## SCHOLIUM ON ABSOLUTE SPACE AND TIME[1]

*Isaac Newton (1642–1727)*

Hitherto I have laid down the definitions of such words as are less known, and explained the sense in which I would have them to be understood in the following discourse. I do not define time, space, place, and motion, as being well known to all. Only I must observe, that the common people conceive those quantities under no other notions but from the relation they bear to sensible objects. And thence arise certain prejudices, for the removing of which it will be convenient to distinguish them into absolute and relative, true and apparent, mathematical and common.

I. Absolute, true, and mathematical time, of itself, and from its own nature, flows equably without relation to anything external, and by another name is called duration: relative, apparent, and common time, is some sensible and external (whether accurate or unequable) measure of duration by the means of motion, which is commonly used instead of true time; such as an hour, a day, a month, a year.

II. Absolute space, in its own nature, without relation to anything external, remains always similar and immovable. Relative space is some

---

[1] Appended to definitions at the beginning of the *Principia*; cf. F. Cajori (ed.), *Sir Isaac Newton's Mathematical Principles of Natural Philosophy and His System of the World*, A. Motte (trans.), University of California Press, Berkeley, Calif., 1934, pp. 6–12.

movable dimension or measure of the absolute spaces; which our senses determine by its position to bodies; and which is commonly taken for immovable space; such is the dimension of a subterraneous, an aerial, or celestial space, determined by its position in respect of the earth. Absolute and relative space are the same in figure and magnitude; but they do not remain always numerically the same. For if the earth, for instance, moves, a space of our air, which relatively and in respect of the earth remains always the same, will at one time be one part of the absolute space into which the air passes; at another time it will be another part of the same, and so, absolutely understood, it will be continually changed.

III. Place is a part of space which a body takes up, and is according to the space, either absolute or relative. I say, a part of space; not the situation, nor the external surface of the body. For the places of equal solids are always equal; but their surfaces, by reason of their dissimilar figures, are often unequal. Positions properly have no quantity, nor are they so much the places themselves, as the properties of places. The motion of the whole is the same with the sum of the motions of the parts; that is, the translation of the whole, out of its place, is the same thing with the sum of the translations of the parts out of their places; and therefore the place of the whole is the same as the sum of the places of the parts, and for that reason, it is internal, and in the whole body.

IV. Absolute motion is the translation of a body from one absolute place into another; and relative motion, the translation from one relative place into another. Thus in a ship under sail, the relative place of a body is that part of the ship which the body possesses; or that part of the cavity which the body fills, and which therefore moves together with the ship; and relative rest is the continuance of the body in the same part of the ship, or of its cavity. But real, absolute rest is the continuance of the body in the same part of that immovable space, in which the ship itself, its cavity, and all that it contains, is moved. Wherefore, if the earth is really at rest, the body, which relatively rests in the ship, will really and absolutely move with the same velocity which the ship has on the earth. But if the earth also moves, the true and absolute motion of the body will arise, partly from the true motion of the earth, in immovable space, partly from the relative motion of the ship on the earth; and if the body moves also relatively in the ship, its true motion will arise, partly from the true motion of the earth, in immovable space, and partly from the relative motions as well of the ship on the earth, as of the body in the ship; and from these relative motions will arise the relative motion of the body on the earth. As if that part of the earth, where the ship is, was truly moved towards the east, with a velocity of 10010 parts; while the ship itself, with a fresh gale, and full sails, is carried towards the west, with a velocity expressed by 10 of those parts; but a sailor walks in the ship towards the east, with 1 part of the said velocity; then the sailor will be moved truly in immovable space towards the east, with a velocity of 10001 parts, and relatively on the earth towards the west, with a velocity of 9 of those parts.

Absolute time, in astronomy, is distinguished from relative, by the equation or correction of the apparent time. For the natural days are truly unequal, though they are commonly considered as equal, and used for a measure of time; astronomers correct this inequality that they may measure the celestial motions by a more accurate time. It may be, that there is no such thing as an equable motion, whereby time may be accurately measured. All motions may be accelerated and retarded, but the flowing of absolute time is not liable to any change. The duration or perseverance of the existence of things remains the same, whether the motions are swift or slow, or none at all; and therefore this duration ought to be distinguished from what are only sensible measures thereof; and from which we deduce it, by means of the astronomical equation. The necessity of this equation, for determining the times of a phenomenon, is evinced as well from the experiments of the pendulum clock, as by eclipses of the satellites of Jupiter.

As the order of the parts of time is immutable, so also is the order of the parts of space. Suppose those parts to be moved out of their places, and they will be moved (if the expression may be allowed) out of themselves. For times and spaces are, as it were, the places as well of themselves as of all other things. All things are placed in time as to order of succession; and in space as to order of situation. It is from their essence or nature that they are places; and that the primary places of things should be movable, is absurd. These are therefore the absolute places; and translations out of those places, are the only absolute motions.

But because the parts of space cannot be seen or distinguished from one another by our senses, therefore in their stead we use sensible measures of them. For from the positions and distances of things from any body considered as immovable, we define all places; and then with respect to such places, we estimate all motions, considering bodies as transferred from some of those places into others. And so, instead of absolute places and motions, we use relative ones; and that without any inconvenience in common affairs; but in philosophical disquisitions, we ought to abstract from our senses, and consider things themselves, distinct from what are only sensible measures of them. For it may be that there is no body really at rest, to which the places and motions of others may be referred.

But we may distinguish rest and motion, absolute and relative, one from the other by their properties, causes, and effects. It is a property of rest, that bodies really at rest do rest in respect to one another. And therefore as it is possible, that in the remote regions of the fixed stars, or perhaps far beyond them, there may be some body absolutely at rest; but impossible to know, from the position of bodies to one another in our regions, whether any of these do keep the same position to that remote body, it follows that absolute rest cannot be determined from the position of bodies in our regions.

It is a property of motion, that the parts, which retain given positions to their wholes, do partake of the motions of those wholes. For all the parts of revolving bodies endeavor to recede from the axis of motion; and the impetus of bodies moving forwards arises from the joint impetus of all the parts. Therefore, if surrounding bodies are moved, those that are relatively at rest within them will partake of their motion. Upon which account, the true and absolute motion of a body cannot be determined by the translation of it from those which only seem to rest; for the external bodies ought not only to appear at rest, but to be really at rest. For otherwise, all included bodies, besides their translation from near the surrounding ones, partake likewise of their true motions; and though that translation were not made, they would not be really at rest, but only seem to be so. For the surrounding bodies stand in the like relation to the surrounded as the exterior part of a whole does to the interior, or as the shell does to the kernel; but if the shell moves, the kernel will also move, as being part of the whole, without any removal from near the shell.

A property, near akin to the preceding, is this, that if a placed is moved, whatever is placed therein moves along with it; and therefore a body, which is moved from a place in motion, partakes also of the motion of its place. Upon which account, all motions, from places in motion, are no other than parts of entire and absolute motions; and every entire motion is composed of the motion of the body out of its first place, and the motion of this place out of its place; and so on, until we come to some immovable place, as in the before-mentioned example of the sailor. Wherefore, entire and absolute motions can be no otherwise determined than by immovable places; and for that reason I did before refer those absolute motions to immovable places, but relative ones to movable places. Now no other places are immovable but those that, from infinity to infinity, do all retain the same given position one to another; and upon this account must ever remain unmoved; and do thereby constitute immovable space.

The causes by which true and relative motions are distinguished, one from the other, are the forces impressed upon bodies to generate motion. True motion is neither generated nor altered, but by some force impressed upon the body moved; but relative motion may be generated or altered without any force impressed upon the body. For it is sufficient only to impress some force on other bodies with which the former is compared, that by their giving way, that relation may be changed, in which the relative rest or motion of this other body did consist. Again, true motion suffers always some change from any force impressed upon the moving body; but relative motion does not necessarily undergo any change by such forces. For if the same forces are likewise impressed on those other bodies, with which the comparison is made, that the relative position may be preserved, then that condition will be preserved in which the relative motion consists. And therefore any relative motion may be changed when the true motion remains unaltered, and the relative may be preserved when the true suffers some change. Thus, true motion by no means consists in such relations.

The effects which distinguish absolute from relative motion are, the forces of receding from the axis of circular motion. For there are no such forces in a circular motion purely relative, but in a true and absolute circular motion, they are greater or less, according to the quantity of the motion. If a vessel, hung by a long cord, is so often turned about that the cord is strongly twisted, then filled with water, and held at rest together with the water; thereupon, by the sudden action of another force, it is whirled about the contrary way, and while the cord is untwisting itself, the vessel continues for some time in this motion; the surface of the water will at first be plain, as before the vessel began to move; but after that, the vessel, by gradually communicating its motion to the water, will make it begin sensibly to revolve, and recede by little and little from the middle, and ascend to the sides of the vessel, forming itself into a concave figure (as I have experienced), and the swifter the motion becomes, the higher will the water rise, till at last, performing its revolutions in the same times with the vessel, it becomes relatively at rest in it. This ascent of the water shows its endeavor to recede from the axis of its motion; and the true and absolute circular motion of the water, which is here directly contrary to the relative, becomes known, and may be measured by this endeavor. At first, when the relative motion of the water in the vessel was greatest, it produced no endeavor to recede from the axis; the water showed no tendency to the circumference, nor any ascent towards the sides of the vessel; but remained of a plain surface, and therefore its true circular motion had not yet begun. But afterwards, when the relative motion of the water had decreased, the ascent thereof towards the sides of the vessel proved its endeavor to recede from the axis; and this endeavor showed the real circular motion of the water continually increasing, till it had acquired its greatest quantity, when the water rested relatively in the vessel. And therefore this endeavor does not depend upon any translation of the water in respect of the ambient bodies, nor can true circular motion be defined by such translation. There is only one real circular motion of any one revolving body, corresponding to only one power of endeavoring to recede from its axis of motion, as its proper and adequate effect; but relative motions, in one and the same body, are innumerable, according to the various relations it bears to external bodies, and, like other relations, are altogether destitute of any real effect, any otherwise than they may perhaps partake of that one only true motion. And therefore in their system who suppose that our heavens, revolving below the sphere of the fixed stars, carry the planets along with them; the several parts of those heavens, and the planets, which are indeed relatively at rest in their heavens, do yet really move. For they change their position one to another (which never happens to bodies truly at rest), and being carried together with their heavens, partake of their motions, and as parts of revolving wholes, endeavor to recede from the axis of their motions.

Wherefore relative quantities are not the quantities themselves, whose names they bear, but those sensible measures of them (either accurate or inaccurate), which are commonly used instead of the measured quantities themselves. And if the meaning of words is to be determined by their use, then by the names time, space, place, and motion, their (sensible) measures are properly to be understood; and the expression will be unusual and purely mathematical, if the measured quantities themselves are meant. On this account, those violate the accuracy of language, which ought to be kept precise, who interpret these words for the measured quantities. Nor do those less defile the purity of mathematical and philosophical truths, who confound real quantities with their relations and sensible measures.

It is indeed a matter of great difficulty to discover, and effectually to distinguish, the true motions of particular bodies from the apparent; because the parts of that immovable space, in which those motions are performed, do by no means come under the observation of our senses. Yet the thing is not altogether desperate; for we have some arguments to guide us, partly from the apparent motions, which are the differences of the true motions; partly from the forces, which are the causes and effects of the true motions. For instance, if two globes, kept at a given distance one from the other by means of a cord that connects them, were revolved about their common centre of gravity, we might, from the tension of the cord, discover the endeavor of the globes to recede from the axis of their motion, and from thence we might compute the quantity of their circular motions. And then if any equal forces should be impressed at once on the alternate faces of the globes to augment or diminish their circular motions, from the increase or decrease of the tension of the cord, we might infer the increment or decrement of their motions;

and thence would be found on what faces those forces ought to be impressed, that the motions of the globes might be most augmented; that is, we might discover their hindmost faces, or those which, in the circular motion, do follow. But the faces which follow being known, and consequently the opposite ones that precede, we should likewise know the determination of their motions. And thus we might find both the quantity and the determination of this circular motion, even in an immense vacuum, where there was nothing external or sensible with which the globes could be compared. But now, if in that space some remote bodies were placed that kept always a given position one to another, as the fixed stars do in our regions, we could not indeed determine from the relative translation of the globes among those bodies, whether the motion did belong to the globes or to the bodies. But if we observed the cord, and found that its tension was that very tension which the motions of the globes required, we might conclude the motion to be in the globes, and the bodies to be at rest; and then, lastly, from the translation of the globes among the bodies, we should find the determination of their motions. But how we are to obtain the true motions from their causes, effects, and apparent differences, and the converse, shall be explained more at large in the following treatise. For to this end it was that I composed it.

## SPATIAL AND TEMPORAL CONGRUENCE IN PHYSICS: NEWTON[1]

*Adolf Grünbaum (1923–    )*

Newton's fundamental contentions here are that (a) the identity of points in the physical container space in which bodies are located and of the instants of receptacle time at which physical events occur is autonomous and not derivative: physical things and events do not first define, by their own identity, the points and instants which constitute their loci or the loci of other things and events, and (b) receptacle space and time each have their own *intrinsic metric*, which exists quite independently of the existence of material rods and clocks in the universe, devices whose function is at best the purely epistemic one of enabling us to ascertain the intrinsic metrical relations in the receptacle space and time contingently containing them. Thus, for example, even when clocks, unlike the rotating earth, run "equably" or uniformly, these periodic devices merely record but do not first define the temporal metric. And what Newton is therefore rejecting here is a *relational* theory of space

[1] From Adolf Grünbaum, *Philosophical Problems of Space and Time*, pp. 6–8. © Copyright 1963 by Adolf Grünbaum. Reprinted by permission of Alfred A. Knopf, Inc.

and time which asserts that (a) bodies and events first *define* (individuate) points and instants by conferring their identity upon them, thus enabling them to serve as the loci of other bodies and events, and (b) instead of having an intrinsic metric, physical space and time are metrically amorphous pending explicit or tacit appeal to the bodies which are first to define their respective metrics.

To be sure, Newton would also reject quite emphatically any identification or isomorphism of absolute space and time, on the one hand, with the psychological space and time of conscious awareness whose respective metrics are given by unaided ocular congruence and by psychological estimates of duration, on the other. But one overlooks the essential point here, if one is led to suppose with F. S. C. Northrop[2] that the relative, apparent and common space and time which Newton contrasts with absolute, true and mathematical space and time are the private visual space and subjective psychological time of immediate sensory experience. For Newton makes it unambiguously clear, as shown by the quoted passages, that his relative space and time are indeed that public space and time which is defined by the system of relations between material bodies and events, and not the egocentrically private space and time of phenomenal experience. The "sensible" measures discussed by Newton as constitutive of "relative" space and time are those furnished by the public bodies of the physicist, not by the unaided ocular congruence of one's eyes or by one's mood-dependent psychological estimates of duration. This interpretation of Newton is fully attested by the following specific assertions of his:

1. "Absolute and relative space are the same in figure and magnitude," a declaration which is incompatible with Northrop's interpretation of *relative* space as "the immediately sensed spatial extension of, and relation between, sensed data (which is a purely private space, varying with the degree of one's astigmatism or the clearness of one's vision.)"[3]

2. As examples of merely "relative" times, Newton cites any "sensible and external (whether accurate or unequable [non-uniform]) measure of duration" such as "an hour, a day, a month, a year."[4] And he adds that the apparent time commonly used as a measure of time is based on natural days which are "truly unequal," true equality being allegedly achievable by astronomical corrections compensating for the non-uniformity of the earth's rotational motion caused by tidal friction, etc.[5]

[2] Cf., e.g., F. S. C. Northrop, *The Meeting of East and West*, Macmillan, New York, 1946, pp. 76–77.

[3] *Ibid.*, p. 76.

[4] Newton, *Principia*, p. 6.

[5] The logical status of the criterion of uniformity implicitly invoked here will be discussed in some detail in Chapter Two [of Grünbaum's book].

But Northrop erroneously takes Newton's relative time to be the "immediately sensed time" which "varies from person to person, and even for a single person passes very quickly under certain circumstances and drags under others" and asserts incorrectly that Newton identified with absolute time the public time "upon which the ordinary time of social usage is based."

3. Newton illustrates *relative* motion by reference to the kinematic relation between a body on a moving ship, the ship, and the earth, these relations being defined in the customary manner of physics without phenomenal space or time.

Northrop is entirely right in going on to say that Einstein's conceptual innovations in the theory of relativity cannot be construed, as they have been in certain untutored quarters, as the abandonment of the distinction between physically public and privately or egocentrically sensed space and time. But Northrop's misinterpretation of the Newtonian conception of "relative" space and time prevents him from pointing out that Einstein's philosophical thesis can indeed be characterized epigrammatically as the enthronement of the very relational conception of the space-time framework which Newton sought to interdict by his use of the terms "relative," "apparent," and "common" as philosophically disparaging epithets!

## SPACE IS SOMETHING MERELY RELATIVE[1]

*Gottfried Wilhelm (von) Leibniz (1646–1716)*

. . . As for my own opinion, I have said more than once, that I hold space to be something merely relative, as time is; that I hold it to be an order of coexistences, as time is an order of successions. For space denotes, in terms of possibility, an order of things which exist at the same time, considered as existing together; without enquiring into their manner of existing. And when many things are seen together, one perceives that order of things among themselves.

5. I have many demonstrations, to confute the fancy of those who take space to be a substance, or at least an absolute being. But I shall only use, at the present, one demonstration, which the author here gives me occasion to insist upon. I say then, that if space was an absolute being, there would something happen for which it would be impossible there should be a sufficient reason. Which is against my axiom. And I prove it thus. Space is something absolutely uniform; and, without the

[1] From H. Alexander (ed.), *The Leibniz-Clarke Correspondence*, Manchester University Press, Manchester, England, 1956.

things placed in it, one point of space does not absolutely differ in any respect whatsoever from another point of space. Now from hence it follows (supposing space to be something in itself, besides the order of bodies among themselves) that 'tis impossible there should be a reason, why God, preserving the same situations of bodies among themselves, should have placed them in space after one certain particular manner, and not otherwise; why every thing was not placed the quite contrary way, for instance, by changing East into West. But if space is nothing else, but that order or relation; and is nothing at all without bodies but the possibility of placing them; then those two states, the one such as it now is, the other supposed to be the quite contrary way, would not at all differ from one another. Their difference therefore is only to be found in our chimerical supposition of the reality of space in itself. But in truth the one would exactly be the same thing as the other, they being absolutely indiscernible; and consequently there is no room to enquire after a reason of the preference of the one to the other.

6. The case is the same with respect to time. Supposing any one should ask, why God did not create every thing a year sooner; and the same person should infer from thence, that God has done something, concerning which 'tis not possible there should be a reason, why he did it so, and not otherwise: the answer is, that his inference would be right, if time was any thing distinct from things existing in time. For it would be impossible there should be any reason, why things should be applied to such particular instants, rather than to others, their succession continuing the same. But then the same argument proves, that instants, consider'd without the things, are nothing at all; and that they consist only in the successive order of things: which order remaining the same, one of the two states, viz. that of a supposed anticipation, would not at all differ, nor could be discerned from, the other which now is. . . .

33. Since space in itself is an ideal thing, like time; space out of the world must needs be imaginary, as the schoolmen themselves have acknowledged. The case is the same with empty space within the world; which I take also to be imaginary, for the reasons before alleged. . . .

47. I will here show, how men come to form to themselves the notion of space. They consider that many things exist at once and they observe in them a certain order of co-existence, according to which the relation of one thing to another is more or less simple. This order, is their *situation* or distance. When it happens that one of those co-existent things changes its relation to a multitude of others, which do not change their relation among themselves; and that another thing, newly come, acquires the same relation to the others, as the former had; we then say, it is come into the place of the former; and this change, we call a motion in that body, wherein is the immediate cause of the change. And though

many, or even all the co-existent things, should change according to certain known rules of direction and swiftness; yet one may always determine the relation of situation, which every co-existent acquires with
respect to every other co-existent; and even that relation which any
other co-existent would have to this, or which this would have to any
other, if it had not changed, or if it had changed any otherwise. And
supposing, or feigning, that among those co-existents, there is a sufficient number of them, which have undergone no change; then we may
say, that those which have such a relation to those fixed existents, as
others had to them before, have now the *same place* which those others
had. And that which comprehends all those places, is called *space*.
Which shows, that in order to have an idea of place, and consequently
of space, it is sufficient to consider these relations, and the rules of their
changes, without needing to fancy any absolute reality out of the things
whose situation we consider. And, to give a kind of a definition: *place* is
that, which we say is the same to A and, to B, when the relation of the
co-existence of B, with C, E, F, G, etc. agrees perfectly with the relation
of the co-existence, which A had with the same C, E, F, G, etc. supposing
there has been no cause of change in C, E, F, G, etc. It may be said also
without entering into any further particularity, that *place* is that, which
is the same in different moments to different existent things, when their
relations of co-existence with certain other existents, which are supposed
to continue fixed from one of those moments to the other, agree entirely
together. And *fixed existents* are those, in which there has been no motion. Lastly, *space* is that, which results from places taken together.[2]

[2] For a commentary on Leibniz's views that situates them in their historical context, cf.
Mary B. Hesse, Forces and Fields, Philosophical Library, New York, 1962, pp. 157–162.

## NEWTON'S VIEWS OF TIME, SPACE AND MOTION[1]

*Ernst Mach (1838–1916)*

1. In a scholium which he appends immediately to his definitions,
Newton presents his views regarding time and space which we must
examine more in detail. . . .[2]

2. It would appear as though Newton in the remarks here cited still
stood under the influence of the medieval philosophy, as though he had
grown unfaithful to his resolves to investigate only actual facts. When
we say a thing A changes with the time, we mean simply that the con-

[1] From Ernst Mach, The Science of Mechanics, Open Court Publishing Company, LaSalle,
III., 1960 (original English edition 1893), pp. 271–276, 279–281, and 283–284.
[2] Mach here cites a passage from Newton; cf. above, pp. 136 and 138.

ditions that determine a thing *A* depend on the conditions that determine another thing *B*. The vibrations of a pendulum take place *in time* when its excursion *depends* on the position of the earth. Since, however, in the observation of the pendulum, we are not under the necessity of taking into account its dependence on the position of the earth, but may compare it with any other thing (the conditions of which of course also depend on the position of the earth), the illusory notion easily arises that *all* the things with which we compare it are unessential. Nay, we may, in attending to the motion of a pendulum, neglect entirely other external things, and find that for every position of it our thoughts and sensations are different. Time, accordingly, appears to be some particular and independent thing, on the progress of which the position of the pendulum depends, while the things that we resort to for comparison and choose at random appear to play a wholly collateral part. But we must not forget that all things in the world are connected with one another and depend on one another, and that we ourselves and all our thoughts are also a part of nature. It is utterly beyond our power to *measure* the changes of things by *time*. Quite the contrary, time is an abstraction, at which we arrive by means of the changes of things; made because we are not restricted to any one *definite* measure, all being interconnected. A motion is termed uniform in which equal increments of space described correspond to equal increments of space described by some motion with which we form a comparison, as the rotation of the earth. A motion may, with respect to another motion, be uniform. But the question whether a motion is *in itself* uniform, is senseless. With just as little justice, also, may we speak of an "absolute time"—*of a time independent of* change. This absolute time can be measured by comparison with no motion; it has therefore neither a practical nor a scientific value; and no one is justified in saying that he knows aught about it. It is an idle metaphysical conception.

It would not be difficult to show from the points of view of psychology, history, and the science of language (by the names of the chronological divisions), that we reach our ideas of time in and through the interdependence of things on one another. In these ideas the profoundest and most universal connection of things is expressed. When a motion takes place in time, it depends on the motion of the earth. This is not refuted by the fact that mechanical motions can be reversed. A number of variable quantities may be so related that one set can suffer a change without the others being affected by it. Nature behaves like a machine. The individual parts reciprocally determine one another. But while in a machine the position of one part determines the position of *all* the other parts, in nature more complicated relations obtain. These relations are best represented under the conception of a number, *n*, of quantities that satisfy a lesser number, $n'$, of equation. Were $n = n'$, nature would be invariable. Were $n' = n - 1$, then with one quantity all the rest would be controlled. If this latter relation obtained in nature, time could be reversed the moment this had been accomplished with any one single motion. But the true state of things is represented by a different relation between $n$ and $n'$. The quantities in question are partially determined by one another; but they retain a greater indeterminateness, or freedom, than in the case last cited. We ourselves feel that we are such a partially determined, partially undetermined element of nature. In so far as a portion only of the changes of nature depends on us and can be reversed by us, does time appear to us irreversible, and the time that is past as irrevocably gone.

We arrive at the idea of time—to express it briefly and popularly—by the connection of that which is contained in the province of our memory with that which is contained in the province of our sense-perception. When we say that time flows on in a definite direction or sense, we mean that physical events generally (and therefore also physiological events) take place only in a definite sense. Differences of temperature, electrical differences, differences of level generally, if left to themselves, all grow less and not greater. If we contemplate two bodies of different temperatures, put in contact and left wholly to themselves, we shall find that it is possible only for greater differences of temperature in the field of memory to exist with lesser ones in the field of sense-perception, and not the reverse. In all this there is simply expressed a peculiar and profound connection of things. To demand at the present time a full elucidation of this matter, is to anticipate, in the manner of speculative philosophy, the results of all future special investigation, that is, a perfected physical science.

As in the study of thermal phenomena we take as our measure of temperature an *arbitrarily chosen indicator of volume,* which varies in almost parallel correspondence with our sensation of heat, and which is not liable to the uncontrollable disturbances of our organs of sensation, so, for similar reasons, we select as our measure of time an *arbitrarily chosen motion,* (the angle of the earth's rotation, or path of a free body), which proceeds in almost parallel correspondence with our sensation of time. If we have once made clear to ourselves that we are concerned only with the ascertainment of the *interdependence* of phenomena, as I pointed out as early as 1865 ..., all metaphysical obscurities disappear. ...

I have endeavored also (*Principles of Heat,* German edition, page 51) to point out the reason for the natural tendency of man to hypostatize the concepts which have great value for him, particularly those at which he arrives instinctively, without a knowledge of their development. The considerations which I there adduced for the concept of temperature may be easily applied to the concept of time, and render the origin of Newton's concept of "absolute" time intelligible. Mention is also made there (page 338) of the connection obtaining between the concept of energy and the irreversibility of time, and the view is advanced that the entropy of the universe, if it could ever possibly be determined, would actually represent a species of absolute measure of time. . . .

3. Views similar to those concerning time, are developed by Newton with respect to space and motion. . . .[3]

If, in a material spatial system, there are masses with different velocities, which can enter into mutual relations with one another, these masses present to us forces. We can only decide how great these forces are when we know the velocities to which those masses are to be brought. *Resting* masses too are forces if *all* the masses do not rest. Think, for example, of Newton's rotating bucket in which the water is not yet rotating. If the mass $m$ has the velocity $v_1$ and it is to be brought to the velocity $v_2$, the force which is to be spent on it is $p = m(v_1 - v_2)/t$, or the work which is to be expended is $ps = m (v_1^2 - v_2^2)$. *All* masses and *all* velocities, and consequently *all* forces, are relative. There is no decision about relative and absolute which we can possibly meet, to which we are forced, or from which we can obtain any intellectual or other advantage. When quite modern authors let themselves be led astray by the Newtonian arguments which are derived from the bucket of water, to distinguish between relative and absolute motion, they do not reflect that the system of the world is only given *once* to us, and the Ptolemaic or Copernican view is *our* interpretation, but both are equally actual. Try to fix Newton's bucket and rotate the heaven of fixed stars and then prove the absence of centrifugal forces.

4. It is scarcely necessary to remark that in the reflections here presented Newton has again acted contrary to his expressed intention only to investigate *actual facts*. No one is competent to predicate things about absolute space and absolute motion; they are pure things of thought, pure mental constructs, that cannot be produced in experience. All our principles of mechanics are, as we have shown in detail, experimental knowledge concerning the relative positions and motions of bodies. Even in the provinces in which they are now recognized as valid, they could not, and were not, admitted without previously being subjected to experimental tests. No one is warranted in extending these principles beyond the boundaries of experience. In fact, such an extension is meaningless, as no one possesses the requisite knowledge to make use of it.

We must suppose that the change in the point of view from which the

---

[3] Mach again cites a long passage from Newton; cf. above, pp. 136–137, 138, 140–142.

system of the world is regarded which was initiated by Copernicus, left deep traces in the thought of Galileo and Newton. But while Galileo, in his theory of the tides, quite naively chose the sphere of the fixed stars as the basis of a new system of coordinates, we see doubts expressed by Newton as to whether a given fixed star is at rest only apparently or really (*Principia*, 1687, p. 11). This appeared to him to cause the difficulty of distinguishing between true (absolute) and apparent (relative) motion. By this he was also impelled to set up the conception of *absolute space*. By further investigations in this direction—the discussion of the experiment of the rotating spheres which are connected together by a cord and that of the rotating water-bucket (pp. 9, 11)—he believed that he could prove an absolute rotation, though he could not prove any absolute translation. By absolute rotation he understood a rotation relative to the fixed stars, and here centrifugal forces can always be found. "But how we are to collect," says Newton in the Scholium at the end of the Definitions, "the true motions from their causes, effects, and apparent differences, and *vice versa*; how from the motions, either true or apparent, we may come to the knowledge of their causes and effects, shall be explained more at large in the following Tract." The resting sphere of fixed stars seems to have made a certain impression on Newton as well. The natural system of reference is for him that which has any uniform motion or translation without rotation (relatively to the sphere of fixed stars). But do not the words quoted in inverted commas give the impression that Newton was glad to be able now to pass over to less precarious questions that could be tested by experience?

Let us look at the matter in detail. When we say that a body $K$ alters its direction and velocity solely through the influence of another body $K'$, we have asserted a conception that it is impossible to come at unless other bodies A, B, C . . . are present with reference to which the motion of the body $K$ has been estimated. In reality, therefore, we are simply cognizant of a relation of the body $K$ to A, B, C. . . . If now we suddenly neglect A, B, C . . . and attempt to speak of the deportment of the body $K$ in absolute space, we implicate ourselves in a twofold error. In the first place, we cannot know how $K$ would act in the absence of A, B, C . . . ; and in the second place, every means would be wanting of forming a judgment of the behavior of $K$ and of putting to the test what we had predicated—which latter therefore would be bereft of all scientific significance. . . .

5. Let us now examine the point on which Newton, apparently with sound reasons, rests his distinction of absolute and relative motion. If the earth is affected with an *absolute* rotation about its axis, centrifugal forces are set up in the earth: it assumes an oblate form, the acceleration of gravity is diminished at the equator, the plane of Foucault's pendulum

rotates, and so on. All these phenomena disappear if the earth is at rest and the other heavenly bodies are affected with absolute motion round it, such that the same *relative* rotation is produced. This is, indeed, the case, if we start *ab initio* from the idea of absolute space. But if we take our stand on the basis of facts, we shall find we have knowledge only of *relative* spaces and motions. *Relatively,* not considering the unknown and neglected medium of space, the motions of the universe are the same whether we adopt the Ptolemaic or the Copernican mode of view. Both views are, indeed, equally *correct;* only the latter is more simple and more *practical.* The universe is not *twice* given, with an earth at rest and an earth in motion; but only *once,* with its *relative* motions, alone determinable. It is, accordingly, not permitted us to say how things would be if the earth did not rotate. We may interpret the one case that is given us, in different ways. If, however, we so interpret it that we come into conflict with experience, our interpretation is simply wrong. The principles of mechanics can, indeed, be so conceived, that even for relative rotations centrifugal forces arise.

Newton's experiment with the rotating vessel of water simply informs us, that the relative rotation of the water with respect to the sides of the vessel produces *no* noticeable centrifugal forces, but that such forces *are* produced by its relative rotation with respect to the mass of the earth and the other celestial bodies. No one is competent to say how the experiment would turn out if the sides of the vessel increased in thickness and mass till they were ultimately several leagues thick. The one experiment only lies before us, and our business is, to bring it into accord with the other facts known to us, and not with the arbitrary fictions of our imagination.

## HAS THE GENERAL THEORY OF
## RELATIVITY REPUDIATED ABSOLUTE SPACE?[1]

*Adolf Grünbaum (1923–    )*

The literature of recent decades on the philosophy and history of science has nurtured and given wide currency to a myth concerning the present status of the dispute between the absolutistic and relativistic theories of space. In particular, that literature is rife with assertions that the post-Newtonian era has witnessed "the final elimination of the concept of absolute space from the conceptual scheme of modern physics"[2] by

[1] From Adolf Grünbaum, *Philosophical Problems of Space and Time*, pp. 418–424. © Copyright 1963 by Adolf Grünbaum. Reprinted by permission of Alfred A. Knopf, Inc.

[2] Max Jammer, *Concepts of Space*, Harvard, Cambridge, Mass., 1954, p. 2.

Einstein's general theory of relativity and that the Leibniz-Huygens polemic against Newton and Clarke has thus been triumphantly vindicated.[3] In this vein, Philipp Frank recently reached the following verdict on Einstein's success in the implementation of Ernst Mach's program for a *relativistic* account of the *inertial* properties of matter: "Einstein started a new analysis of Newtonian mechanics which eventually vindicated Mach's reformulation [of Newtonian mechanics]."[4]

I shall now show that the history of the GTR does not at all bear out the widespread view set forth in the quotations from Max Jammer and Philipp Frank. And it will then become apparent in what precise sense there is ample justification for Einstein's own admission of 1953 as follows: the supplanting of the concept of absolute space is "a process which is probably by no means as yet completed."[5]

Mach had urged against Newton that both translational and rotational inertia are intrinsically dependent on the large-scale distribution and relative motion of matter. Assuming the indefinite extensibility of terrestrial axes to form an unlimited Euclidean rigid system $S_e$, the rotational motion of the stars seemed to be clearly defined with respect to $S_e$. Unfortunately, however, the GTR was not entitled to make use of $S_e$: the linear velocity of rotating mass points increases with the distance from the axis of rotation, and hence the existence of a system $S_e$ of unrestricted size would allow *local* velocities greater than that of light, in contravention of the requirement of the local validity of the STR. But to deny, as the GTR therefore must, that $S_e$ can extend even as far as the planet Neptune is to assert that the Machian concept of the *relative* motion of the earth and the stars is no more meaningful physically than the Newtonian bugaboo of the *absolute* rotation of a solitary earth in a space which is structured independently of any matter that it might contain accidentally and indifferently![6] Accordingly, the earth must be held to rotate *not* relative to the stars but with respect to the local "star-compass" formed at the earth by stellar light rays whose paths are determined by the local *metrical field*.

At Einstein's hands, Mach's thesis underwent not only this modification but also the following generalization: Einstein found that *both* the geometry of material rods and clocks *and* the inertial behavior of par-

[3] A very useful modern edition by H. G. Alexander of *The Leibniz-Clarke Correspondence* has been published in 1956 by the Manchester University Press and by the Philosophical Library in New York.

[4] P. Frank, *Philosophy of Science*, Prentice-Hall, Englewood Cliffs, N.J., 1957, p. 153.

[5] Foreword to Jammer, *op. cit.*, p. 15.

[6] For details, see H. Weyl, "Massenträgheit und Kosmos," *Naturwissenschaften*, vol XII, p. 197, 1924. See also F. E. A. Pirani, "On the Definition of Inertial Systems in General Relativity," in *Bern Jubilee of Relativity Theory*, suppl. IV of *Helvetica Physica Acta*, Birkhauser Verlag, Basel, 1956, pp. 198–203.

ticles and light in the context of that geometry are functionally related to the same physical quantities. Probably unaware at the time that Riemann had previously conjectured the dependence of the geometry of physical space on the action of matter via a different line of reasoning,[7] Einstein named his own organic fusion of Riemann's and Mach's ideas "Mach's Principle."[8] And he sought to implement that principle by requiring that the metrical field given by the quantities $g_{ik}$ be *exhaustively* determined by properties and relations of ponderable matter and energy specified by the quantities $T_{ik}$. On this conception a single test particle would have no inertia whatever if all other matter and energy were either annihilated or moved indefinitely far away.

But when the problem of solving the nonlinear partial differential equations which connect the derivatives of the $g_{ik}$ to the $T_{ik}$ was confronted, it became apparent that, far from having been exorcised by the GTR, the ghost of Newton's absolute space is nothing less than a haunting incubus. For to obtain a solution of these equations, it is necessary to supply the boundary conditions "at infinity." And to assume, as is done in Schwarzchild's solution, that there are certain preferred coordinate systems in which the $g_{ik}$ have the Lorentz-Minkowski values at infinity is to violate Mach's Principle in the following twofold sense: first, the boundary conditions at infinity then assume the role of Newton's absolute space, since it is not the influence of matter that determines what coordinate systems at infinity are the Galilean ones of special relativity; and second, instead of being the *source* of the *total* structure of space-time, matter then merely *modifies* the latter's otherwise autonomously flat structure. In 1916 Einstein first attempted to avoid this most unwelcome consequence by reluctantly altering the above field equations through the introduction of the cosmological constant $\lambda$, which yielded a solution in which space was closed (finite). But this rather forced step did not provide an escape from the troublesome philosophical difficulties that had cropped up in the boundary conditions at infinity, since these difficulties reappeared when W. de Sitter showed that the now *modified* equations violated Mach's Principle by allowing a universe essentially devoid of matter to have a definitely structured space-time. The attempt to dispose of the difficulty at infinity by laying down the finitude of space as a *boundary condition* governing the solution of the *unmodified* field equations is unavailing for the purpose of rescuing Mach's Principle *as it was orginally conceived*, since such a speculative assumption in-

---

[7] Cf. B. Riemann, *Uber die Hypothesen welche der Geometrie zu Grunde liegen*, 3d. ed., H. Weyl (ed.), Julius Springer, Berlin, 1923, pp. 3 and 20. The reader will find a brief account of the relevant part of Riemann's reasoning in Chapters One and Fifteen of the present book [Grünbaum's].

[8] A. Einstein, "Prinzipielles zur allgemeinen Relativitätstheorie," *op. cit.*, p. 241.

volves a nonintrinsic connection between the over-all structure of space and the properties of matter. In 1951 the Machian hope of subordinating space-time ontologically to matter was further dashed when A. H. Taub showed that there are conditions under which the *unmodified* field equations yield *curved* space in the absence of matter.[9]

These results inescapably raise the question of whether the failure of the GTR to implement Mach's Principle is to be regarded as an inadequacy on the part of that theory or as a basis for admitting that the GTR was right in philosophically retaining Newton's absolute space to a significant extent, thinly disguised under new structural trappings. Einstein's own attitude in his last years seems to have been one of unmourning abandonment of Mach's Principle. His reason appears to have been that although matter provides the *epistemological* basis for the metrical field, this fact must *not* be held to confer *ontological* primacy on matter over the field: matter is merely part of the field rather than its source.[10]

This is indeed a very far cry from, nay the very antithesis of, Max Jammer's "final elimination of the concept of absolute space from the conceptual scheme of modern physics."[11] In fact, Jammer himself quotes a recent passage from Einstein in which Einstein says that if the *space-time field* were removed, there would be no space.[12] Yet Jammer gives no indication whatever that this is a drastically different thesis from Einstein's earlier one that if all matter were annihilated, then metric space would vanish as well.[13]

It is now clear that the GTR *cannot* be said to have resolved the controversy between the absolutistic and relativistic conceptions of space in favor of the latter on the issue of the implementation of Mach's Principle. Instead, the current state of knowledge supports the following summary assessment given in 1961 by the physicists C. Brans and R. H. Dicke:

[9] A. H. Taub, "Empty Space-Times Admitting a Three Parameter Group of Motions," *Annals of Mathematics*, vol. LIII, p. 472, 1951.

[10] For a discussion of the status of Einstein's program of field theory, see J. Callaway, "Mach's Principle and Unified Field Theory," *Physical Review*, vol. XCVI, p. 778, 1954. For an alternative theory of gravitation inspired by the aim of strict conformity to Mach's principle but incomplete in other respects, see D. W. Sciama, "On the Origin of Inertia," *Monthly Notices of the Royal Astronomical Society*, vol. CXIII, p. 35, 1953, and "Inertia," *Scientific American*, vol. CXCVI, pp. 99–109, February, 1957. Cf. also F. A. Kaempffer, "On Possible Realizations of Mach's Program," *Canadian Journal of Physics*, vol. XXXVI, pp. 151–159, 1958, and O. Klein, "Mach's Principle and Cosmology in their Relation to General Relativity," in *Recent Developments in General Relativity*, Polish Scientific Publishers, Warsaw, 1962, pp. 293–302.

[11] M. Jammer, *Concepts of Space, op. cit.*, p. 2.

[12] *Ibid.*, p. 172.

[13] Jammer has since taken account of these criticisms on pp. 12 and 195 of the revised Harper Torchbook edition of his book, published in New York in 1960.

The ... view that the geometrical and inertial properties of space are meaningless for an empty space, that the physical properties of space have their origin in the matter contained therein, and that the only meaningful motion of a particle is motion relative to other matter in the universe has never found its complete expression in a physical theory. This picture is ... old and can be traced from the writings of Bishop Berkeley[14] to those of Ernst Mach.[15] These ideas have found a limited expression in general relativity, but it must be admitted that, although in general relativity spatial geometries are affected by mass distributions, the geometry is not uniquely specified by the distribution. It has not yet been possible to specify boundary conditions on the field equations of general relativity which would bring the theory into accord with Mach's principle. Such boundary conditions would, among other things, eliminate all solutions without mass present.[16]

The difficulties encountered by the attempt to incorporate Mach's Principle as originally conceived into the GTR have most recently prompted two kinds of responses from leading investigators, which illustrate the lack of a uniform conception of this principle. Brans and Dicke[17] have put forward a *modified* relativistic theory of gravitation which is apparently compatible with Mach's principle, and is closely related to the theory of P. Jordan.[18] But J. A. Wheeler has articulated the important modifications which must be made in the original program of Mach's Principle, if Mach's ideas are to preserve their relevance to the GTR in its current state. Wheeler's substantial reformulation of Mach's Principle is as follows: "the specification of a sufficiently regular closed three-dimensional geometry at two immediately succeeding instants, and of the density and flow of mass-energy, is to determine the geometry of space-time, past, present, and future, and thereby the inertial properties of every infinitesimal test particle."[19] In Wheeler's view, then, Mach's

14 "G. Berkeley: *The Principles of Human Knowledge*, Paragraphs 111–17, 1710-*De Motu* (1726)."

15 "E. Mach: *Conservation of Energy*, note No. 1, 1872 (reprinted by Open Court Publishing Company, LaSalle, Illinois, 1911), and *The Science of Mechanics*, 1883 (reprinted by Open Court Publishing Company, LaSalle, Illinois, 1902, Chapter II, Sec. VI)."

16 C. Brans and R. H. Dicke, "Mach's Principle and a Relativistic Theory of Gravitation," *Physical Review*, vol. CXXIV, p. 925, 1961. See also R. H. Dicke, "Mach's Principle and Invariance under Transformation of Units," *Physical Review*, vol. CXXV, p. 2163, 1962, and "The Nature of Gravitation," in L. V. Berkner and H. Odishaw (eds.), *Science in Space*, McGraw-Hill, New York, 1961, chap. 3, sec. 3.1, "Mach's Principle," pp. 93–95. For an account of statements which might be regarded as modified versions of Mach's principle and which are valid in the GTR, see C. H. Brans, "Mach's Principle and the Locally Measured Gravitational Constant in General Relativity," *Physical Review*, vol. CXXV, p. 396, 1962.

17 C. Brans and R. H. Dicke, "Mach's Principle and a Relativistic Theory of Gravitation," *op. cit.*

18 P. Jordan, *Schwerkraft und Weltall*, Friedrich Vieweg und Sohn, Braunschweig, 1955.

19 J. A. Wheeler, "Mach's Principle as a Boundary Condition for Einstein's Field Equations and as a Central Part of the 'Plan' of General Relativity," report given at the Conference on Relativistic Theories of Gravitation, Warsaw, July, 1962.

Principle can be implemented in the GTR in the following drastically altered form: if we are *given* (1) that the *three*-dimensional geometry of space at some initial instant and at some closely succeeding instant does *not* extend to infinity and does *not* show infinite curvature, and (2) the distribution of mass and mass-flow, then the *four*-dimensional geometry of space-time or the "geometrodynamics" and hence the inertial properties of infinitesimal test particles are thereby determined. For Wheeler then, the modified form of Mach's Principle simply *requires ab initio* that the universe be *spatially* closed or finite. In this way, it constitutes a principle for *selecting* out of the many conceivable solutions of Einstein's field equations those for which the three-geometry at a given instant is closed and free from singularity, thereby making possible the determination of the four-geometry and of the inertial behavior of infinitesimal test particles.[20]

## SUMMARY OF POINTS FOR DISCUSSION

1. A defender of Newton, especially when fortified by the incisive points made by Grünbaum, should be able to show that absolute space is still, after Einstein, a virtually essential part of physical measurement. This is particularly true of the imaginative structuring or modeling of theories about measureable bodies in the universe. What is difficult for the Newtonian to defend—because it is in no sense entailed by or essential for his theory of measurement—is the *physical reality* or ontological status of absolute space.

2. Defenders of a relational view of space (or, in Aristotle's terms, of "place" as the basic principle of measurement) can point to the success of Einstein's relativistic formulation as a strong support for their view, though relativity theory certainly does not resolve the ontological problem of space versus place. In addition, relational approaches remain basic for nearly all purposes of *de facto* measurement in science. Where such views run into difficulty, however, is in the formidable technicalities of the mathematical extensions of relativity as well as in the near impossibility of visualizing or imagining bodies as *located*, quantitatively and definitively, anywhere except against a background of spatial extension.

3. The most realistic view might in fact be one that (a) pragmatically assumes local reference frames as most useful for purposes of measurement

---

[20] J. A. Wheeler ("The Universe in the Light of General Relativity," *The Monist*, vol. XLVII, no. 1, pp. 40–76, 1962) has given a very brief statement of the meaning of his reformulation of Mach's principle as applied to a universe which is empty of all "real" mass in the sense of the vision of Clifford and Einstein. For details on the latter universe, see C. W. Misner and J. A. Wheeler, "Geometrodynamics," *Annals of Physics*, vol. II, pp. 525–614, 1957; J. A. Wheeler, "Curved Empty Space-Time as the Building Material of the Physical World: An Assessment," in E. Nagel, P. Suppes, and A. Tarski (eds.), *Logic, Methodology and Philosophy of Science*, Proceedings of the 1960 International Congress, Stanford, Stanford, Calif., 1962, pp. 361–374, and J. G. Fletcher, "Geometrodynamics," in L. Witten (ed.), *Gravitation*, Wiley, New York, 1962, chap. 10, pp. 412–437.

(even theoretical measurement, as for instance in "thought experiments"), yet (*b*) insists upon *some* spatial geometry as an essential background for conceptualization. This need not be taken as a Kantian category, nor must the geometry be Euclidean (though it is easiest and most natural), but at least a spatial frame of reference of some sort, involving some form of infinity, is virtually demanded for the sort of mathematical theorizing essential to modern science.

## BIBLIOGRAPHY

### Classics

Alexander, H. (ed.): *The Leibniz-Clarke Correspondence*, Philosophical Library, New York, 1956; Manchester University Press, Manchester, Eng., 1956.

Cajori, F. (ed.): *Sir Isaac Newton's Mathematical Principles of Natural Philosophy and His System of the World*, A. Motte (trans.) (1729), University of California Press, Berkeley, Calif., 1934.

Mach, E.: *The Science of Mechanics*, Open Court, LaSalle, Ill., 1960 (original English edition 1893).

### Modern Treatments of Space

Alexander, S.: *Space, Time, and Deity*, 2 vols., Dover paperback, New York, 1966 (original edition 1920).

Eddington, Sir A.: *Space, Time, and Gravitation*, Harper & Row, New York, 1959 (original edition 1920).

Grünbaum, A.: *Philosophical Problems of Space and Time*, Knopf, New York, 1963.

Hesse, M.: *Forces and Fields: The Concept of Action at a Distance in the History of Physics*, Philosophical Library, New York, 1962.

Jammer, M.: *Concepts of Space*, 2d ed. rev., Harper & Row, New York, 1960 (original edition, Harvard, Cambridge, Mass, 1954).

Munitz, M.: *Space, Time and Creation*, Free Press, New York, 1957.

Reichenbach, H.: *The Philosophy of Space and Time*, Dover, New York, 1958 (original German edition 1928).

Smart, J. (ed.): *Problems of Space and Time*, Macmillan, New York, 1964.

# Chapter

# 7

# Time in
# Classical
# Physics

SPACE AND TIME—KANT MADE THEM the fundamental categories in terms of which we perceive the world. Absolute space and absolute time were the foundations of this idea in Kant, and for Newton they were the twin foundations of all measurement in science. This could lead one to suspect that a treatment of absolute time should exactly parallel that of absolute space. And in a sense it does; the chief philosophical problem once again is a conflict between upholders of *absolute* time and defenders of a *relational* view of time. Yet this is not the whole story, for time, in contrast with space, is much more difficult to delimit for investigation, to "pin down," so to speak, long enough for careful examination. As a result, the very existence of time—its objectivity and dependence on the perceiving mind—is also an important philosophical question that has been answered in various ways.

In addition, this reference to the *perception* of time brings up many psychological and even physiological problems—for instance about the existence of a "sense of time." And the regularity of activity among animals, with respect to (apparently) perceived time, brings up further questions of biological evolution and biological clocks. What is the relation between these conceptions of time—as well as the "sacred time" of comparative religion, time in music or grammar, and the philosophical questions about time already mentioned—and time as it is used in physics?

Only a cross-discipline or interdisciplinary study could really answer this question.[1] Almost never is it the case that physicist and biologist compare their conceptions of time, and neither would be likely to think they should compare their views with sacred time or distortions of time perception in psychiatry.

The whole question of time, in fact, brings up emotional attitudes and hostilities; people differ markedly in the way they perceive time as an object of investigation.[2] It has even been claimed, by Fraser, that "the *Weltanschauung* of an individual and of an age, that is, the perception of life and concept of things preferred, is essentially a view of time."[3]

All this suggests that there is a *single* reality (or perhaps a single mental construct) of time that either permeates all these usages or is their foundation. This itself is a problematic assumption, as is the implication that could be drawn from it—namely that different approaches to time, scientific, literary, philosophical, will turn out to be complementary. In short, the problems associated with time are many and complex. Those that are of interest here pertain to philosophical discussions of scientific issues.

As was true of space, so also with time there has been a long history of philosophical discussion on its nature. Rather than give a survey of this history, however, it seems preferable to present a few brief but influential passages from classical authors. Discussions of time were already important in the Athens of Plato and Aristotle, and Aristotle introduces his treatment of time in the *Physics* with a clear presentation of the *problem of time*. This problem was given a rephrasing by St. Augustine that has become such a classic that no discussion of time should omit it.

[1] An excellent start on this project has been made by J. T. Fraser (ed.), *The Voices of Time*, Braziller, New York, 1966.

[2] Fraser's work, for instance, can be contrasted with the literary study of J. Buckley, *The Triumph of Time*, Harvard, Cambridge, Mass., 1966.

[3] *Op. cit.*, p. xxi.

## WHAT IS TIME?[1]

*St. Augustine (354–430)*

For what is time? Who can easily and briefly explain it? Who even in thought can comprehend it, even to the pronouncing of a word concerning it? But what in speaking do we refer to more familiarly and knowingly than time? And certainly we understand when we speak of it; we understand also when we hear it spoken of by another. What, then, is time? If no one ask of me, I know; if I wish to explain to him who asks,

[1] St. Augustine, *Confessions*, book XI, chap. 14; cf. W. Oates (ed.), *Basic Writings of St. Augustine*, Random House, New York, 1948, vol. I, p. 191.

I know not. Yet I say with confidence, that I know that if nothing passed away, there would not be past time; and if nothing were coming, there would not be future time; and if nothing were, there would not be present time. Those two times, therefore, past and future, how are they, when even the past now is not, and the future is not as yet? But should the present be always present, and should it not pass into time past, truly it could not be time, but eternity. If, then, time present—if it be time—only comes into existence because it passes into time past, how do we say that even this is, whose cause of being is that it shall not be— namely, so that we cannot truly say that time *is*, unless because it tends *not to be*?

**Editor's Note:** Aristotle's classic formulation of the nature of time, in response to questions like those of St. Augustine, is given in the following passage.

# THE NATURE OF TIME[1]

*Aristotle (384–322 B.C.)*

As to what time is or what is its nature, the traditional accounts give us as little light as the preliminary problems which we have worked through.

Some assert that it is (1) the movement of the whole, others that it is (2) the sphere itself.

(1) Yet part, too, of the revolution is a time, but it certainly is not a revolution: for what is taken is part of a revolution, not a revolution. Besides, if there were more heavens than one, the movement of any of them equally would be time, so that there would be many times at the same time.

(2) Those who said that time is the sphere of the whole thought so, no doubt, on the ground that all things are in time and all things are in the sphere of the whole. The view is too naive for it to be worth while to consider the impossibilities implied in it.

But as time is most usually supposed to be (3) motion and a kind of change, we must consider this view.

Now (a) the change or movement of each thing is only *in* the thing which changes or *where* the thing itself which moves or changes may chance to be. But time is present equally everywhere and with all things.

Again, (b) change is always faster or slower, whereas time is not: for "fast" and "slow" are defined by time—"fast" is what moves much in a short time, "slow" what moves little in a long time; but time is not defined by time, by being either a certain amount or a certain kind of it.

---

[1] Aristotle, *Physics*, book IV, chaps. 10–11; 218a32–219b8. From *The Oxford Translation of Aristotle*, by permission of the Clarendon Press, Oxford.

Clearly then it is not movement. (We need not distinguish at present between "movement" and "change.")

But neither does time exist without change; for when the state of our own minds does not change at all, or we have not noticed its changing, we do not realize that time has elapsed, any more than those who are fabled to sleep among the heroes in Sardinia do when they are awakened; for they connect the earlier "now" with the later and make them one, cutting out the interval because of their failure to notice it. So, just as, if the "now" were not different but one and the same, there would not have been time, so too when its difference escapes our notice the interval does not seem to be time. If, then, the non-realization of the existence of time happens to us when we do not distinguish any change, but the soul seems to stay in one indivisible state, and when we perceive and distinguish we say time has elapsed, evidently time is not independent of movement and change. It is evident, then, that time is neither movement nor independent of movement.

We must take this as our starting-point and try to discover—since we wish to know what time is—what exactly it has to do with movement.

Now we perceive movement and time together: for even when it is dark and we are not being affected through the body, if any movement takes place in the mind we at once suppose that some time also has elapsed; and not only that but also, when some time is thought to have passed, some movement also along with it seems to have taken place. Hence time is either movement or something that belongs to movement. Since then it is not movement, it must be the other.

But what is moved is moved from something to something, and all magnitude is continuous. Therefore the movement goes with the magnitude. Because the magnitude is continuous, the movement too must be continuous, and if the movement, then the time; for the time that has passed is always thought to be in proportion to the movement.

The distinction of "before" and "after" holds primarily then, in place; and there in virtue of relative position. Since then "before" and "after" hold in magnitude, they must hold also in movement, these corresponding to those. But also in time the distinction of "before" and "after" must hold, for time and movement always correspond with each other. The "before" and "after" in motion identical in substratum with motion yet differs from it in definition, and is not identical with motion.

But we apprehend time only when we have marked motion, marking it by "before" and "after"; and it is only when we have perceived "before" and "after" in motion that we say that time has elapsed. Now we mark them by judging that A and B are different, and that some third thing is intermediate to them. When we think of the extremes as different from the middle and the mind pronounces that the "nows" are two, one before and one after, it is then that we say that there is time, and this that we say is time. For what is bounded by the "now" is thought to be time—we may assume this.

When, therefore, we perceive the "now" as one, and neither as before and after in a motion nor as an identity but in relation to a "before" and an "after," no time is thought to have elapsed, because there has been no motion either. On the other hand, when we do perceive a "before" and an "after," then we say that there is time. For time is just this— number of motion in respect of "before" and "after."

Hence time is not movement, but only movement in so far as it admits of enumeration. A proof of this: we discriminate the more or the less by number, but more or less movement by time. Time then is a kind of number. (Number, we must note, is used in two senses—both of what is counted or the countable and also of that with which we count. Time obviously is what is counted, not that with which we count: these are different kinds of thing.)

**Editor's Note:** Aristotle's views are often contrasted with those of Plato, and on the topic of time this contrast approach would be as suggestive as anywhere else. Certainly the mythical flavor of the Timaeus immediately serves to set it off from the dry scholastic treatment of time in the Physics. Yet there is another more obvious difference: for Plato gives as his fundamental definition of time that it is the "moving image of eternity" (37d), a view that would seem at first glance totaly unacceptable to Aristotle. And in fact the quasi-theological approach of Plato has been interpreted as an "unconscious prophecy" of what was to come in twentieth-century science.


## THE CONCEPT OF TIME IN THE TIMAEUS[1]

*A. E. Taylor (1869–1945)*

To come back to the *Timaeus*. The main point to be dwelt on at once— though all that has been said will be found to be relevant in the end, when we have the account of space before us—is that Plato rightly distinguishes between time and the fundamental "passage" of Nature itself. Time is not the same thing as γένεσις or τὸ γίγνεσθαι but a numerical "measure" of it. It is precisely this distinction between what happens and a way of measuring what happens that is so commonly overlooked, and it is the overlooking of it which makes it seem paradoxical to say that there can be many time-systems and that events which are simultaneous in one of them are not necessarily simultaneous in another. I do not mean that Timaeus or his creator is to be supposed alive to such a development. Timaeus implies what Aristotle expressly teaches in the

---

[1] From A. E. Taylor, *A Commentary on Plato's "Timaeus,"* Clarendon Press, Oxford, 1928, pp. 689 and 691. By permission of the Clarendon Press, Oxford.

*Physics* that there is just one space-order and one time-order in which events are set. But he has carefully made the distinction between time and "passage," on the making of which the whole recent development rests, and as the uniqueness of order in time is only implied, not actually affirmed, his account could be adopted by an exponent of the "Theory of Relativity." Indeed, since there would be a want of complete coincidence between the time-order as we work it out and the order which would be worked out even by inhabitants of a neighbouring planet of our own system, we may fairly say that the express insistence on the point that the periods of all the planets are "time," and the happy use of the plural χρόνοι in the phrase ὄργανα χρόνων applied to the planets at 41e5 is an "unconscious prophecy" of things to come. . . .

[Note that up to this point there would only be a minor disagreement with Aristotle, who would also "carefully make the distinction between time and passage." But Taylor goes on to fit the "unconscious prophecy" in the context of Plato's "moving image of eternity."]

If we keep firmly before our minds the difference between the actual "passage of Nature" and the representation of it in a given space-and-time system, and the contrast between the plurality of these systems and the unity of the "passage" itself, we shall see the full happiness of the phrase that time is a *"moving* image of eternity." "Passage" itself does not "pass." It is a permanent character by which Nature is distinguished from what is above Nature. Thus Nature itself in its concrete reality may be said at any rate to belong to *aevum*.[2] But when we try to represent the passage of Nature in the time-system correlated with our space-system, to get a *perspective* of it, what we get is an endless series of occurrences in an order which would not be the same for observers with a different space-system. Every system of measures depends on the arbitrary selection of a special ποῦ στῶ, and therefore we cannot create a system which starts from no one particular ποῦ στῶ at all. The view of Nature we could get by pursuing science for ever would, after all, be only one among an infinity of equally legitimate perspectives, all differing. Such a view is exactly what Timaeus calls it, a *shadow*, and a "moving" or "variable" shadow of the eternal.

Editor's Note: However, the principal focus of this chapter should be on classical (Newtonian) physics rather than classical (ancient) philosophy. Thus the starting point is Newton himself, whose views on absolute time (along with absolute space) have been given in the last chapter. To summarize here, Newton defines "absolute, true, and mathematical time" as that which "flows equally without relation to anything external," and distinguishes it from "relative, apparent, and common time." As is often the case in the *Principia*, it is unclear whether Newton himself, in setting down this definition, thought of absolute time

---

[2] This medieval term had been explained earlier by Taylor. He defines it as "endlessly prolonged succession without a beginning" and places it halfway between true time and the eternity of God.

as a *reality* or merely a prerequisite for his mathematical theories. Nevertheless, he was taken to mean that absolute time is a reality, and it is with this view that modern controversies about time can be said to begin.

There are four basic questions with respect to time and its nature: "Does time exist?" "How should it be defined?" "What is the relation of time to matter or physical bodies in general?" and "Is there a universal time or a fundamental time from which all other 'times' are derived?" Newton's view can be considered an answer to the last question. (Doing so safeguards the theoretical importance of absolute time even if it is decided that absolute time is only theoretical and not a reality.) Leibniz would be the next major thinker on time, and his relational view is elaborated in conscious opposition to Newton viewed as holding for absolute time as a reality; this takes the discussion back to the second question, on the nature of time. Kant then enters the picture, accepts Newton's view, but makes of time a mental category rather than a physical reality—which reraises the ancient and radical question, "Does time exist?" For classical Newtonians, especially of the late nineteenth century, this question was virtual nonsense, and the only important point was to emphasize the independence of time from matter—the subject of the selection from Capek below. Finally, in reaction against this mechanistic view, Bergson returned to the question of the basic nature of time and made it the basic "stuff" of the universe—a view not totally unrelated to the notion of space-time, to be taken up in the next chapter.

## ABSOLUTE TIME AND RELATIONAL TIME[1]

G. J. Whitrow (1912–    )

### Absolute Time

"Absolute, true and mathematical time," wrote Newton, "of itself, from its own nature, flows equably without relation to anything external." This famous definition which appears at the beginning of the *Principia* has been one of the most criticized, and justly so, of all Newton's statements. It reifies time and ascribes to it the function of flowing. If time were something that flowed then it would itself consist of a series of events in time and this would be meaningless. Moreover, it is equally difficult to accept the statement that time flows "equably" or uniformly, for this would seem to imply that there is something which controls the rate of flow of time so that it always goes at the same speed. But if time can be considered in isolation "without relation to anything external," what meaning can be attached to saying that its rate of flow is not uniform? If no meaning can be attached even to the possibility of non-uniform flow, then what significance can be attached to specifically stipulating that the flow is "equable"?

Newton was not a philosopher in the modern professional sense of the term, and so it is perhaps not surprising that he gave no critical analysis of his definitions but generally contented himself with their practical use. What is surprising, however, is that his definition of absolute time has no practical use! In practice we can only observe events and use

[1] From G. J. Whitrow, *The Natural Philosophy of Time*, Nelson, London, 1961, pp. 33–39.

processes based on them for the measurement of time. The Newtonian theory of time assumes, however, that there exists a unique series of moments and that events are distinct from them but can occupy some of them. Thus temporal relations between events are complex relations formed by the relation of events to the moments of time which they occupy and the before-and-after relation subsisting between distinct moments of time. [Strictly speaking, "universal" and "absolute" are not synonymous when applied to time, though time for Newton was both absolute and universal.]

Why did Newton introduce this complicated metaphysical concept? Two reasons can be advanced: one physical and the other mathematical. Physically, Newton must have regarded the concept as the essential correlative of absolute space and absolute motion. It is well known that he had definite empirical evidence which he interpreted as a conclusive argument in favour of his belief in absolute motion. This evidence was dynamical. "True motion is neither generated nor altered but by some force impressed upon the body moved, but relative motion may be generated and altered without any force impressed upon the body." The actual effects by which Newton believed that absolute motion could be distinguished from relative were the centrifugal forces associated with motion in a circle. "For there are no such forces in a circular motion purely relative, but in a true and absolute circular motion they are greater or less according to the quantity of the motion. If a vessel, hung by a long cord, is so often turned about that the cord is strongly twisted, then filled with water and held at rest together with the water, thereupon by the sudden action of another force it is whirled about the contrary way, and while the cord is untwisting itself the vessel continues for some time in this motion, the surface of the water will at first be plain, as before the vessel began to move; but after that the vessel, by gradually communicating its motion to the water, will make it begin sensibly to revolve and recede by little and little from the middle, and ascend to the sides of the vessel, forming itself into a concave figure (as I have experienced); and the swifter the motion becomes, the higher will the water rise, till at last, performing its revolutions in the same times with the vessel, it becomes relatively at rest in it."

This experimental evidence shows that after the pail begins to spin there is at first relative motion between the water and the pail which gradually diminishes as the water takes up the motion of the pail. Newton pointed out that when the *relative* motion was greatest it produced no effect on the surface of the water, but that as it diminished to zero and the rotational motion of the water increased, the surface became more and more concave. He interpreted this as evidence that rotational motion is absolute. Consequently, it is not necessary to refer to any other body to attach a definite physical meaning to saying that a particular body rotates, and from this he argued that time, as well as space, must be absolute.

Mathematically, Newton seems to have found support for his belief in absolute time by the need, in principle, for an ideal rate-measurer. He pointed out that, although commonly considered equal, the natural days are in fact unequal. "It may be," he wrote, "that there is no such thing as an equable motion, whereby time may be accurately measured. All motions may be accelerated and retarded, but the flowing of absolute time is not liable to any change. The duration or perseverance of the existence of things remains the same, whether the motions are swift or slow, or none at all; and therefore this duration ought to be distinguished from what are only sensible measures thereof." Newton regarded the moments of absolute time as forming a continuous sequence like that of the real numbers and believed that the rate at which these moments succeed each other is a variable which is independent of all particular events and processes.

An argument which has been used by Bertrand Russell in favour of the absolute theory of time turns on the relation of time to position [*The Principles of Mathematics*, 2d ed., G. Allen, London, 1937, p. 265]. When the time is given, the position of a material particle is uniquely determined, but when the position is given then there may be a number, indeed there may be an infinity, of corresponding moments. Thus, the relation of time to position is not one-one but may be many-one. From this consideration he claims that the time sequence must form an independent variable existing in its own right, and that the correlation of events is made possible only through their prior correlation with moments of absolute time.

Despite Newton's advocacy and Russell's erstwhile support (which he later abandoned), the absolute theory of time has found little favour with philosophers. That moments of absolute time can exist in their own right is now generally regarded as an unnecessary hypothesis. Events are simultaneous not because they occupy the same moment of time, but simply because they happen together. As [J. Alexander] Gunn has so forcefully remarked, "They correlate themselves because they co-exist, and they have no need of an entity 'moment of absolute time' to do this, but rather because they happen, we speak of a moment, and this moment is not a temporal entity existent in its own right, it is simply the class of co-existent events themselves. We derive time from events, not vice versa." [*The Problem of Time*, G. Allen, London, 1929, p. 323.] For the temporal correlation of events which do not co-exist, it is sufficient to postulate that there is a linear sequence of states of the universe, each of which is the class of events simultaneous with a given event, and that these states have the simple before-and-after relation.

Relational Time

The theory that events are more fundamental than moments—which do not exist in their own right, but are classes of events defined by the concept of simultaneity—is usually known as the relational (or relative) theory of time. It was formulated by Leibniz who opposed it to Newton's absolute theory. Leibniz's theory was founded on his principles of sufficient reason, identity of indiscernibles, and pre-established harmony.

According to the first of these principles, nothing happens without there being a reason why it should be thus rather than otherwise. "Truths of reasoning," Leibniz wrote, "are necessary and their opposite is impossible; truths of fact are contingent and their opposite is possible. . . . But there must also be a sufficient reason for contingent truths or truths of fact." [*The Monadology*, R. Latta, (trans.), Geoffrey Cumberlege, Oxford, London, 1925 (original edition, 1898), p. 236.] A particular form of this rather ill-defined general principle is that symmetry of causes must persist in the symmetry of effects. For example, as Leibniz himself pointed out in the second of his five letters to Clarke, the defender of Newton, "Archimedes, wishing to proceed from mathematics to physics in his book *On Equilibrium*, was compelled to make use of a particular case of the great principle of sufficient reason; he takes it for granted that if there is a balance in which everything is the same on both sides, and if, further, two equal weights be hung on the two ends of the balance, the whole will remain at rest. This is because there is no reason why one side should go down rather than the other." [*Philosophical Writings*, Mary Morris (trans.), Dent, London, 1934, p. 194.]

Leibniz applied this principle to time in a famous passage of his third letter. "Suppose someone asks why God did not create everything a year sooner; and that the same person wants to infer from that that God did something for which He cannot possibly have had a reason why He did it thus rather than otherwise, we should reply that his inference would be true if time were something apart from temporal things, for it would be impossible that there should be reasons why things should have been applied to certain instants rather than to others, when their succession remained the same. But this itself proves that instants apart from things are nothing, and that they only consist in the successive order of things; and if this remains the same, the one of the two states (for instance that in which the Creation was imagined to have occurred a year earlier) would be nowise different and could not be distinguished from the other which now exists." [*Philosophical Writings*, p. 200.]

According to the principle of the identity of indiscernibles, which Leibniz deduced from his principle of sufficient reason, it is impossible that there should exist things which differ *sole numero*, or only because they are two, and are otherwise completely similar. In his fourth letter to Clarke he wrote, "To suppose two things indiscernible is to suppose the same thing under two names. Thus the hypothesis that the universe should have originally had another position in time and place from that which it actually had, and yet all the parts of the universe should have had the same position with regard to one another as that which they have in fact received, is an impossible fiction." [*Philosophical Writings*, p. 204.]

Leibniz's monads [atoms endowed, in varying degrees, with the power of perception] are mutually independent but, in order that they should form one universe, each mirroring the whole course of the universe from its own point of view, the famous principle of pre-established harmony stipulated that the states of all monads at every instant correspond with each other. Leibniz illustrated this principle by the simile of the two clocks which may be made to keep perfect time with one another in three different ways. They may be physically connected, as in Huygens's experiment in which two pendulums hung on a bar of wood were set swinging out of time with one another but ultimately swung in harmony as the result of the mutual transference of vibrations through the wood. Alternatively, they could be kept in time by the continual intervention of a skilled workman. Finally, they may have been so perfectly constructed that they keep time without either mutual influence or external assistance. The last possibility corresponds to the pre-established harmony.

Thus, in Leibniz's theory, neither space nor time can exist in their own right independently of bodies, except as ideas in the mind of God. Space is the order of co-existences, and time is the order of succession of phenomena. This order is the same for all monads, for since each of the latter mirrors the whole universe, they must necessarily keep pace with one another. Consequently, in so far as the temporal aspect of the universe is concerned, Leibniz's principle of harmony is equivalent to the postulate of universal time. He was very clear on the question of the temporal origin of the universe. "It is a similar, that is to say an impossible fiction, to suppose that God had created the world several million years sooner. Those who incline towards such kinds of fiction will be unable to reply to those who are in favour of the eternity of the world. For since God does nothing without a reason, and since there is no reason assignable why He did not create the world sooner, it will follow either that He created nothing at all, or that He produced the world before any assignable time, which is to say that the world is eternal. But when we show that the beginning, whatever it was, is always the same thing, the question why it was not otherwise ceases to exist. If space and time were something absolute, that is to say if they were something other than certain orders of things, what I am saying would be a contradiction. But since this is not the case, the hypothesis is contradictory, that is to say it is an impossible fiction." [*Philosophical Writings*, p. 206.]

Leibniz does not seem to have formulated any detailed criticism of Newton's strongest argument for absolute time which was based, as we have seen, on his belief that rotational motion is absolute. The first attack on this interpretation of the rotating bucket experiment was made by Berkeley, whose whole philosophy was founded on the rejection of abstract general ideas and, in particular, on the rejection of absolute space and time as objective realities existing independently of our perception. In his essay *De Motu*, published in 1721, he showed that the crucial point in Newton's argument was his implicit assumption that the experiment would yield the same result if it were performed in empty space, whereas in fact the pail was at first rotating and then at rest relative to the Earth. Its motion was only apparently, and not truly, circular, because it is necessary to take into account the rotation of the Earth about its axis, the revolution of the Earth about the Sun, and so on. He concluded that the phenomena cited by Newton merely indicated rotation relative to the other bodies of the universe and that it is not necessary to introduce the idea of absolute rotation. The same point was made by Mach, in the latter part of the nineteenth century, in his classic *Science of Mechanics*. He remarked that the only experimental test that could be imagined for disproving the idea that rotational motion is relative (with respect to the universe as a whole) would be to compare Newton's experiment as he performed it with one in which the bucket is left undisturbed and the universe is made to rotate around it. This test is impossible to carry out and so we are not compelled to accept Newton's interpretation of his experiment. Consequently, his case for absolute time collapses.

## THE CONCEPT OF TIME[1]

*Immanuel Kant (1724–1804)*

### Metaphysical Exposition of the Concept of Time

1. Time is not an empirical concept that has been derived from any experience. For neither coexistence nor succession would ever come within our perception, if the representation of time were not presupposed as underlying them *a priori*. Only on the presupposition of time can we represent to ourselves a number of things as existing at

From Immanuel Kant, *Critique of Pure Reason*, 2d ed. rev., N. K. Smith (trans.), 1933, 74–78, by permission of Macmillan & Co. Ltd., London, The Macmillan Company of ada Ltd., and St. Martin's Press Inc., New York.

one and the same time (simultaneously) or at different times (successively).

2. Time is a necessary representation that underlies all intuitions. We cannot, in respect of appearances in general, remove time itself, though we can quite well think time as void of appearances. Time is, therefore, given *a priori*. In it alone is actuality of appearances possible at all. Appearances may, one and all, vanish; but time (as the universal condition of their possibility) cannot itself be removed.

3. The possibility of apodeictic principles concerning the relations of time, or of axioms of time in general, is also grounded upon this *a priori* necessity. Time has only one dimension; different times are not simultaneous but successive (just as different spaces are not successive but simultaneous). These principles cannot be derived from experience, for experience would give neither strict universality nor apodeictic certainty. We should only be able to say that common experience teaches us that it is so; not that it must be so. These principles are valid as rules under which alone experiences are possible; and they instruct us in regard to the experiences, not by means of them.

4. Time is not a discursive, or what is called a general concept, but a pure form of sensible intuition. Different times are but parts of one and the same time; and the representation which can be given only through a single object is intuition. Moreover, the proposition that different times cannot be simultaneous is not to be derived from a general concept. The proposition is synthetic, and cannot have its origin in concepts alone. It is immediately contained in the intuition and representation of time.

5. The infinitude of time signifies nothing more than that every determinate magnitude of time is possible only through limitations of one single time that underlies it. The original representation, *time*, must therefore be given as unlimited. But when an object is so given that its parts, and every quantity of it, can be determinately represented only through limitation, the whole representation cannot be given through concepts, since they contain only partial representations; on the contrary, such concepts must themselves rest on immediate intuition.

## The Transcendental Exposition of the Concept of Time

I may here refer to No. 3, where, for the sake of brevity, I have placed under the title of metaphysical exposition what is properly transcendental. Here I may add that the concept of alteration, and with it the concept of motion, as alteration of place, is possible only through and in the representation of time; and that if this representation were not an *a priori* (inner) intuition, no concept, no matter what it might be, could render comprehensible the possibility of an alteration, that is, of a combination of contradictorily opposed predicates in one and the same object, for instance, the being and the not-being of one and the same thing in one and the same place. Only in time can two contradictorily opposed predicates meet in one and the same object, namely, *one after the other*. Thus our concept of time explains the possibility of that body of *a priori* synthetic knowledge which is exhibited in the general doctrine of motion, and which is by no means unfruitful.

### Conclusions from these Concepts

(*a*) Time is not something which exists of itself, or which inheres in things as an objective determination, and it does not, therefore, remain when abstraction is made of all subjective conditions of its intuition. Were it self-subsistent, it would be something which would be actual and yet not an actual object. Were it a determination or order inhering in things themselves, it could not precede the objects as their condition, and be known and intuited *a priori* by means of synthetic propositions. But this last is quite possible if time is nothing but the subjective condition under which alone intuition can take place in us. For that being so, this form of inner intuition can be represented prior to the objects, and therefore *a priori*.

(*b*) Time is nothing but the form of inner sense, that is, of the intuition of ourselves and of our inner state. It cannot be a determination of outer appearances; it has to do neither with shape nor position, but with the relation of representations in our inner state. And just because this inner intuition yields no shape, we endeavour to make up for this want by analogies. We represent the time-sequence by a line progressing to infinity, in which the manifold constitutes a series of one dimension only; and we reason from the properties of this line to all the properties of time, with this one exception, that while the parts of the line are simultaneous the parts of time are always successive. From this fact also, that all the relations of time allow of being expressed in an outer intuition, it is evident that the representation is itself an intuition.

(*c*) Time is the formal *a priori* condition of all appearances whatsoever. Space, as the pure form of all *outer* intuition, is so far limited; it serves as the *a priori* condition only of outer appearances. But since all representations, whether they have for their objects outer things or not, belong, in themselves, as determinations of the mind, to our inner state; and since this inner state stands under the formal condition of inner intuition, and so belongs to time, time is an *a priori* condition of all appearance whatsoever. It is the immediate condition of inner appearances (of our souls), and thereby the mediate condition of outer appearances. Just as I can say *a priori* that all outer appearances are in space, and are determined *a priori* in conformity with the relations of space, I can also say, from the principle of inner sense, that all appearances whatsoever, that is, all objects of the senses, are in time, and necessarily stand in time-relations.

If we abstract from *our* mode of inwardly intuiting ourselves—the mode of intuition in terms of which we likewise take up into our faculty of representation all outer intuitions—and so take objects as they may be in themselves, then time is nothing. It has objective validity only in respect of appearances, these being things which we take as *objects of our senses*. It is no longer objective, if we abstract from the sensibility of our intuition, that is, from that mode of representation which is peculiar to us, and speak of *things in general*. Time is therefore a purely subjective condition of our (human) intuition (which is always sensible, that is, so far as we are affected by objects), and in itself, apart from the subject, is nothing. Nevertheless, in respect of all appearances, and therefore of all the things which can enter into our experience, it is necessarily objective. We cannot say that all things are in time, because in this concept of things in general we are abstracting from every mode of their intuition and therefore from that condition under which alone objects can be represented as being in time. If, however, the condition be added to the concept, and we say that all things as appearances, that is, as objects of sensible intuition, are in time, then the proposition has legitimate objective validity and universality *a priori*.

What we are maintaining is, therefore, the *empirical reality* of time, that is, its objective validity in respect of all objects which allow of ever being given to our senses. And since our intuition is always sensible, no object can ever be given to us in experience which does not conform to the condition of time. On the other hand, we deny to time all claim to absolute reality; that is to say, we deny that it belongs to things absolutely, as their condition or property, independently of any reference to the form of our sensible intuition; properties that belong to things in themselves can never be given to us through the senses. This, then, is what constitutes the *transcendental ideality* of time. What we mean by this phrase is that if we abstract from the subjective conditions of sensible intuition, time is nothing, and cannot be ascribed to the objects in themselves (apart from their relation to our intuition) in the way either of subsistence or of inherence. This ideality, like that of space, must not, however, be illustrated by false analogies with sensation, because it is then assumed that the appearance, in which the sensible predicates inhere, itself has objective reality. In the case of time, such objective reality falls entirely away, save in so far as it is merely empirical, that is, save in so far as we regard the object itself merely as appearance.

## THE CONCEPT OF TIME IN THE CLASSICAL PICTURE OF THE PHYSICAL WORLD[1]

*Milic Capek (1909–     )*

### The Independence of Time from Its Physical Content

Time is the second fundamental concept of classical physics. While space was defined as the three-dimensional manifold of coexisting homogeneous terms, time was regarded as the one-dimensional manifold of successive terms. The basic relation in space is juxtaposition; the basic relation in time is *succession*. The points of space are *beside* one another; the instants of time *follow* one another. While we keep this fundamental difference in mind, we can apply a large part of what has just been said about space to time as well. Both space and time were regarded as species of manifold, and both were believed to share the property of being homogeneous. As in the case of space, the basic attributes of time followed from its homogeneity: its independence of its physical content, its infinity, continuity, and uniformity. The uniformity of time was a counterpart of the immutability of space; it might be more expressively designated *uniform fluidity*. Thus it is only natural that the principles of relativity of magnitude and of position have their counterparts in the doctrine of classical time.

The independence of time in regard to concrete changes which take place in it was again explicitly formulated by Newton:

> Absolute true and mathematical time, of itself and by its own nature, flows uniformly, without regard to anything external. It is also called *duration*. Relative, apparent and vulgar time, is some sensible and external measure of absolute time (duration), estimated by the motions of bodies, whether accurate or unequable, and is commonly used instead of true time; such as an hour, a day, a month, a week.

According to this view, time flows no matter whether something changes or not; in its own nature time is *empty* and is only in an accessory and contingent way filled by changes. Changes are *in* time; they are not *time* itself. This distinction between time and concrete becoming is at the very foundations of classical physics. As space does not imply matter,

[1] From Milic Capek, *The Philosophical Impact of Contemporary Physics*, Van Nostrand, Princeton, N.J., 1961, pp. 35–38 and 49–51.

time does not imply motion nor change in general. This had been clearly stated by Newton's tutor and predecessor Isaac Barrow, whose influence on the formation of Newton's concept of time was as important as the influence exerted by Henry More on Newton's view of space:

> But does time imply motion? Not at all, I reply, as far as its absolute, intrinsic nature is concerned; no more than rest; the quantity of time depends on neither essentially; whether things run or stand still, whether we sleep or wake, time flows in its even tenor. Imagine all the stars to have remained fixed from their birth; nothing would have been lost to time; as long would that stillness have endured as has continued the flow of this motion. Before, after, at the same time (as far as concerns the rise and disappearance of things), even in that tranquil state would have had their proper existence, and might by a more perfect mind have been perceived. [*Mathematical Works of Isaac Barrow D.D.*, Whewell ed., Cambridge, 1860, vol. II, pp. 160f.[2]]

This could hardly be stated more explicitly.

Basically the same argument was still used at the beginning of this century. When Bertrand Russell in 1901 defended the absolute theory of time, he began by defending the fundamental distinction between the temporal series itself and its qualitative content:

> In the absolute theory, we have two classes of entities, 1) those which *are* positions, 2) those which *have* positions. Any two terms of the first class have an asymmetrical transitive relation; in the present case either *before* or *after*. The terms which have positions are terms each of which has, to one or more of the terms which are positions, a certain specific relation, which may be expressed by saying that the new terms are *at the* positions, or that they occupy the positions.... We may call *qualities* the terms which have positions in time; thus quality may be at many moments, or even at all moments. ["Is Position in Space Absolute or Relative?" *Mind*, vol. X, p. 294, 1901.]

The argument is more general and the language evidently more abstruse than that of Barrow, but its substance is the same. Barrow tried to show that the absence of motion does not prevent time from flowing; Russell gave the argument a more general form by pointing out that no absence of *any* change (not only of change of position) affects the flow of time; a certain quality can endure through *many* moments or even through *all* moments. Barrow and Russell had an identical target at which they were aiming: the relational theory of time. Russell's distinction between "qualities" and "moments" is equivalent to the assertion that the physical content of time is underivable from time itself just as matter is underivable from space. What Russell said of space may be

---

2 Capek then adds references to E. A. Burtt: *The Metaphysical Foundations of Modern Physical Science*, 2d ed. rev., Doubleday, Garden City, N.Y., 1954 (original edition, 1924), pp. 150ff; and G. Windred, "The History of Mathematical Time," *Isis*, vol. XIX, pp. 126–138, 1933.

repeated word for word of time: "There is no logical implication of other entities in [time]. It does not follow, merely because there is [time], that therefore there are things in it." Because the concept of matter as well as that of motion cannot be logically derived from the concepts of space and time respectively, we must recognize that both are indefinable:

> What is meant by *occupying* a point or instant, analysis cannot explain; this is a fundamental relation, expressed by *in* or *at*, asymmetrical and intransitive, indefinable and simple. [Bertrand Russell, *The Principles of Mathematics*, Cambridge, Cambridge, Eng., 1903, p. 465.]

This means that time—if not *de facto*, at least *de iure*—is empty.

The use of the term *occupancy* for both space and time is characteristic of the whole of classical thought. The term itself is distinctly spatial in its original meaning, and its use suggests the close analogy between space and time in which classical physics as well as classical philosophy so firmly believed. Just as matter *fills* or *occupies* portions of space, so motions or, more generally, changes *fill* or *occupy* portions of time. Just as space is a container of all matter, so time is a receptacle of all changes or, in Barrow's words, "Time is in some sort the Space of Motion" [*Mathematical Works*, lecture X]. This was the basic dogma of classical science.

The influence of the Newtonian view of time was far deeper than is generally believed, for it went beyond the limits of physical science. In the thought of Kant, for instance, time was regarded also as a sort of homogeneous frame or container which is filled out from outside by the changing material of sensations. It is true that time for Kant did not possess extramental reality, being only an a priori form of intuition, but this does not alter the fact that the sharp distinction between an immutable homogeneous container and its changing and heterogeneous content is essentially Newtonian in its nature. In this respect we can speak of a certain *isoformism* between the thought of Kant and Newton. Even today we are hardly aware that when we speak of our psychological states as occurring *in* time, we retain this distinction between the receptor and its content, the distinction which under the double impact of Newton and Kant still dominates to a great extent our mode of thinking. . . .

### The Problem of the Duration of Space

There was, however, a certain ambiguity in this assertion of the timelessness of space. Apparently, in the relation of juxtaposition which is the essence of spatiality, there is no reference to time; conversely, in the relation of succession no trace of spatiality can be found. In Kant's words: "Time has only one dimension; different times are not simultaneous, but successive (just as different spaces are not successive, but simultaneous)" [*Critique of Pure Reason*, N. K. Smith (trans.), Humanities Press, New York, 1950, p. 75]. By completing the assumption of the timelessness of space by the spacelessness of time, Kant drew between space and time a sharp line which no physicist dared to blur before the advent of the theory of relativity.

But even before the revolution in physics there were certain obtrusive questions concerning the relation of space and time which were difficult to ignore. Granting that diverse portions of space are *juxtaposed* or *coexisting* and never successive; is not there at least an indirect reference to time by silently assuming that the juxtaposed terms are thought of as being *simultaneous*, i.e., as being at *the same time?* It was possible to avoid this question by claiming that simultaneity is not a temporal relation at all. This is what Kant did, though he was not always consistent in this respect [cf. N. K. Smith, *Commentary on Kant's Critique of Pure Reason*, Macmillan, London, 1918, pp. 135–136, 358–359].

But there was a far more serious question. Even if we grant with Newton, Locke, Maxwell, and nearly all other classical thinkers that the structure of space is completely devoid of any change and in this sense is "eternal," it cannot be denied that space, though immutable, *still endures through time*. Otherwise, how could we speak of motion occurring *in* space? Are not the successive positions of a moving body not only in different points of space but also *in different instants of time?* If so, then Kant's statement about the impossibility of different successive spaces is not valid. It is true that these successive spaces are not qualitatively different and this is the reason why we are inclined to fuse them into a single unchanging timeless space, but this timeless space is merely a convenient label applied to what is in truth an *infinite series of successive instantaneous spaces* which, though qualitatively identical, still differ by their positions in the universal flow of time.

Thus, although it is true to say that classical space was immutable, it is *not* true that it was timeless. As has been shown above, changelessness and duration were not incompatible according to the classical doctrine of time. True timelessness belonged only to individual successive spaces, each of which, in virture of its instantaneous character, contained only purely spatial relations. Thus even classical science seemed to lead to the conclusion that time is a receptacle not only of the changing physical material but of *space itself* [cf. A. N. Whitehead, *The Concept of Nature*, Cambridge, Cambridge, Eng., 1920, p. 71]. But this implicit subordination of space to time was rarely emphasized, and in most cases the opposite tendency prevailed: to subordinate time to space, and even to deny the objective status of time entirely. This opposite tendency was due to the habit of regarding the properties of time as analogous to those of space and was strengthened by some implications of the classical concept of causality which will be analyzed later.

# TIME AS PURE DURATION[1]

*Henri Bergson (1859–1941)*

If space is to be defined as the homogeneous, it seems that inversely every homogeneous and unbounded medium will be space. For, homogeneity here consisting in the absence of every quality, it is hard to see how two forms of the homogeneous could be distinguished from one another. Nevertheless it is generally agreed to regard time as an unbounded medium, different from space but homogeneous like the latter: the homogeneous is thus supposed to take two forms, according as its contents co-exist or follow one another. It is true that, when we make time a homogeneous medium in which conscious states unfold themselves, we take it to be given all at once, which amounts to saying that we abstract it from duration. This simple consideration ought to warn us that we are thus unwittingly falling back upon space, and really giving up time. Moreover, we can understand that material objects, being exterior to one another and to ourselves, derive both exteriorities from the homogeneity of a medium which inserts intervals between them and sets off their outlines: but states of consciousness, even when successive, permeate one another, and in the simplest of them the whole soul can be reflected. We may therefore surmise that time, conceived under the form of a homogeneous medium, is some spurious concept, due to the trespassing of the idea of space upon the field of pure consciousness. At any rate we cannot finally admit two forms of the homogeneous, time and space, without first seeking whether one of them cannot be reduced to the other. Now, externality is the distinguishing mark of things which occupy space, while states of consciousness are not essentially external to one another, and become so only by being spread out in time, regarded as a homogeneous medium. If, then, one of these two supposed forms of the homogeneous, namely time and space, is derived from the other, we can surmise *a priori* that the idea of space is the fundamental datum. But, misled by the apparent simplicity of the idea of time, the philosophers who have tried to reduce one of these ideas to the other have thought that they could make extensity out of duration. While showing how they have been misled, we shall see that time, conceived under the form of an unbounded and homogeneous medium, is nothing but the ghost of space haunting the reflective consciousness.

The English school tries, in fact, to reduce relations of extensity to more or less complex relations of succession in time. When, with our eyes shut, we run our hands along a surface, the rubbing of our fingers against the surface, and especially the varied play of our joints, provide

[1] From Henri Bergson, *Time and Free Will*, F. L. Pogson (trans.), G. Allen, London, 1910, pp. 98–102.

a series of sensations, which differ only by their *qualities* and which exhibit a certain order in time. Moreover, experience teaches us that this series can be reversed, that we can, by an effort of a different kind (or, as we shall call it later, *in an opposite direction*), obtain the same sensations over again in an inverse order: relations of position in space might then be defined as reversible relations of succession in time. But such a definition involves a vicious circle, or at least a very superficial idea of time. There are, indeed, as we shall show a little later, two possible conceptions of time, the one free from all alloy, the other surreptitiously bringing in the idea of space. Pure duration is the form which the succession of our conscious states assumes when our ego lets itself *live*, when it refrains from separating its present state from its former states. For this purpose it need not be entirely absorbed in the passing sensation or idea; for then, on the contrary, it would no longer *endure*. Nor need it forget its former states: it is enough that, in recalling these states, it does not set them alongside its actual state as one point alongside another, but forms both the past and the present states into an organic whole, as happens when we recall the notes of a tune, melting, so to speak, into one another. Might it not be said that, even if these notes succeed one another, yet we perceive them in one another, and that their totality may be compared to a living being whose parts, although distinct, permeate one another just because they are so closely connected? The proof is that, if we interrupt the rhythm by dwelling longer than is right on one note of the tune, it is not its exaggerated length, as length, which will warn us of our mistake, but the qualitative change thereby caused in the whole of the musical phrase. We can thus conceive of succession without distinction, and think of it as a mutual penetration, an interconnexion and organization of elements, each one of which represents the whole, and cannot be distinguished or isolated from it except by abstract thought. Such is the account of duration which would be given by a being who was ever the same and ever changing, and who had no idea of space. But, familiar with the latter idea and indeed beset by it, we introduce it unwittingly into our feeling of pure succession; we set our states of consciousness side by side in such a way as to perceive them simultaneously, no longer in one another, but alongside one another; in a word, we project time into space, we express duration in terms of extensity, and succession thus takes the form of a continuous line or a chain, the parts of which touch without penetrating one another. Note that the mental image thus shaped implies the perception, no longer successive, but simultaneous, of a *before* and *after*, and that it would be a contradiction to suppose a succession which was only a succession, and which nevertheless was contained in one and the same instant. Now, when we speak of an *order* of succession in duration, and of the reversibility of this order, is the succession we are dealing with pure succession, such as we have just defined it, without any admixture of extensity, or is it succession developing in space, in such a way that we can take in at once a number of elements which are both distinct and set side by side? There is no doubt about the answer: we could not introduce *order* among terms without first distinguishing them and then comparing the places which they occupy; hence we must perceive them as multiple, simultaneous and distinct; in a word, we set them side by side, and if we introduce an order in what is successive, the reason is that succession is converted into simultaneity and is projected into space. In short, when the movement of my finger along a surface or a line provides me with a series of sensations of different qualities, one of two things happens: either I picture these sensations to myself as in duration only, and in that case they succeed one another in such a way that I cannot at a given moment perceive a number of them as simultaneous and yet distinct; or else I make out an order of succession, but in that case I display the faculty not only of perceiving a succession of elements, but also of setting them out in line after having distinguished them: in a word, I already possess the idea of space. Hence the idea of a reversible series in duration, or even simply of a certain *order* of succession in time, itself implies the representation of space, and cannot be used to define it.

## SUMMARY OF POINTS FOR DISCUSSION

Because of the complex nature of discussions about time, straightforward contrasts cannot be made—not even those between absolute and relative (relational) views of time. What may be of more use is to repeat, from the introduction to the chapter, (p. 164), the four basic philosophical questions concerning time and invite reflection on them:

*1. Does time exist?* After Kant's reflection on Newton, this question takes on an urgency it had not had since ancient times. Does it make any difference, for *measurements* in science, whether time is real or not, whether it is only a construct of the perceiving subject?

*2. What is the nature of time?* Is it a reality in itself apart from the motions and changes it measures? Is it merely the perception of these motions? Or is it the perception of them as requiring *measurement*, at least of some sort?

*3. What is the relation of time to matter?* Is it as independent as classical mechanists would say, or is time the very "stuff" out of which the world is made? And if someone claims it is the latter, can his statement be verified by the methods of empirical science?

*4. Is there a universal time?* Or, to state the question another way, is the time unfolding of the universe a *unified* process, such that local variations of rate are determinable with respect to some absolute, overall time process?

Obviously several of these questions clearly suggest *relativity* and problems of relativistic space-time. Nevertheless, they are interesting problems in themselves and can be debated on their own terms—i.e., within the limits of classical Newtonian physics.

## BIBLIOGRAPHY

### Classics

Alexander, H. (ed.): *The Leibniz-Clarke Correspondence*, Philosophical Library, New York, 1956; Manchester University Press, Manchester, Eng., 1956.

Bergson, H.: *Time and Free Will*, Macmillan, New York, 1910.

Cajori, F. (ed.): *Sir Isaac Newton's Mathematical Principles of Natural Philosophy and His System of the World*, A. Motte, trans. (1729), University of California Press, Berkeley, Calif., 1934.

Mach, E.: *The Science of Mechanics*, Open Court, La Salle, Ill., 1960 (original English edition, 1893).

### Works of Philosophical or Historical Interest on the Nature of Time

Alexander, S.: *Space, Time, and Deity*, 2 vols., Dover paperback, New York, 1966 (original edition, 1920).

Callahan, J.: *Four Views of Time in Ancient Philosophy*, Harvard, Cambridge, Mass., 1948.

Eddington, Sir A.: *Space, Time, and Gravitation*, Harper & Row, New York, 1959 (original edition, 1920).

Fraser, J. (ed.): *The Voices of Time*, Braziller, New York, 1966.

Gale, Richard M. (ed.): *The Philosophy of Time*, Doubleday, Garden City, N.Y., 1967.

Grünbaum, A.: *Philosophical Problems of Space and Time*, Knopf, New York, 1963.

Munitz, M.: *Space, Time and Creation*, Free Press, New York, 1957.

Reichenbach, H.: *The Philosophy of Space and Time*, Dover, New York, 1958 (original German edition, 1928).

Smart, J. (ed.): *Problems of Space and Time*, Macmillan, New York, 1964.

Toulmin, S., and J. Goodfield: *The Discovery of Time*, Harper & Row, New York, 1965.

Whitrow, G.: *The Natural Philosophy of Time*, Nelson, London, 1961.

MacKinnon, Edward: "Time and Contemporary Physics," International Philosophical Quarterly, vol. II, pp. 428–457, 1962.

# Chapter

# 8*

# Relativity and the
# Space-Time Continuum:
# Static and
# Dynamic Views

THERE HAS BEEN TALK AMONG PHILOSOPHERS in recent decades of a "final elimination of the concept of absolute space from the conceptual scheme of modern physics." (The same attitude would necessarily also have to be taken toward absolute time.) We have seen in Chapter 6 how Grünbaum would counter this claim, especially in terms of the formidable mathematical obstacles to carrying out the implications of relativity. Undoubtedly there are difficulties—and these will be duly referred to—but in one sense Grünbaum has missed the point. For Einstein, though he does admit that the "process . . . is probably by no means as yet completed," nevertheless speaks also of a "victory over the concept of absolute space." Perhaps it is not final, but a victory there has surely been. And Einstein explains its nature. "The victory over the concept of absolute space . . . became possible only because the concept of the material object was gradually replaced as the fundamental concept of physics by that of the field."[1] Continuous, field-theory models of the physical world have become standard today, and the concomitant philo-

---

[1] All the quotations in this paragraph are from either the Foreword or the Introduction to M. Jammer, *Concepts of Space*, 2d ed. rev., Harper & Row, New York, 1960; cf. above, Chap. 6, where Einstein's Foreword is given as a selection.

sophical view of a "unification of the physical world" has intrigued more and more philosophers familiar with the findings of science.

The most radical of such unification views would be something like the Heraclitean version of process philosophy proposed by Milic Capek. (See the selection from Capek below.) So radical is Capek's rethinking of the problems of space and time, in terms of relativity and interacting field theories, that he prefers to speak of "time-space" rather than the more customary space-time. As a result, his views in a sense belong more properly among the discussions of Chapter 9, on emergence. These views do, however, at the same time, serve to emphasize the possibility of a *radically dynamic* view of the space-time universe.

More moderate in his presentation of the "unification of the physical world" is another process philosopher, Errol Harris. In summing up his main point in this connection, he says:

> What we wish to emphasize here is that, through a continuous series of generalizations of Euclidean geometry and Newtonian mechanics, all physical phenomena have been resolved into the structure of space-time in a unified world. First, the special theory of relativity showed length and duration, mass and energy to be inseparably united; then the general theory geometrized the gravitational field; Weyl's extension of the theory assimilated to it the phenomena of electrodynamics, and, finally, Eddington attempted to include the structure of matter within the geometry of the four-dimensional whole.[2]

He then goes on to make the point more forcibly, in terms of the *intent* of the scientist:

> The effort of the scientist is . . . to bring all physical phenomena under laws, each of which is a specific expression or special exemplification of the pervasive metrical properties of the space-time continuum. The world is conceived as an unbroken, unified whole, or four-dimensional process, not indeed blankly uniform, but richly differentiated into distinguishable parts and elements variously determining the metrical properties of the locality. These differentiations, however, are not fixed and simply located in space-time, but depend on the particular system of interrelated elements with reference to which they are considered, and of such systems there is an indefinite possible variety. Nevertheless, the relativisitic principle (or set of principles) governing the variations from one system to another is universal and regulates the structure of the whole.[3]

Is this "intent" of physicists "to bring all physical phenomena under laws . . . of the space-time continuum" a fact or a figment of the imagination of philosophers? This is, of course, a factual question for the historian rather than the philosopher of science. Nevertheless, it seems safe to say that the supposed intent, if it is true of anyone, belonged to the great scientist-

---

[2] *The Foundations of Metaphysics in Science*, Humanities Press, New York, 1965, p. 61.

[3] *Ibid.*, p. 62.

philosophers of an earlier generation more than it does to present-day physicists. One indication of this is the current attitude toward Einstein's project of a "unified field theory." A recent reviewer attempts to indicate reasons for "concern with unified field theories gradually to dwindle," and speaks of a "current lack of interest in unified field theories," of "whether there is any value in pursuing the subject" (he thinks there is), and of such theories as "at the moment out of fashion."[4] Nor is unified field theory the only indication, at present, of a lack of universality among physicists of the kind of "intent" Harris ascribes to them. Nonetheless, field theories are very much a part of contemporary science, and—as indicated in Chapter 5, on continuity and discontinuity—they even offer a very attractive invitation to think of the entire universe in terms of field-theory continuity.

One of the most interesting disciplines in current science where this is especially true is *cosmology*—the study of the large-scale structure of the universe. In this area, a great part of the theorizing consists in attempts to give solutions of the field theories of general relativity. "Each cosmological solution of the field equations gives us a model of the universe, by which is meant an account of the history of the universe . . . [i.e.,] of the past and future of the very large-scale features of the universe—say, of the clusters of galaxies."[5] No account of problems of the space-time continuum could be complete without reference to these various models of the universe and various solutions of the field equations of general relativity. One classification lists three types of relativistic models of the universe: (*a*) expanding models without the "cosmological (lambda) term," (*b*) expanding models with the cosmological term (static views), and (*c*) expanding and rotating models.[6] Many great names in recent physics are associated with these attempts, such as Milne and Eddington, and Einstein's name is associated with more than one of them.

All this serves to illustrate what Grünbaum has already suggested—that the "victory" of relativity is by no means complete, nor is it without manifold problems on several levels. Yet it remains true to say that Einstein's space-time continuum is *fundamental* in contemporary physics. One final effort to utilize the concept—one which would have been repudiated violently by Einstein himself—can now be introduced as another background to the discussions of this chapter. This is the attempt to treat *empty space-time* as the building material of the universe, i.e., to revive a sort of Cartesian view of matter as *extension*.

With this last view Grünbaum, in the selection from his work presented below, is in thorough agreement. Its principal contemporary proponent, how-

[4] A. Komar, review of M. Tonnelat, *Einstein's Unified Field Theory*, Gordon and Breach, New York, 1966, in *Science*, vol. 155, p. 1233, Mar. 10, 1967.

[5] W. Bonnor, *The Mystery of the Expanding Universe*, Macmillan, New York, 1964, p. 92.

[6] *Ibid.*, pp. 155–156.

ever, is the physicist John A. Wheeler, and in fact he has entitled one of his articles on the topic "Curved Empty Space-Time as the Building Material of the Physical World: An Assessment."[7] Reference should also be made to an article by C. W. Misner, an associate of Wheeler, with the significant title, "Mass as a Form of Vacuum."[8]

In sum, the unity of a space-time (field) theory of the physical world, in one form or another, is appealing to a great many interpreters of science as *the* ultimate foundation either of measurement in science or of measurable science itself. This by no means implies (as Grünbaum would quickly note) that the absolute space and time of Newton have been entirely eliminated. Even so, the present chapter will presume the utility of the space-time orientation, and the discussions will center on the dynamic-versus-static aspects of a space-time universe. In this context the first selection, by Milic Capek, begins with a clear presentation of the alternative, static and dynamic, views, then argues vigorously for the dynamic view. This is followed, first, by a selection from Adolf Grünbaum arguing for a static view of time (or, to be perfectly fair, for the static character of the *time axis* in physical space-time), and then by a selection from Errol Harris criticizing Capek from within the school of process philosophy.

[7] In E. Nagel, P. Suppes, and A. Tarski (eds.), Logic, Methodology, and Philosophy of Science, Stanford, Stanford, Calif., 1962, pp. 361–374. Cf. also, J. A. Wheeler, "The Universe in the Light of General Relativity," Monist, vol. XLVII, pp. 40–76, 1962.

[8] In E. McMullin (ed.), The Concept of Matter, University of Notre Dame Press, Notre Dame, Ind., 1963, pp. 596–608.

## TIME IN RELATIVITY THEORY: ARGUMENTS FOR A PHILOSOPHY OF BECOMING[1]

Milic Capek (1909–    )

Einstein was not alone in his vacillations on this point. Hermann Weyl, Sir James Jeans, Hans Reichenbach and others shifted their views on this subject, sometimes even within one and the same book. A more consistently negative attitude toward the static interpretation was shown by Paul Langevin and, contrary to what Meyerson claimed, by Arthur S. Eddington [*La Déduction relativiste*, p. 97];[2] and among philosophers by Bergson and Whitehead. It is true that the attitude of the latter two was mostly inspired by their general philosophical outlook, even though the effort to grasp the concrete physical meaning of the relativistic

[1] George Braziller, Inc.—from The Voices of Time, edited by J. T. Frazer. Reprinted with the permission of the publisher, copyright © 1966 by J. T. Frazer, pp. 437–438 and 443–447.

[2] Capek adds a reference to his own article, "Relativity and the Status of Space," *Review of Metaphysics*, vol. IX, p. 160, 1955.

formulae was not lacking in either of them. Despite all criticisms, the spatializing interpretation still lingers, though more in the minds of philosophers than in those of physicists. Besides the relatively recent essay by Gödel (1949), there was Professor Donald Williams' article with the challenging title "The Myth of Passage" (1951) [*Journal of Philosophy*, vol. XLVIII, p. 457, 1951]. Even more recently, Professor Willard Quine claimed that the discovery of the principle of relativity "leaves no reasonable alternative to treating time as space-like" [*Word and Object*, M.I.T., Cambridge, Mass., 1960, p. 172]. Among contemporary philosophers of science two most vigorous defenders of the becomingless view of space-time are Olivier Costa de Beauregard and Adolf Grünbaum. The former speaks of matter as "displayed statically in space-time," ("*statiquement déployée dans l'espace-temps*") [*Le Second principe de la science du temps*, Seuil, Paris, 1963, p. 132], while the latter says explicitly that "coming into being is only coming into awareness" [*Philosophical Problems of Space and Time*, Knopf, New York, 1963, p. 329]. Thus the opinion is still divided—sometimes divided within one and the same mind. This shows clearly how complex and difficult the problem of correct interpretation of the relativistic fusion of space and time still is. . . .

## The Dynamic Character of Time-Space

Our conclusions are then as follows:

a. The succession of causally related events is preserved in *all* frames of reference. In other words, the irreversibility of the world lines, which are constituted by causal successions of events, is a *topological invariant*.

b. The succession of causally unrelated events is completely relativized.

c. Equally fully relativized is the simultaneity of all events with an apparently trivial exception of the simultaneity of each event with itself. The last part of this statement can be expressed in the following way: *absolute coincidences*, that is coincidences both in space and time, are as much topologically invariant as the temporal order of causally related events.

The propositions *b* and *c* are not logically independent. The relativization of the succession of causally unrelated events and the relativity of simultaneity of distant events are two related consequences of the fact that *the temporal order of all causally unrelated events remains undetermined*. A pair of such events can appear in certain temporal order in some systems, in a reversed order in other systems, and finally simultaneous in the third category of systems which constitute, so to speak, a boundary case separating the first two groups of frames of reference. No events can be judged simultaneous unless they are causally unrelated. Only if there were instantaneous causal connections in nature would the simultaneity of causally (in this case instantaneously) related events be possible.

This, indeed, was the case of Newtonian mechanics, and it is certainly not accidental that Galileo's transformation is obtained when we substitute an infinite value for the velocity $c$ in the Lorentz transformation. Infinite velocity means instantaneous interaction. It is true that classical physics knew since Olaf Roemer's discovery in 1675 the finite velocity of light which in the nineteenth century was found equal to the velocity of electromagnetic waves; but it remained completely unaware of the limiting character of this velocity. No upper limit was imposed on the range of possible velocities, that is, on the speed of causal interactions. Thus for a considerable time the velocity of gravitation was believed to be infinite. Laplace still believed that it was at least 50,000,000 times larger than that of light [cf., with respect to Laplace's error, W. Wien, "Über die Möglichkeit einer elektromagnetischen Begründung der Mechanik," *Wiedemann's Annalen*, p. 501, 1901].

In truth, the assumed existence of the Newtonian space, spread instantaneously and orthogonally with respect to the "axis of time," was an embodiment of instantaneous connections; every geometrical distance in such space can in virtue of its instantaneous character be regarded as a world line of a point moving with instantaneous velocity. This network of instantaneous geometrical relations constituting "space at an instant," was at the same time an objective substrate of absolutely simultaneous events. When we say, for instance: "Sirius is eight light years from the earth," it has in classical physics the following meaning: 1) that there is an instantaneous space at this particular moment in which the events both on the earth and on Sirius are located; 2) that because of its finite velocity, the luminous message which I perceive now left Sirius eight years ago. It is clear that the difference between "Now" and "Seen now" was fully recognized by classical physics; but although the objective "Now" was by definition unperceivable, it was in principle inferable and calculable on the basis of the classical theorem for the addition of velocities which was applied to the relative motion of the luminous source and the observer.

The belief in the distinction between "Now" and "Seen now" was due to the fact that classical physics—unlike the general theory of relativity today—accepted the distinction between static geometrical space and its changing physical content. "Now," that is, absolute simultaneity, belonged to the former; "Seen now," that is, the perceived, spurious simultaneity, belonged to the latter. It was this distinction which inspired the search for an absolute frame of reference which would be the substrate of the objective simultaneity. It is sufficiently known how this search, carried on by the experiments of Michelson, Morley, Trouton, Noble, Tomaschek, and Chase, ended in the failure which inspired the most comprehensive and revolutionary revision of the traditional concepts of space and time. The profound and far-reaching meaning of this revision is still not always fully understood now, more than a half century after the formulation of the special theory of relativity.

Thus we read frequently, and not only in semi-popular treatises, that the simultaneity of distant events, absolute for Newton, "was made relative by Einstein." To use such a language is highly misleading. It suggests almost inevitably that behind the inherent relativity of the human frames of reference there lies hidden the true absolute simultaneity, the absolute "Now," even if it may remain forever inaccessible to our knowledge. It is far more accurate to say that the simultaneity of distant events was *eliminated* instead of being merely relativized. What objective status could possibly exist for an entity which is unobservable by definition, and which is an inferential construct different in different frames of reference, none of which possesses a privileged character? It is thus not sufficient to join the adjective "relative" to the noun "simultaneity"; the noun itself should be dropped because of its lurking ontological connotation. Einstein himself did not hesitate to do it:

> There is no such thing as simultaneity of distant events; consequently there is also no such thing as immediate action at a distance in the sense of Newtonian mechanics. ["Autobiographical Notes," in *Albert Einstein: Philosopher-Scientist*, Tudor, New York, 1949, p. 61.]

This correlation between simultaneity of distant events and the network of instantaneous connections can be expressed in a far more explicit way. The class of objectively simultaneous events constitutes the space of classical physics at a certain instant. Conversely, any instantaneous three-dimensional cut across the four-dimensional world process contains the events objectively simultaneous at that instant. Thus the simultaneity of distant events implies their juxtaposition and vice versa. This is what Newton had in mind when he claimed that "every indivisible moment of duration is everywhere" [S. Horsley (ed.), *Opera*, London, 1779–1785, vol. III, p. 8]. The cosmic "Now," in virtue of its universality, is instantaneously spread everywhere; this is the meaning of the classical correlation of absolute simultaneity and absolute space.

But such instantaneous three-dimensional cuts, admissible in the physics of Newton and Laplace, are excluded by the physics of relativity. Contrary to Newton's belief, there is no moment of time which is present everywhere. This lack of correlation between Now and Everywhere was expressed by various thinkers in different ways. In Eddington's words, there are no "world-wide instants" [Sir A. Eddington, *The Nature of the Physical World,* Cambridge, Cambridge, Eng., 1933, p. 42], according to Whitehead, there is not such a thing as "nature at an instant" [A. Whitehead, *Science and the Modern World,* Macmillan, New York, 1926, p. 172], or, as A. A. Robb said, "there is no identity of instants at different places at all"; in other words, "the present instant, properly speaking, does not extend beyond here" [*The Absolute Relations of Time and Space,* Cambridge, Cambridge, Eng., 1921, p. 12]. *Since there is no absolute space correlated with each instant of time, there is no absolute juxtaposition which would serve as a substratum of absolutely simultaneous events.* But while there is no juxtaposition of events which would be a juxtaposition for all frames of reference, *there are certain types of succession which remain such in all systems.* As we have seen, these types of succession are represented by causal chains, that is, by the world lines of material and luminous "particles." Unlike spatial juxtaposition, the irreversibility of the world lines has an *absolute* significance, independent of the conventional choice of the system of reference. We can hardly have a more convincing illustration of the dynamic character of space-time.

We may anticipate the following objection: what about the relativization of the succession of the causally unrelated events? Is it not as fatal to the ontological status of time as the relativization of juxtaposition is to the ontological status of space? Not speaking of the fact that the succession of causally related events still remains invariant, we must not forget that the relativization of the simultaneity of distant events and the relativization of the succession of causally unrelated events entail each other (see above). If we substitute with Einstein the term "elimination" for that of "relativization," it becomes clear that the succession of causally unrelated events is as much devoid of concrete physical meaning as the simultaneity of remote events. Nothing in nature corresponds to either of them. To continue to refer to them as something "real, though relative" betrays the pre-relativistic modes of thought. Such expressions result from an incongruous overlapping of two incompatible languages, the Newtonian and relativistic; it is the resistance of our Newtonian subconscious which prevents us from saying boldly and consistently that simultaneity of distant events as well as the succession of causally independent events simply does not exist.

For there are only two types of relations in the relativistic universe: that of successive causal connections and that of contemporary causal independence. Since the universe consists of the dynamical network of the irreversible causal lines, their irreversibility which remains absolute in the relativity theory is conferred to the universe as a whole. Needless to say, it is not the irreversibility of the Newtonian time. The world process, according to Newton, consisted of the irreversible series of the world-wide instants, that is, of the Now-Everywhere planes; and we have seen that no such cleavage planes are admissible in the relativistic universe. We have seen that a three-dimensional space, at any moment, is an arbitrary instantaneous cut in the four-dimensional process and that such artificial cuts were superseded by the four-dimensional regions of causal independence ("elsewhere" of Eddington, "co-presence" of Whitehead) which separates the front cone of causal future from the rear cone of the causal past. But this does or at least should make clear two important points. First, the impossibility of three-dimensional instantaneous cuts radically transforms the classical concept of space; space now is incorporated into the four-dimensional world process in which the classical space of Newton is a mere artificial instantaneous cross-section. Second, the fact that the past and the future are now more effectively separated than in classical physics certainly does not weaken the objective status of succession. Thus, all these evidences point to one important conclusion: the relativistic union of space with time is far more appropriately characterized as a *dynamization of space* rather than a spatialization of time.

## IS THERE A "FLOW" OF TIME OR TEMPORAL "BECOMING"?[1]

*Adolf Grünbaum (1923–    )*

I believe that the issue of determinism *vs.* indeterminism is *totally irrelevant* to whether becoming is a significant attribute of the time of physical nature independently of human consciousness. And I wish to explain now why I regard the thesis of Reichenbach, Eddington, Bondi, Whitrow, and of many others that indeterminism confers flux onto physical time as untenable. I have given my reasons for likewise rejecting Reichenbach's further claim that "The paradox of determinism and planned action is a genuine one"[2] in other publications.[3]

In the indeterministic quantum world, the relations between the sets

[1] From Adolf Grünbaum, *Philosophical Problems of Space and Time*, pp. 321–329. © Copyright 1963 by Adolf Grünbaum. Reprinted by permission of Alfred A. Knopf, Inc.

[2] H. Reichenbach, *The Direction of Time*, University of California Press, Berkeley, Calif., 1956, p. 12.

[3] Cf. Adolf Grünbaum, "Causality and the Science of Human Behavior," reprinted from *American Scientist*, vol. XL, pp. 665–676, 1952, in H. Feigl and M. Brodbeck (eds.), *Readings in the Philosophy of Science*, Appleton-Century-Crofts, New York, 1953, pp. 766–778; "Das Zeitproblem," *Archiv für Philosophie*, vol. VII, pp. 203–206, 1957; "Complementarity in Quantum Physics and Its Philosophical Generalization," *Journal of Philosophy*, vol. LIV, pp. 724–727, 1957; and "Science and Man," *Perspectives in Biology and Medicine*, vol. V, pp. 483–502, 1962. See also J. J. C. Smart's telling criticisms [*Philosophical Quarterly*, vol. VIII, esp. p. 76, 1958] of Reichenbach's contention that we can "change the future" but not the past.

of measurable values of the state variables characterizing a physical system at different times are, in principle, not the one-to-one relations linking the states of classically behaving closed systems. But this holds for a given state of a physical system and its absolute future quite independently of whether that state occurs at midnight on December 31, 1800 or at noon on March 1, 1984. Moreover, if we consider *any one* of the temporally successive regions of space-time, we can assert the following: the events belonging to its particular absolute past could be (more or less) uniquely specified in records which are a part of that region, whereas its particular absolute future is thence quantum mechanically unpredictable. Accordingly, every "now," be it the "now" of Plato's birth or that of Reichenbach's, always constitutes a divide in Reichenbach's sense between its own recordable past and its unpredictable future, thereby satisfying Reichenbach's definition of the "present." But this fact is fatal to his avowed aim of providing a physical basis for a "unique," transient "now" and thus for "becoming."[4] Reichenbach's recent characterization of the determinacy of the past as recordability as opposed to the quantum mechanical indeterminacy of the future can therefore not serve to vindicate his conception of becoming any more than did his paper of 1925,[5] which was penetratingly criticized by Hugo Bergmann. . . .[6]

I maintain with Bergmann that the transient now with respect to which the distinction between the past and the future of common sense and psychological time acquires meaning has no relevance at all apart from the egocentric perspectives of a conscious (human) organism and from the immediate experiences of that organism. If this contention is correct, then *both* in an indeterministic *and* in a deterministic world, *the coming into being or becoming of an event, as distinct from its merely being, is thus no more than the entry of its effect(s) into the immediate awareness of a sentient organism (man).* For what is the difference between these two worlds in regard to the determinateness of future events? The difference concerns only the type of functional connection linking the attributes of the future events to those of present or past events. But this difference does not make for a precipitation of future events into existence in a way in which determinism does not. Nor does indeterminacy make for any difference whatever at any time in regard to the *attribute-specificity* of the future events themselves. For in either

---

4 This aim is stated by him in "Die Kausalstruktur der Welt und der Unterschied von Vergangenheit und Zukunft," in *Berichte der Bayerischen Akademie München, Mathematisch-Naturwissenschaftliche Abteilung*, pp. 139–142, November, 1925.

5 *Ibid.*

6 H. Bergmann, *Der Kampf um das Kausalgesetz in der jüngsten Physik*, Vieweg, Braunschweig, 1929, pp. 27–28. Wilfrid Sellars has independently developed the basis for similar criticisms of the alleged connection between indeterminism and becoming as part of his penetrating study of a complex of related issues; cf. W. Sellars, "Time and the World Order," in *Minnesota Studies in the Philosophy of Science*, vol. III, pp. 527–616.

kind of universe, it is a fact of logic that what will be, will be! The result of a future quantum mechanical measurement may not be definite prior to its occurrence in relation to earlier states, and thus our prior knowledge of it correspondingly cannot be definite. But as an event, it is as fully attribute-definite and occurs just as a measurement made in a deterministic world does. The belief that in an indeterministic world, the future events come into being or become actual or real with the passage of time would appear to confuse two quite different things: (1) the *epistemological* precipitation of the actual event-properties of future events out of the wider matrix of the possible properties allowed by the quantum-mechanical probabilities, and (2) an existential coming into being or becoming actual or real. Only the *epistemological* precipitation is affected by the passage of time through the transformation of a statistical expectation into a definite piece of information. But this does *not* show that in an indeterministic world there is any kind of *precipitation into existence* or *coming into being* with the passage of time. And even in a deterministic world, the effects of physical events come into our awareness at a certain time and *in that sense* can be thought of as coming into being.

Bergmann's demonstration . . . that an indeterminist universe fails to define a *non*-psychological objective transient now can be extended in the following sense to justify his contention that the concept "now" involves features peculiar to consciousness: the "flux of time" or transiency of the "now" has a meaning only in the context of the egocentric perspectives of *sentient* organisms and does *not also* have relevance to the relations between purely inanimate individual recording instruments and the environmental physical events they register, as Reichenbach claims. For what can be said of every state of the universe can also be said, *mutatis mutandis*, of every state of a given inanimate recorder. Moreover, the relevance of the transient now to the accretion of time-tagged marks or traces on an inanimate recording tape also emerges from William James's and Hans Driesch's correct observation that a simple isomorphism between a succession of *brain traces* and a succession of states of awareness does not explain the now-contents of such psychological phenomena as melody awareness. For the hypothesis of isomorphism of traces and states of awareness renders only the succession of states of awareness but not the *instantaneous awareness of succession*,[7] which is an essential ingredient of the meaning of "now": the now-content, when viewed as such in awareness, includes an awareness of the order of succession of events in which the occurrence of that awareness constitutes a *distinguished element*. And the transiency of the

[7] Cf. W. James, *The Principles of Psychology*, Dover, New York, 1950, pp. 628–629; and H. Driesch, *Philosophische Gegenwartsfragen*, Reinicke, Leipzig, 1933, pp. 96–103.

now or the "flux" of time arises from the *diversity* of the now-contents having the latter attributes: there are striking differences in the *membership* of the set of remembered (recorded) and/or forgotten events of which we have instantaneous awareness.

I cannot see, therefore, that Reichenbach is justified in considering the accretion of time-tagged marks or traces on an *inanimate* recording tape so as to form an expanding spatial series as illustrating the "flux" of time. Thus, Bergmann's exclusively psychologistic conception of this flux or becoming must be upheld against Reichenbach: the flux depends for its very *existence* on the perspectival role of consciousness, since the coming *into* being (or becoming) of an event is no more than the entry of its effect(s) into the immediate awareness of a sentient organism (man).

We saw earlier that the locution "Here-Now" of the relativistic Minkowski diagram does not commit that entirely non-psychological theory to the transient now encountered in common sense time. Hence the purely physical character of the special theory of relativity *cannot* be adduced to show that the transient now is relevant to physical time, i.e., it cannot be adduced to refute our claim of the dependence of the "now" and, correlatively, of the transient division of the time continuum into "past" and "future," on the perspectival role of consciousness.[8]

It was none other than the false assumption that "flux" must be a feature of physical no less than of psychological (common sense) time that inspired Henri Bergson's misconceived polemic against the mathematical treatment of motion, which he unfoundedly charged with having erroneously *spatialized* time by a description which leaves out the flux of becoming and renders only the "static" relations of earlier and later.[9]

Hermann Weyl has given a metaphorical rendition of the dependence of coming into being on consciousness by writing:[10] "The objective world simply *is*, it does not *happen*. Only to the gaze of my consciousness, crawling[11] upward along the life- [i.e., world-] line of my body, does a

---

8 Neither does Minkowski's use of the locution "Here-Now" show conversely that the special theory of relativity makes essential use of psychological temporal categories in its assertive content (as distinct from the pragmatics of its verification by us humans).

9 Cf. H. Bergson, *Creative Evolution*, Random House, New York, 1944, and *Matière et Mémoire*, Skira, Geneva, 1946. Related criticisms of Bergson's treatment of other aspects of time are given in A. Grünbaum, "Relativity and the Atomicity of Becoming," *Review of Metaphysics*, vol. IV, pp. 144–155, 1950.

10 H. Weyl, *Philosophy of Mathematics and Natural Science*, Princeton, Princeton, N.J., 1949, p. 116.

11 The metaphor "crawling" must not, of course, be taken to suggest the "metaphysical error" charged against it by J. J. C. Smart ["Spatializing Time," *Mind*, vol. CXIV, p. 240, 1955] that psychologically time itself "flows" spatially at a certain rate measured in some nonexistent hypertime. We shall see shortly that the concept of the "forward" shifting now does not involve this logical blunder.

section of this world come to life as a fleeting image in space which continuously changes in time." This poetic but sound declaration has given rise to serious misunderstandings, as shown by the following objection from Max Black:

> But this picture of a "block universe," composed of a timeless web of "world-lines" in a four-dimensional space, however strongly suggested by the theory of relativity, is a piece of gratuitous metaphysics. Since the concept of change, of something happening, is an inseparable component of the commonsense concept of time and a necessary component of the scientist's view of reality, it is quite out of the question that theoretical physics should require us to hold the Eleatic view that nothing happens in "the objective world." Here, as so often in the philosophy of science, a useful limitation in the form of representation is mistaken for a deficiency of the universe.[12]

But contrary to Black, Weyl's claim that the time of inanimate nature is devoid of *happening* in the sense of *becoming* is not at all tantamount to the Eleatic doctrine that *change* is an illusion of the human mind! It is of the essence of the relativistic account of the inanimate world as embodied in the Minkowski representation that there is change in the sense that different kinds of events can (do) occur at different times: the attributes and relations of an object associated with any given world-line may be different at different times (e.g., its world-line may intersect with different world-lines at different times). Consequently, the total states of the world (when referred to the simultaneity criterion of a particular Galilean frame) are correspondingly different at different times, i.e., they change with time. It is Blacks' own misidentification of mere change with becoming ("happening") which leads him to the astonishing and grotesque supposition that Weyl's mentalistic account of becoming bespeaks Weyl's unawareness that "the concept of change . . . is . . . a necessary component of the scientist's view of reality." Black refers to the web of earlier-later relations represented by the world-lines as "timeless" just because they do not make provision for becoming. And he suggests that Weyl conceives of them as forming a four-"space" in the sense in which physical space *excludes* the system of temporal relations obtaining with respect to "earlier than." It is apparent that Black's use of the terms "timeless" and "space" in this context is misleading to the point of conveying question-begging falsehoods. Weyl's thesis is that coming into being ("happening"), as contrasted with simply being, is only coming into the present awareness of a sentient organism. And that thesis is not vulnerable to Black's charge of having mistaken "a useful limitation in

12 M. Black, "Review of G. J. Whitrow's The Natural Philosophy of Time," Scientific American, vol. 206, pp. 181–182, April, 1962.

the form of representation" for "a deficiency of the universe," all the less so, since Weyl makes a point of the difference between space and time by speaking of the world as "a (3 + 1)-dimensional metrical manifold"[13] rather than as a 4-dimensional one.

In an endeavor to erect a *reductio ad absurdum* of Weyl's thesis, M. Capek has given an even more grotesque account of that thesis than Black did. Capek writes:

> ... although the world scheme of Minkowski eliminates succession in the physical world, it recognizes at least the *movement of our consciousness* to the future. Thus arises an absurd dualism of the timeless physical world and temporal consciousness, that is, a dualism of two altogether disparate realms whose correlation becomes completely unintelligible.... [In] such a view ... we are already dead without realizing it now; but our consciousness creeping along the world line of its own body will certainly reach any pre-existing and nominally future event which in its completeness *waits* to be finally reached by our awareness.... To such strange consequences do both spatialization of time and strict determinism lead.[14]

But Capek states a careless and question-begging falsehood by declaring that on Weyl's view the physical world is "timeless." For what Weyl is contending is only that the physical world is devoid of becoming, while fully granting that the states of physical systems are ordered by an "earlier than" relation which is isomorphic, in important respects, with its counterpart in consciousness. Capek's claim of the unintelligibility of the correlation between physical and psychological time within Weyl's framework is therefore untenable, especially in the absence of an articulation of the kind (degree) of correlation which Capek requires and also of a *justification* of that requirement. More unfortunate still is the grievous mishandling of the meaning of Weyl's metaphor in Capek's attempt at a *reductio ad absurdum* of Weyl's view, when Capek speaks of our "already" being dead without realizing it now and of our completed future death *waiting* to be finally "reached" by our awareness. This gross distortion of Weyl's metaphorical rendition of the thesis that coming *into* being is only *coming into present awareness* rests on a singularly careless abuse of the temporal and/or kinematic components of the meanings of the words "already," "completed," "wait," "reach," etc.

13 H. Weyl, *Space-Time-Matter*, Dover, New York, 1950, p. 283.

14 M. Capek, *The Philosophical Impact of Contemporary Physics*, Van Nostrand, Princeton, N.J., 1961, p. 165.

# CO-EXISTENCE AND SUCCESSION[1]

*Errol E. Harris (1908–     )*

[An] oversight seems to affect the argument put forward by Capek [Milic Capek, *The Philosophical Impact of Contemporary Physics*, Van Nostrand, Princeton, N.J., 1961, chap. XI] for the complete abolition of co-existence and of juxtaposition in space. For these he substitutes "extensive becoming." Relativity, he says, has wholly eliminated instantaneous co-existence and has infused time into all space, so that the conception of pure spatial extensity is no longer legitimate. We may now speak only of contemporaneous durations. On the other hand, time has not been spatialized in the sense that the time axis has become a fourth static space dimension, but no more is it left as a mere unidimensional series of unextended and durationless instants. Time has an expanded and expanding content, it has breadth and volume. But the spatial implications of these terms have not their former timeless significance, for distance has meaning only in terms of causal sequences and so is never devoid of temporal succession. In Capek's view, therefore, while pure space has been altogether discarded, temporal progression still has an important place in the contemporary world-picture.

In the main all this is sound enough so long as we remember that *pure* time and space are *pure* abstractions and that neither are components of the real world. The actuality is the process of events out of which neither space nor time can be independently extracted. But it is equally true that even relativistic physics can completely dispense with neither space nor time. The extensive becoming of the world is no less spatial than temporal. Its extensiveness still requires co-existence, and juxtaposition cannot be altogether abolished, though it ceases to be a purely spatial idea and is, perhaps, better conceived as contiguity. For any expanse must have co-existent parts, otherwise it is not an expanse but a mere multiplicity of *un*related points—precisely what Capek would promptly reject.

For, as he admits, in relativistic thinking simultaneity of distant events is not annihilated; it is only made relative.[2] Distant events, as he concedes, are contemporaneous, but their simultaneity cannot be simply or absolutely determined. In [a] diagram[3] representing the relativistic four-dimensional world, the "here-now" is the apex of a double cone, the

---

[1] From Errol E. Harris, *The Foundations of Metaphysics in Science*, Humanities Press, New York, 1965, pp. 73–77. Used by permission of Humanities Press and George Allen & Unwin, Ltd., London.

[2] This is a mistake on Harris' part; Capek does not say such simultaneity is "annihilated," but he does say it is *eliminated* (above, p. 187), and he goes on to show that Einstein did not hesitate to speak the same way.

[3] Harris gives such a diagram at this point, but it is not essential to the argument.

meeting point of absolute past and absolute future, but the interval between the two cones is not a void. Schrödinger felicitously called it a *"Toleranzbreite"* ["tolerance-breadth"]. It is the contemporary world filled with events whose precise location in space-time is not simple but varies with the frame of reference. In this respect, however, they are no different from any other events, for in different frames different time series will be applicable, and simple dating is no more possible than simple location.

The temporality of causation and the consecutiveness of causal process undoubtedly remain essential for relativity. But the consequence of this is that causal chains linking distant events always have the form of motion (e.g. the propagation of radiation), and motion can occur only between contiguous positions in space, which must therefore be *juxtaposed*. This juxtaposition is, as it were, pushed further afield in the causal process, and its propagation (so to call it) is both spatial and temporal. The truth of the matter is that juxtaposition has not been abolished but it has become temporal as well as spatial, and can never be one without the other. Similarly, if time is to have structure and expanse as well as bare succession, there must be co-existence of places, if not we are restricted to bundles of unrelated causal lines, each without any spatial breadth, and without mutual communication. Capek seems to lean towards such an idea; but this, as we have seen, is not what the relativity theory demands. There is a connection between contemporary events but they are differently correlated in different frames. There is co-existence, but it is not instantaneous, and simultaneity is not a timeless cut across the four-dimensional manifold but a *Toleranzbreite*.

Capek is anxious to put out of court those who assert the unreality of time, but he seems to forget that, of those who do, the majority deny the reality of space for the same or similar reasons. He himself, in company with Bergson, is not unwilling to degrade space to the level of appearance, but is reluctant to forego the reality of time. But, on his own showing, the two are "inseparable." To speak of appearance and reality is not very fruitful without defining terms. Capek is well aware that any appearance must be founded in, and explained in terms of, reality (who more than Kant and Bradley have insisted on this), and that if temporal succession is confined to the mind, it still remains a feature of experience and is not eliminated from the real. But it must not be forgotten that our awareness of time is curiously ambiguous because, while it is incurably successive, it is so only so far as our consciousness spans an epoch of some duration and apprehends it as a whole within which the succession takes place. Bare "nows" cannot constitute a succession and cannot maintain continuity. They must coalesce in a "specious present," which, as J. D. Mabbott has convincingly argued [*Mind*, vol. LX, 1951], is emphatically *specious,* and may comprehend almost any span depending upon the universe of reference of our thought. It is not, and cannot be, wholly perceptual and can constitute a time-series (as Kant saw [*Critique of Pure Reason,* Second Analogy, A189, B233ff]) only if conceptually ordered as an objective sequence. This objective sequence must be conceived as a whole or else the succession within it, if at all it could then properly be recognized as such, becomes incoherent and devoid of order.

Time is no more than the metric of becoming, which is the presentational form of the concrete reality that becomes. Capek explains lucidly how a single space-time interval between two events may be differently measured by two observers in different frames of reference because they use different metrics [*op. cit.,* p. 218]. The result is different local times; but they are secondary characters which do not affect the actual process of "creative advance." In a valid sense they are different appearances of it. In this sense, then, time is mere appearance, though the process of events is not. And this process, we should have learnt from Whitehead, is one of "*concrescence,*" of continuous realization of "definiteness," wholeness, or form. Mere succession is meaningless and unintelligible. It must be a sequence or series of continuous and coherent structures. What has no form can be no part of a succession, so successive instants are strictly inconceivable, and the idea serves a purpose only as an abstraction from that of successive changes. What changes must have some form, and this form must alter to produce the change and the succession. Succession necessarily implies difference and "successive identities" is a contradiction in terms. *A fortiori,* empty, identical instants cannot succeed one another. If succession thus implies form and structure, it equally requires continuity of successive forms in the process of change. That is to say, it equally involves pattern of change in order to be intelligibly continuous and successive. This is the foundation on which the idea of causality rests and Kant's recognition of it constitutes his great advance upon Hume. Without recognizably continuous pattern of change, successive "*Vorstellungen*" are purely subjective, disordered and incapable of precise temporal relation. The same, of course, is true of spatial order, but there the aspect of togetherness is easier to recognize than in the case of time, while the equally essential aspect of differentiation gets somehow frozen, and the wholeness of space appears static and binding, while the wholeness of time tends to escape notice altogether.

This wholeness or totality is what frightens Capek, who very rightly is anxious to avoid "the night in which all cows are black," the block-universe, *tout donné;* and he feels that the continuous flow of time can save us from these. Indeed it can, but not because it breaks the bounds of wholeness and structure; not because it is for ever incomplete—for it as much implies completion as does spatial order. It saves us from the blank unity of the Parmenidean One, because it is the primary form of diversity and differentiation. As soon as diversification of a uniform being is contemplated, it takes the form of change and must be presented serially. This is why relativity forces upon us the infusion of space with time—to diversify its otherwise blank and unintelligible oneness. Difference of position is distance; and distance takes time to traverse.

## SUMMARY OF POINTS FOR DISCUSSION

*1.* The crux of Grünbaum's argument for a static view of space-time is contained in two sentences. "Nor does indeterminacy make for any difference whatever at any time in regard to the *attribute-specificity* of the future events themselves. For in either kind of universe [deterministic or (quantum) indeterministic], it is a fact of logic that what will be, will be!" Does this mean that for Grünbaum time is unreal? No, it is still an axis of space-time. (Nevertheless, one should note with Grünbaum that, "The theory of relativity conceives of events as simply being and sustaining relations of earlier and later, but not as 'coming *into* being.' ") Does this mean that the *passage* of time, the transient "now," is unreal? Grünbaum again replies in the negative: It is not unreal, though it is a fact that it "involves features peculiar to consciousness."

This last point should be readily assented to by almost anyone; time always bears a relationship to the *perception* (or, at the minimum, to the perceptibility) of time, in almost any theory. Most would also agree that "relativity conceives of events as simply being" (in the sense that an event can always be *definitely located* relative to temporal or spatial coordinates). If Capek counters that when a relativistic formula uniquely isolates an event, the determination is dynamic rather than static, with the temporal-unfolding aspect as fundamental, Grünbaum could retort: "Yes, *provided* that time does 'flow,' and provided that this cannot be explained by reference to consciousness."

Are we left, then, with *no passage or becoming* in the real world? Not necessarily. Grünbaum's arguments show convincingly that the *passage of time* is not a part of the real world, but that does not rule out *all* passage or becoming. Furthermore, this exception gains plausibility *if one claims that becoming, by definition, cannot have the logical attribute-specificity looked for by Grünbaum.* "Passage" or "becoming," in this view, cannot be the sort of finished reality which *results from* passage or becoming.

To sum up, it can be asked, "Is not Grünbaum simply *presuming* that to be physically real a thing must have 'logical attribute-specificity'?"

*2.* Conversely, Capek also seems to be presuming, rather than proving, the physical existence of a dynamic reality of passage, process, or becoming—

which he then identifies with the time axis in his "time-space." Does not his "topological invariance of causally related events in all frames of reference" presuppose dynamic features in reality? How could a succeeding causally dependent event depend on anything else but the (dynamic) *activity* of the preceding cause?

3. It thus appears as though each of these views presupposes what it is arguing for—either a world in which nothing exists unless it has *logical attribute-specificity*, or one in which the time axis of space-time is both more fundamental than the space dimensions and also *radically dynamic*. (Neither author needs to be accused of arguing in a vicious circle; each could be presuming the truth of his position until he feels the other party has disproved it.) Against this background Harris attempts to formulate a middle position. He does so by way of a correction of Capek: The latter's view, he says, "is sound enough so long as we remember that *pure* time and space are *pure* abstractions and that neither are components of the real world. The actuality is the process of events out of which neither space nor time can be extracted."

This might seem the obvious—and the obviously correct—answer. But the state of affairs in philosophy is seldom that tidy. Discussions should be recalled here from earlier chapters, and one point of view that loomed large in them, that of the *positivists* or *logical empiricists*, would have a ready answer for Harris. They would ask, "Can we really know his 'process of events' as it is in the external world? Or are we limited to the hypothetical knowledge of physical theory? Is it in fact this kind of 'physical reality'—namely, inclusion in a theory of physics—that Grünbaum is denying to becoming?"

## BIBLIOGRAPHY

Bondi, H.: *The Universe at Large*, Doubleday, Garden City, N.Y., 1960.

Bonnor, J.: *The Mystery of the Expanding Universe*, Macmillan, New York, 1964.

Capek, M.: *The Philosophical Impact of Contemporary Physics*, Van Nostrand, Princeton, N.J., 1961.

Eddington, Sir A.: *Space, Time, and Gravitation*, Harper & Row, New York, 1959 (original edition, 1920).

Fraser, J. (ed.): *The Voices of Time*, Braziller, New York, 1966.

Gamow, G.: *The Creation of the Universe*, Viking, New York, 1952.

Harris, E.: *The Foundations of Metaphysics in Science*, Humanities Press, New York, 1965.

Hoyle, F.: *The Nature of the Universe*, Harper & Row, New York, 1950.

Jammer, M.: *Concepts of Space*, 2d ed. rev., Harper & Row, New York, 1960 (original edition, Harvard, 1954).

Munitz, M.: *Space, Time and Creation,* Free Press, New York, 1957.

Reichenbach, H.: *The Philosophy of Space and Time,* Dover, New York, 1958 (original German edition, 1928).

Russell, B.: *The ABC of Relativity,* Harper & Row, New York, 1925.

Smart, J. (ed.): *Problems of Space and Time,* Macmillan, New York, 1964.

Weyl, H.: *Space-Time-Matter,* Dover, New York, 1950.

Whitehead, A.: *An Enquiry concerning the Principles of Natural Knowledge; The Concept of Nature;* and *The Principle of Relativity,* Cambridge, Cambridge, Eng., 1919, 1920, and 1922, respectively.

Whitrow, G.: *The Structure and Evolution of the Universe,* Hillary House, London, 1959; and *The Natural Philosophy of Time,* Nelson, London, 1961.

# Part 3

# EMERGENCE, CAUSALITY, AND SCIENCE

IN AN ARISTOTELIAN PERSPECTIVE this final part of the philosophy of science should be the place for a discussion of activity, physical causality, and "agents" or "movers" (including "forces") responsible for the various changes measurable in terms of space and time. It should especially be the place to consider the movers responsible for local motion, and in the corresponding sections of Aristotle's *Physics* this is where he states such principles as, "everything in motion must be set in motion by something external to itself," "motion requires contact with the mover," and "there is no process to infinity in movers."

However, in the world of the 1960s, it is worthwhile at this point to consider some related problems of greater interest to our contemporaries. The most fascinating of these is the problem raised by a *radical alternative* to everything said up to this point. This alternative is opposed not only to Aristotelianism but to its opponents, mechanism and positivism. The "new view" is that of *emergence* or *process philosophy* in one or another of its various forms.

A second contemporary problem, less radical than the first, is of great interest to logical empiricists—it is that of the *physical interpretation of causality.* This problem will then offer a natural opening for the introduction of further problems, of a more advanced nature, on methodological and epistemological issues.

Emergence will be the subject of discussion in Chapter 9, physical causality will be taken up in Chapter 10, and a brief introduction to some advanced topics will be given in two Appendixes.

# Chapter

# 9

# How
# Radical is
# Emergence?

AS IT WILL BE CONSIDERED HERE, the basic question at issue in *emergence* is this: Is some form of process—energy, wave motion, dynamic field—the basic "stuff," ontologically speaking, of which the universe is made, with bodies only particular "configurations" or "condensations" or "discontinuous mathematical functions"? Or is substance, or body, or matter, the more fundamental, and energy, activity, and process derivative?

This complex question can be rewritten in terms appropriate to modern physics, but also acceptable to such "process" thinkers as Teilhard de Chardin and Harris (in the selections below): Is *energy* or *substance* more radical in the explanation of the universe? It should be noted in passing that this question, in spite of similarities, is not the same as the continuity-discontinuity question of Chapter 5; an Aristotelian can opt for continuity, yet still maintain that substance is more fundamental than energy or activity.

In the present chapter the discussion will be set up around an Aristotelian thesis: "Energy is not a physical reality; it is a *measure* of the actual or impeded natural motions of bodies." (See the article on energy below.) "Process" or "radical emergentist" views will be set off in opposition to this thesis. The reason for this procedure is clear. By now it should be obvious, from the Introduction, from the treatment of natural change, and from the selections in the chapters on space and time, that Aristotle's view is through-and-through relativist and dynamic—as opposed to, say, a Newtonian clock-work universe, and in spite of many detractors ridiculing Aristotle as a "static Greek" thinker. Therefore, if some form of reductionism or mechanism is ever going to be defensible in the face of emergentist objections, a dynamic relativist Aristotelianism is a fortiori going to be more defensible. Thus "reductive" views will be represented here only by Aristotle (who is not a "reductionist" in the logical-empiricist sense of the term), and the emergentists will be set off in opposition to him.

With respect to the question, "Is *energy* or *substance* more radical?" several opinions are possible. (1) Most traditional interpretations of Aristotle and his medieval followers would say substance is more radical and would interpret substance in this context in an *absolute* sense. As Raymond Nogar points out in the introductory selection, this view is completely untenable in an evolutionary intellectual climate like our own. (2) Aristotle as interpreted by John Herman Randall, Jr. (correctly, I think) would make substance more radical, but would also note that substance itself is to be treated as *radically relative* to its activities or functions. In general, many reductionists would be absolutists in some sense, all positivists would be relativists. (3) "Process philosophers" like Alfred North Whitehead and Errol Harris would make energy the more radical, though each would have his own view on how the term "energy" is to be taken. In basic accord with this view is that of Pierre Teilhard de Chardin, though he interprets energy in terms of an unfolding "complexity-consciousness." (4) Finally, an even more radical emergent view is possible—as for instance in Nogar's new book, *The Lord of the Absurd*—in which "unfolding energy" is taken as random and disorganized; no selection will be given defending this view.

The basic polarization is between the editor's "Energy—An Aristotelian Interpretation" and two opposing views. The first of these is a selection from Harris, filled out by a representative quote from Whitehead; the second is from Teilhard de Chardin.

The discussions implicit in this confrontation are introduced by a careful selection from Nogar in which he sets up the basic argument for an emergent interpretation of the world, then outlines some acceptable and unacceptable "philosophies of novelty." The chief argument for emergence, quite obviously, is the fact of evolution. However, it becomes urgent chiefly when evolution is interpreted in ontological terms and becomes a sort of "spirit of the times"—which is very much the case today. The chief candidates for a "philosophy of novelty" are here taken as a dynamic Aristotelianism, a Whiteheadian process metaphysics, and a philosophy based on the intuition of Teilhard de Chardin.

The following selection from Nogar, then, is an excellent introduction to the discussions of this chapter.

# TOWARD A PHILOSOPHY OF NOVELTY[1]

*Raymond J. Nogar (1916–1967)*

Although scientific evolution may not warrant the excesses of ideological evolutionisms, this new-found epigenic unfolding of nature in the various sectors of reality demands the close attention of philosophers and theologians, especially those of the Western tradition. Evolution needs a philosophy. It is equally true to say that realistic philosophy (and theology) needs evolution. One of the most serious shortcomings of traditional world-views, based fundamentally upon a Platonic or an Aristotelian approach to reality, is their failure to account for the place of space-time (history) in the understanding of the universe and man. Since the time of Hegel, and especially since the upsurge of the science of origins and development of cosmic entities, the great scandal of traditional metaphysics and Christian theology has been to regard the historical unfolding of nature [as] irrelevant. Preoccupation with the necessary, the eternal, the immutable provided the tradition with an ontological blind spot. It could not see what the contemporary mind with its gaze upon the space-time contingency of existence could see only too well: that the historical unfolding of cosmic being and the life of man belongs, not to the realm of the incidental, but to the very heart of reality. Any philosophy or theology which neglected the timely for the timeless and eternal could not be but illusory.

Thus the philosophies of "essence" have given way today to the philosophies of existence and history. And scientific evolution, with its concentration on origins, development, and epigenic newness of nature is playing its role of focusing attention on the contingency of reality. The old cosmic world-views are dead: determinism on the microscopic, macroscopic, and megaloscopic planes has given way to indeterminism and dynamic transformation. The stability which science studies today is not the static universe of the ancients: it is an ever-changing dynamic stability. There is order, but the order is constantly being replaced by another order, and each is a function of space and time. Even in the human sphere, man may not be *merely* his history, but he is not a man without his history. Nor are his morals, spirituality, and religion untouched by time and space.

This consideration raises an old question. What is the relation between stability and change in nature? The ancients answered by neutralizing time and history—and hence evolution. Species were eternal. But evolutionary science has set the cosmos and the world of man into an essential space-time spin. The universe is not so stable, so orderly as

[1] From Raymond J. Nogar, "The Wisdom of Evolution," *Theology Digest*, vol. XIII, pp. 276–278, 1965. This article is a summary, by the author, of his *The Wisdom of Evolution*, Doubleday, Garden City, N.Y., 1963.

we once thought. Change in space and time touch the very essence of reality. We need a new philosophy of evolution, of epigenic unfolding of nature. But it must avoid the excesses of the past which attended to the timeless to the neglect of the timely, and the excesses of contemporary thought which attends to the timely and neglects the timeless and the eternal.

The problem for any philosophy of evolution is to account for the origins and development of natural species in terms of ultimate natural explanation. Hence the account must be (1) philosophical, (2) evolutionary, (3) natural. In this explanation, both stability and change must be fully accounted for and their roles in the emergence of natural being properly assessed.

In evolution, just as in individual generation and development, two natural tendencies prevail: *constancy* and *variation*. The marks of constancy in nature are three: constancy of regularity, constancy of type, and constancy of unicity. In natural generation, the regularities of physical, chemical, and biological agents and materials are everywhere observed. In a sense, every biological law places restrictions upon evolution, and without the regularity of nature, science would be inoperative. Too, when nature generates, it reproduces a type: the parent is the model of the progeny. The third constancy of unfolding nature is the unique development of each species. On the other hand, evolutionary nature is equally inconstant. That is to say, nature is subject to variation in its developmental activity. This variation is especially marked in the long-term evolutionary picture where the effects of novelty and extinction are dramatic. The ancients thought that constancy was primary (per se) and variation in species was incidental. Today we see them as natural correlatives.

Evolutionary philosophy, then, must stress the historical *contingency* of natural being. Space and time are no longer incidental, and variation of species lies at the heart of natural being. Evolution is the potentiality or virtuality of natural being to change in species. The very metaphysics of the philosophy of evolution will stress the potential and the contingent instead of stressing exclusively the actual and the necessary. The world of evolutionary being is a balanced dualism of stability and change, of the actual and the potential, of the necessary and the contingent. Evolutionary essence must be a space-time existent; the timely and the timeless must be equally acknowledged.

Can the natural philosopher find a fundamental concept of stability and change which expresses this balanced dualism of constancy and novelty? Casting a glance back into the wisdoms of tradition, is there a basic view of the universe which avoids the rigidity of the archetype (Plato) and the fluidity of incomprehensible matter (Heraclitus)? Perhaps Heidegger is not far from this important discovery when he goes back to the Greek concept *phusis* which has entered the Aristotelian tradition and come down to us as nature (*natura*). But it would not be an acceptable concept for the evolutionary problem unless it is purified of the later excessive rigidity given to it by a platonizing of the tradition of natural philosophy.

Originally, nature in the sense of *phusis* meant the entire being in process of unfolding from birth until maturity and death. This developmental concept was drawn from the life sciences and was intended to designate the ground of natural being, the intrinsic spring and source of spontaneous, yet characteristic activity. The concept was intended to express both stability and change, type and variety, to the extent that each was found in reality. But because the ancients had very poor instruments of natural science and natural species seemed to be immutable, the concept *nature* came to mean the unchanging *essence* of natural being, thought to be necessary, immutable, and eternal. The change of species could not be observed, nature was viewed as a mathematical species, and the static cosmos with its metaphysics of essence obscured and almost obliterated the dynamic aspect of the original concept of nature.

Many natural philosophers of the Aristotelian tradition attempted to preserve the relativistic, fluid aspect of the concept "nature," St. Thomas among them. But without an empirical knowledge of evolution of natural species, it was difficult to find reason to accent the timely, the contingent, historical unfolding of nature. Most of the resistance of traditional philosophers to evolutionary claims, even today, stems from an excessive typological concept of nature in which fixity and stability are so stressed that time-space contingent history is a secondary, incidental, and even uninteresting philosophical consideration. This excessive rigidity of the concept "nature" is an accretion, however, and if the primitive meaning is maintained, then we do have the possibility of a basic evolutionary concept which can retain both stability and novelty in realistic balance.

*Editor's Analysis:*

## ENERGY—AN ARISTOTELIAN INTERPRETATION[1]

An *Aristotelian interpretation of energy* was suggested as an introductory foil against which to see the radical alternatives that process philosophy offers to traditional philosophy. Nogar's introductory selection, in spite of its persuasive argument for a reinterpreted Aristotle, is not a

---

[1] For a balanced philosophical view, two things were needed at this point: (1) elimination of mystifying aspects of the term "energy," and (2) presentation of a traditional realist view for discussion. Since no selection could be found to fill these needs, the present analysis was composed expressly for this book.

presentation of an Aristotelian view. It is, rather, an open invitation, directed toward Aristotelians and others, to come up with a philosophy that will do justice to evolutionary unfolding. No well-elaborated Aristotelian response has been given to this challenge, but it is possible to sketch the main lines of such a response.

An Aristotelian would begin the discussion by attempting to be very clear about just what process philosophers mean by the "process" or "energy" that they take to be more fundamental than substance. And a good place to begin here is with the concept *energy* and its basic meaning in physics.

1. *The meaning of energy in physics*   "Energy," as a concept in physical science, is defined as the capacity to do work. Work is defined as the product of the force exerted on a body times the distance over which the body travels under the influence of that force. The relation between energy and work then can be defined by saying that energy diminishes when work is done, the amount of diminution being equal to the amount of work done; the units of energy are thus the same as the units of work (ergs, joules, foot-pounds).

There are two fundamental types of energy, kinetic and potential. Kinetic energy is that which is associated with mechanical motion; potential energy, on the other hand, is not directly associated with mechanical motion, although it can always in principle be converted into kinetic energy (and this in fact represents the principal utility of the concept in physics).

The kinds of potential energy are numerous—gravitational, chemical, atomic, nuclear, electromagnetic, and even the energy of an elastic body such as a spring. Electromagnetic energy exists in quanta or discrete units of electromagnetic radiation (such as photons). Heat is a special case: The "kinetic theory of heat" takes the energy of a hot body to be the sum of the (statistical average of the) kinetic energy of the particles in the body.

The general formula for kinetic energy is $1/2mv^2$. As the velocity of a particle approaches the speed of light, this formula becomes inaccurate and another must be substituted: $T = (m - m_0)c^2$. It is from this formula, by appropriate substitution, that the mass-energy equivalence, $E = mc^2$, is derived. This mass-energy equivalence, finally, requires a revision in the classical energy-conservation principle, and the principle is now sometimes referred to as the "principle of the conservation of mass-energy."

The *historical background* of this elaborate theoretical construction is complex. An excellent summary has been given by Max Jammer.[2] His summary is built up around three stages in the development of the con-

2 M. Jammer, "Energy," in *New Catholic Encyclopedia*, vol. 5, McGraw-Hill, New York, 1967, pp. 343–346.

cept: (1) a preliminary stage in which energy was not yet differentiated from force and the chief problem was that of deriving an acceptable quantitative formulation; (2) the second stage was concerned with the development of the conservation-of-energy principle; and (3) the development of a generalized conception of energy in the nineteenth century. Work on the nature of heat and the mechanical equivalents of heat aided greatly in the development of this general concept of energy. The latest stage in the development is, of course, the Einsteinian reinterpretation of the generalized concept of energy in terms of the mass-energy equivalence. Jammer cites Einstein as concluding from the equivalence that "the mass of a body is a measure of its energy-content." He then summarizes the present state of affairs: "Modern field theory bases its program for interpreting the mass values of fundamental particles as energy eigen-values on the energy-mass equivalence."[3]

2. *Theoretical status of the energy concept*  This fundamental character of energy in contemporary physics could lead someone to think that energy is in fact the basic stuff of the universe. Heisenberg claims, for instance, "All the elementary particles are made of the same substance, which we may call energy or universal matter.[4] This kind of view was anticipated, though with respect to the nineteenth-century generalized conception of energy, by the "energetics" school most often associated with the name of Ostwald. For these late nineteenth-century thinkers, energy was simply projected from physical theory into the external world; as Jammer puts it, energy "was *the* actuality of nature, all physical phenomena merely being manifestations of energy."

It would be possible to argue against these views of Ostwald and Heisenberg, to prove that energy cannot be the sort of substantial entity (even a potential substantial entity, as Heisenberg would have it) that these theories require. However, it seems enough for present purposes simply to point out that the projection of a physical theoretical construct like energy into the real world is naïve and illogical.

As Ernan McMullin notes:

> Energy is a complex, constructed concept, whose justification must be found . . . in an evaluation of the entire conceptual network of which it is an integral part. Kinetic energy is defined in terms of mass and velocity, and these in turn are defined by means of a group of measure-operations as well as a sophisticated set of mechanical theories and working assumptions. . . . If this interlocking structure provides correct predictions, . . . the concept of energy is thereby validated, and assertions about the energy of a ball become meaningful and testable. This does not make energy either a substance or an accident.[5]

[3] *Ibid.*, p. 346, col. 1.

[4] W. Heisenberg, *Physics and Philosophy*, Harper & Row, New York, 1958, p. 160; see above, p. 97.

[5] E. McMullin, "Energy" (Philosophical Analysis), *New Catholic Encyclopedia*, vol. 5, p. 348, col. 1.

In short, energy is a theoretical construct involving an interrelated set of operational definitions. In Aristotelian terms, such a construct has the status of a hypothetical entity, a "saving of the appearances." Both Aristotle and St. Thomas had warned against the naïve assumption that such hypothetical entities give an explanation of physical reality as it is. Something underlying the hypothetical entity "energy" may be a substance or an accident, but the quantitative construct itself cannot be presumed to be such.

3. *Is there a reality underlying the concept "energy," and can it be known?* Generally speaking, philosophers of science today do not attempt to get at the reality underlying scientific constructs. Is such a project even worth pursuing? In the present case, it does seem worthwhile. The attempt of a scientist like Heisenberg, who in the quotation given above identifies energy with "universal matter," already makes any other attempt intellectually respectable. But beyond this is the urgency that almost certainly was behind Heisenberg's attempt: the fact, namely, that many thinkers have taken the mass-energy equivalence to be a philosophical paradox. Even more urgent, and demanding of a reply, are suggestions that it is really *matter* and energy that are convertible. Gaston Bachelard speaks of a "neo-materialism in which *substance* and energy are interchangeable entities."[6] Finally, there is Einstein's own remark, cited by Jammer, that "the mass of a body is a measure of its energy-content."

Is it possible to know the reality (if any) underlying the concept of energy? How would one go about discovering it? An Aristotelian would go about the business by way of an analogy. Just as there is a simple, quantitative piece of reasoning that justifies the existence of the theoretical physical construct "energy," so there is possible a bit of qualitative reasoning that would argue to the existence of a reality underlying the construct "energy." The two reasoning processes would be exactly parallel.

The quantitative argument is the solution of a problem: How can changes in motion (for instance in a collision of bodies) be measured in terms of simple quantities that will allow calculation of the results of interactions? The solution must involve three elements: (1) a measurable effect external to the motion itself (work); (2) the basic quantity itself (first supplied by Leibniz' *vis viva*, $mv^2$, patterned after Galileo's law of free fall, and later averaged as $1/2mv^2$); (3) a generalization that will allow conservation of the basic quantity and thus make possible straightforward solutions of equations involving it (the generalized concept of energy, including interconvertible kinetic and potential energy).

---

6 P. Schilpp (ed.), *Albert Einstein: Philosopher-Scientist*, Tudor, New York, 1949, p. 578 (italics added).

*4. What is the reality (if any) underlying the concept energy?* Granting the utility of a philosophical clarification of the reality measured by the energy construct (as argued above), Aristotle might well have proposed the following as a candidate: *Energy is the measurement of the actual or impeded natural local motion of bodies.*

Many of the pioneers of modern science objected violently to the "natures" implied in the concept of natural motion, as "occult qualities" useless in quantitative science. However, the concepts involved in natural motion, though they definitely are not of direct application in quantitative science, are no more "occult" than any of the concepts invoked by Galileo or Newton. For Aristotle, the more known explanatory principle was not—as it was so often taken to be by his followers—the nature or essence, from which natural motions would somehow be deduced; rather, nature and natural motions were inseparably interrelated, and whatever could be known about the nature of a thing was derived from its operations.

Nonetheless, natures remain useless in science, and the concept of nature generally tells nothing more about a thing than a listing of its properties. In spite of a constant denial of natures and natural properties on the part of classical scientists, however, science of any kind would be impossible without presuming a distinction between what is essential to bodies and what is accidental (what is able to be left out of account): It is impossible, for instance, even to talk about elementary particles or chemical elements without distinguishing them in terms of their determining properties. In any case, it is generally recognized today that Einstein once again made useful the concept of natural place (at least as a theoretical construct).[7]

If, then, natural motion is no longer as suspect scientifically as it once was, is there any reason to think it can still be made philosophically meaningful? One philosopher who thinks so is John Herman Randall, Jr.; his *Aristotle* includes an eloquent section on Aristotle's "functionalism" and "contextualism" as "far closer to present-day physical theory than are the ideas of the nineteenth century."[8] (Randall also notes, of course, that Aristotle's contextualism has to be brought up to date in "exact, analytical and mathematical formulation.") The conception basic to Aristotelian functionalism is *physis,* usually unhappily translated as "nature." No word is intrinsically objectionable, of course, but this translation is unfortunate both because of the absolute character traditionally associated with natures and essences, and also because of the repudiation by scientists of these as "occult qualities." Aristotelian

---

[7] Cf. Einstein's Foreword to Max Jammer, *Concepts of Space,* 2d ed. rev., Harper & Row, New York, 1960, above, pp. 133–134; and Milic Capek, *The Philosophical Impact of Contemporary Physics,* Van Nostrand, Princeton, N.J., 1961, p. 272.

[8] J. H. Randall, Jr., *Aristotle,* Columbia, New York, 1960, p. 167; cf. above, p. 25.

*physis*, on the contrary, is an *essentially relative* term: Not only is the *physis* of each being necessarily related to its natural operations, but all physical beings are interrelated in a quasi-organic, functional system in which each has its appropriate place and functions.

In searching for examples of natural changes, the very complexity of the functional activities required for human life makes man a poor example of natural changes (contrary to what is implied by the tiresome repetition of *animal rationale* as a standard example in scholastic textbooks). The most appropriate examples are simple ones: Since Aristotle was a biologist, it would be tempting to describe something like the amoeba in terms of its biological and ecological functions. But even this is still too complex for the present discussion on energy. Instead, a good example is something with as few natural changes as possible—for instance, a mineral crystal (say that of diamond), one of the most resistant to change of all natural substances.

There are two points to note here. *(a)* The structure of a crystal is maintained by the bonding between atomic constituents—the "forces" of ionic, covalent, metallic, or Van der Waals bonding; and these forces require characteristic *motions, with definite energy levels*—complete cessation of atomic and molecular motions, absolute zero, is theoretically and practically unattainable. *(b)* Further, there is a reason for the characteristic crystal structure of solids:

> When atoms or molecules condense into a solid phase from a liquid or gaseous phase, the *lowest energy state* is achieved if they become arranged in as regular a way as possible, usually by forming a small basic unit of structure which is repeated indefinitely throughout the solid to form a *crystal*.[9]

The analogy with Aristotle's "natural place" conception of "earth" and "earthy substances" is striking: The solid state is characterized by low energy level (relative physical inertness), great structural stability, and function as dense stabilizing support relative to higher-energy, more active liquids and gases. In addition, the basic physical properties of these solids are determined by natural motions *associated with characteristic bonding forces and energy levels*. (Hence the hardness of the diamond crystal, for instance, caused by the difficulty of breaking the carbon bonds.)

Can natural motion be measured? The sort of temporal divisibility Aristotle mentions[10] would hardly suffice for the building up of a quantitative science of motion. But that does not mean Aristotelians *could not* have developed measurements of natural local motion (and indirectly of the other kinds). In order to do so, they would first have had to

---

[9] R. Besançon (ed.), *The Encyclopedia of Physics*, Reinhold, New York, 1966, p. 146.
[10] *Physics*, book VI, chaps. 3–4, 233b33–235b5.

determine the *effect* of motion on some other measurable body, and to do this would (ordinarily) require a shift in focus from natural to violent or nonnatural motion.

It is often claimed that in a natural-motion scheme "a whole domain of motion, of the so-called violent motions, is blocked off from explanation entirely."[11] The statement as it stands is simply false; what Aristotle said was that violent motions, to be explained, must be reduced to, must be treated as derivatives of, natural motions.[12] What the statement should have said is that *in fact* the explanation of violent motions was neglected, not that it was ruled out. And if violent motions had been explained (and measured), it would have been through the *interaction of natural* motions impeding or counterbalancing one another—a much neglected aspect of Aristotle's doctrine of nature and natural movement, for an impeded natural motion exerts a (measurable) *force* on a body.

If these ideas are now gathered and summed up, they amount to the first steps in a qualitative argument exactly parallel to the quantitative argument for energy.[13] *If natural motion is to be measured, it must be by way of violent motions impressed or capable of being impressed on other bodies.* When elaborated, these measurements would most naturally take the form of concepts like "work" and "kinetic energy." All that would then be required is a generalization to allow for potential energy, *and this is precisely the point of closest agreement with a natural-change doctrine.* The convertibility of the multiplicity of kinds of potential energy into kinetic energy would exactly parallel the natural potentialities of physical bodies as capable of giving rise to natural local motion.

5. *Implications*  This Aristotelian view of energy would require a great deal of elaboration to take account of, for instance, the multiplicity of mechanical (violent) motions in classical physics, or the energy of high-energy particles and mass-energy conversion. In addition, it raises some immediate questions. The most urgent is, "What would such a naturalist interpretation of energy add to a scientific account?" The answer is simple and straightforward—it would add *nothing*.

However, this does not mean the view would have no bearing on the *interpretation* of science. In particular, the view would have an important implication in the context of contemporary discussions of "emergence," "process philosophy," and the views of such evolutionists as Teilhard de Chardin. The reason is that the view focuses attention once more, after many centuries, on the overriding importance of natural change and dynamic qualities in Aristotle's view of the world. For too long he has

11 Cf. McMullin, in the *NCE* article cited above, p. 346, col. 2.
12 *De caelo*, book III, chap. 2, 300a24.
13 See above, p. 210.

been seen exclusively in terms of a metaphysical doctrine of unchanging essences (and his followers are as guilty of the misinterpretation as his enemies), rather than in the light of his *functional* interpretation of nature and the natural.

It may even be hypothesized that Aristotle would have altered his view of unchanging species and essences under the weight of both the evolutionary evidence *and his own doctrine* of *physis*. For if *physis* is totally relative, with respect to natural functions and functional role in larger systems, there is no reason to believe that the *physis* of a thing cannot evolve under the influence of ecological, environmental, and other external factors influencing its characteristic operations. A doctrine of *physis* is perfectly open to evolution, granted that there is evidence of operational mutation capable of bringing about a radical change in the functional role of a being in its environment.

## THE PHILOSOPHY OF PROCESS AND ORGANISM[1]

*Errol E. Harris (1908–     )*

The world view suggested by our review of the physical sciences is extended, and our notion of the fundamental principles of its general structure reinforced, by reflection upon the sciences of life. The physical world revealed itself as a single totality of distinguishable but inseparable elements, within which were generated microcosms each more fully and adequately embodying principles of order governing the whole. So also the biotic world is seen to be a single interconnected organic system containing a multitude of organisms each a complex whole auturgically maintaining its equilibrium by variations relevant to its own internal principles of order, which reflect and exemplify the general principles of organization governing the biocoenosis.[2] The system of living species, more palpably than that of physical entities, arrays itself as a scale of forms increasingly complex and more closely integrated. Again, more emphatically than at the physical level, living reality reveals itself as essentially dynamic, as perpetual process, even where its structure appears to be most stable and permanent. Not only are the formed organs of the living body in constant process of decay and self-renewal, but the genes themselves, that seem to be the least changeable units of life, suffer constant dynamic breakdown and reconstruction. The living world

---

[1] From Errol E. Harris, *The Foundations of Metaphysics in Science*, Humanities Press, New York, 1965, pp. 279–282. Used by permission of Humanities Press and George Allen & Unwin, Ltd., London.

[2] I.e., the total relationship of an organism to its environment, such that it and other organisms are interrelated in an ecological balance.

is essentially a realm of dynamic wholeness, in which the realization of completeness is through a process of change; in which no whole is static, simple, uniform or undifferentiated; yet in which all movement subserves and tends towards order and coherence.

This dynamic interplay of factors in all living substance makes the separation of parts, however clearly distinguishable within the system, altogether impossible. For they flow into and constitute one another. This is true even on the anatomical level. There is strictly *no* living substance, only a complex of interacting chemical substances which live by the special form of their interaction. Organs have their specific characters (and often even their characteristic shapes) only in their functioning. Detached from the organism they are lumps of matter—proteinous or other —not organs of a living body. And when we remind ourselves that the parts of a living thing are strictly not material structures so much as functional processes, when we remember that the organism is an *open* system, we must at once acknowledge that the distinguishable factors which contribute to its organized make-up are utterly inseparable, are completely interfused and mutually constitutive in a thoroughly inextricable manner. They can of course be distinguished and given separate attention by the biologist, but whenever he forgets their indissoluble interdependence he is liable to gross misinterpretation of experimental findings.

Between the physical and the biotic there is no break, and the scale of organized forms advances by continuous complexification and successive self-enfoldments, as Teilhard asserts. The molecule by self-involution becomes organic. Processes of chemical interaction by returning upon themselves in cyclical reconstitution of substances become metabolic. Energy-producing systems by feed-back of their own products become self-regulating (or cybernetic), and this self-regulation by constant incorporation, harmonization and use of accidental novelties evolves to more efficient, more versatile and more capable organisms. The process generates man, and man with all his shortcomings, acts by deliberate intention, exercising mind. This we shall find is again a "folding back" or reflection upon itself of vital process, an activity supervenient upon the physiological which cannot be separated from the functioning of the body.

Further, the scale continues to be hierarchical. Nothing physical is cancelled by life, which incorporates in itself all the main physical forms —atoms (even when radioactive), molecules, crystals, with all their physical and chemical bonds. The interaction of these forms is still subject to physicochemical laws, if also to more special biological laws; and in some sense nothing is added on the purely material level. The difference is *prima facie* only one of complexity and the type of organization

—a difference of degree—but it is one so marked and so critical that it also amounts to a difference of kind. What was before merely a complex and polyphasic system of chemical reactions, becomes an auturgic, self-adjusting and self-maintaining, living organism. Again, despite the continuity between them, the properties of the inorganic and the living are so divergent, as a result of this critical advance in organization, that they evince opposition, not only by contrast of general character, but also in mutual influence so that the organism maintains itself *against* the destructive tendencies of thermodynamics, *against* the strains and stresses imposed upon it by its environment.

Within the tree of life the same sort of relationship between phases of development and evolution pertains. They are all in various ways continuous with one another, all different degrees of organization and adaptation to special conditions; yet they provide marked contrasts—unicellular as opposed to multicellular, asexual as opposed to sexual, invertebrate as opposed to vertebrate, animals with exoskeletons of dead hard chitinous exudations as opposed to those with living bony endoskeletons, aquatic animals as opposed to terrestrial, instinctive as opposed to intelligent. In the biotic sphere we have, more obviously than at prior levels, a continuous process of development unrolling a scale of forms, both temporally successive and hierarchically coexistent. These are mutually related in three ways: (i) as differing degrees of realization of organic wholeness and adaptation, (ii) as differing kinds—phyla, classes, orders, families, genera, species—(it was mainly biological study that suggested the very notion of classification)—(iii) as contrasting and opposed forms (e.g. plants as opposed to animals) which diverge to opposite poles of a continuous gradation.

Again there is mounting hierarchy. The cell, independent in Protozoa, is still a self-contained unit in Metazoa. Asexual reproduction by self-diremption still continues in the segmentation of eggs and the proliferation of cells in sexually reproducing species. The watery environment of early aquatic life with its characteristic salt concentration is still traceable in the bloodstream (the internal environment) of land animals. Automatic and instinctive activity (as will appear) is still the foundation of all intelligent behaviour.

The philosopher cannot afford to ignore all this in his effort to understand the general nature of things. The logician must take cognizance of it, if he seeks to discover the principles which make it intelligible. Clearly no foundation is provided by biological discoveries for any metaphysical atomism or purely extensional logic. The kind of metaphysic to which it points is Whiteheadian—a metaphysic of process and concrescence, particulate only so far as "the real internal constitution" of "actual entities" is made up by the "ingredience" into them of other actual entities. It portends a metaphysic of internal relations and thoroughgoing interdependence of diverse elements within a single totality. The appropriate philosophy for contemporary science must be, like Whitehead's, a philosophy of organism. "The whole point of the modern doctrine," he writes, "is the evolution of the complex organisms from antecedent states of less complex organisms. The doctrine thus cries aloud for a conception of organism as fundamental for nature. It also requires an underlying activity—a substantial activity—expressing itself in achievements of organism."

**Editor's Note:** This quotation is from Alfred North Whitehead, *Science and the Modern World*, Mentor paperback, New York, 1948, p. 101. To give something more of the original flavor of Whitehead, the following brief selection is added. It is the immediate context of the preceding quote.

## THEORY OF ORGANIC MECHANISM[1]

*Alfred North Whitehead (1861–1947)*

The atomic material entities which are considered in physical science are merely these individual enduring entities, conceived in abstraction from everything except what concerns their mutual interplay in determining each other's historical routes of life-history. Such entities are partially formed by the inheritance of aspects from their own past. But they are also partially formed by the aspects of other events forming their environments. The laws of physics are the laws declaring how the entities mutually react among themselves. For physics these laws are arbitrary, because that science has abstracted from what the entities are in themselves. We have seen that this fact of what the entities are in themselves is liable to modification by their environments. Accordingly, the assumption that no modification of these laws is to be looked for in environments, which have any striking difference from the environments for which the laws have been observed to hold, is very unsafe. The physical entities may be modified in very essential ways, so far as these laws are concerned. It is even possible that they may be developed into individualities of more fundamental types, with wider embodiment of envisagement. Such envisagement might reach to the attainment of the poising of alternative values with exercise of choice lying outside the physical laws, and expressible only in terms of purpose. Apart from such remote possibilities, it remains an immediate deduction that an individual entity, whose own life-history is a part within the life-history

[1] Reprinted with permission of The Macmillan Company from *Science and the Modern World*. by Alfred North Whitehead. Mentor paperback, New York, 1948, pp. 100–102. Copyright 1925 by The Macmillan Company, renewed 1953 by Evelyn Whitehead.

of some larger, deeper, more complete pattern, is liable to have aspects of that larger pattern dominating its own being, and to experience modifications of that larger pattern reflected in itself as modifications of its own being. This is the theory of organic mechanism.

According to this theory the evolution of laws of nature is concurrent with the evolution of enduring pattern. For the general state of the universe, as it now is, partly determines the very essences of the entities whose modes of functioning these laws express. The general principle is that in a new environment there is an evolution of the old entities into new forms.

This rapid outline of a thoroughgoing organic theory of nature enables us to understand the chief requisites of the doctrine of evolution. The main work, proceeding during this pause at the end of the nineteenth century, was the absorption of this doctrine as guiding the methodology of all branches of science. By a blindness which is almost judicial as being a penalty affixed to hasty, superficial thinking, many religious thinkers opposed the new doctrine; although, in truth, a thoroughgoing evolutionary philosophy is inconsistent with materialism. The aboriginal stuff, or material, from which a materialistic philosophy starts is incapable of evolution. This material is in itself the ultimate substance. Evolution, on the materialistic theory, is reduced to the role of being another word for the description of the changes of the external relations between portions of matter. There is nothing to evolve, because one set of external relations is as good as any other set of external relations. There can merely be change, purposeless and unprogressive. But the whole point of the modern doctrine is the evolution of the complex organisms from antecedent states of less complex organisms. The doctrine thus cries aloud for a conception of organism as fundamental for nature. It also requires an underlying activity—a substantial activity —expressing itself in individual embodiments, and evolving in achievements of organism. The organism is a unit of emergent value, a real fusion of the characters of eternal objects, emerging for its own sake.

Thus in the process of analysing the character of nature in itself, we find that the emergence of organisms depends on a selective activity which is akin to purpose. The point is that the enduring organisms are now the outcome of evolution; and that, beyond these organisms, there is nothing else that endures. On the materialistic theory, there is material—such as matter or electricity—which endures. On the organic theory, the only endurances are structures of activity, and the structures are evolved.

Enduring things are thus the outcome of a temporal process; whereas eternal things are the elements required for the very being of the process.

# THE PHENOMENON OF MAN[1]

*Pierre Teilhard de Chardin (1881–1955)*

If this book is to be properly understood, it must be read not as a work on metaphysics, still less as a sort of theological essay, but purely and simply as a scientific treatise. The title itself indicates that. This book deals with man *solely* as a phenomenon; but it also deals with the *whole* phenomenon of man.

In the first place, it deals with man *solely* as a phenomenon. The pages which follow do not attempt to give an explanation of the world, but only an introduction to such an explanation. Put quite simply, what I have tried to do is this; I have chosen man as the centre, and around him I have tried to establish a coherent order between antecedents and consequences. I have not tried to discover a system of ontological and causal relations between the elements of the universe, but only an experimental law of recurrence which would express their successive appearance in time. Beyond these first purely *scientific* reflections, there is obviously ample room for the most far-reaching speculations of the philosopher and the theologian. Of set purpose, I have at all times carefully avoided venturing into that field of the essence of being. At most I am confident that, on the plane of experience, I have identified with some accuracy the combined movement towards unity, and have marked the places where philosophical and religious thinkers, in pursuing the matter further, would be entitled, for reasons of a higher order, to look for breaches of continuity.

But this book also deals with the *whole* phenomenon of man. Without contradicting what I have just said (however much it may appear to do so) it is this aspect which might possibly make my suggestions *look* like a philosophy. During the last fifty years or so, the investigations of science have proved beyond all doubt that there is no fact which exists in pure isolation, but that every experience, however objective it may seem, inevitably becomes enveloped in a complex of assumptions as soon as the scientist attempts to explain it. But while this aura of subjective interpretation may remain imperceptible where the field of observation is limited, it is bound to become practically dominant as soon as the field of vision extends to the whole. Like the meridians as they approach the poles, science, philosophy and religion are bound to converge as they draw nearer to the whole. I say "converge" advisedly, but without merging, and without ceasing, to the very end, to assail the real from different angles and on different planes. Take any book about the universe written by one of the great modern scientists, such as Poincaré, Einstein or Jeans, and you will see that it is impossible to attempt a general scientific interpretation of the universe without *giving the impression* of trying to explain it through and through. But look a little more closely and you will see that this "hyperphysics" is still not a metaphysic.

In the course of every effort of this kind to give a scientific description of the whole, it is natural that certain basic assumptions, on which the whole superstructure rests, should make their influence felt to the fullest possible extent. In the specific instance of the present Essay, I think it important to point out that two basic assumptions go hand in hand to support and govern every development of the theme. The first is the primacy accorded to the psychic and to thought in the stuff of the universe, and the second is the "biological" value attributed to the social fact around us.

The pre-eminent significance of man in nature, and the organic nature of mankind; these are two assumptions that one may start by trying to reject, but without accepting them, I do not see how it is possible to give a full and coherent account of the phenomenon of man. . . .

What has made us in four or five generations so different from our forebears (in spite of all that may be said), so ambitious too, and so worried, is not merely that we have discovered and mastered other forces of nature. In final analysis it is, if I am not mistaken, that we have become conscious of the movement which is carrying us along, and have thereby realised the formidable problems set us by this reflective exercise of the human effort. . . .

We have all forgotten the moment when, opening our eyes for the first time, we saw light and things around us all jumbled up in it and all on one single plane. It requires a great effort to imagine the time when we were unable to read or again to take our minds back to the time when for us the world extended no farther than the walls of our home and our family circle.

Similarly it seems to us incredible that men could have lived without suspecting that the stars are hung above us hundreds of light years away, or that the contours of life stretched out millions of years behind us to the limits of our horizon. Yet we have only to open any of those books with barely yellowing pages in which the authors of the sixteenth, or even as late as the eighteenth, century discoursed on the structure of worlds to be startled by the fact that our great-great-great-grandfathers felt perfectly at ease in a cubic space where the stars turned round the earth, and had been doing so for less than 6,000 years. In a cosmic atmosphere which would suffocate us from the first moment, and in perspectives in which it is physically impossible for us to enter, they breathed without any inconvenience, if not very deeply.

Between them and us what, then, has happened?

I know of no more moving story nor any more revealing of the biological reality of a noegenesis than that of intelligence struggling step by step from the beginning to overcome the encircling illusion of proximity.

In the course of this struggle to master the dimensions and the relief of the universe, space was the first to yield—naturally, because it was more tangible. In fact the first hurdle was taken in this field when long, long ago a man (some Greek, no doubt, before Aristotle), bending back on itself the apparent flatness of things, had an intuition that there were antipodes. From then onwards round the round earth the firmament itself rolled roundly. But the focus of the spheres was badly placed. By its situation it incurably paralysed the elasticity of the system. It was only really in the time of Galileo, through rupture with the ancient geocentric view, that the skies were made free for the boundless expansions which we have since detected in them. The earth became a mere speck of sidereal dust. Immensity became possible, and to balance it the infinitesimal sprang into existence.

For lack of apparent yardsticks, the depths of the past took much longer to be plumbed. The movement of stars, the shape of mountains, the chemical nature of bodies—indeed all matter seemed to express a continual present. The physics of the seventeenth century was incapable of opening Pascal's eyes to the abysses of the past. To discover the real age of the earth and then of the elements, it was necessary for man to become fortuitously interested in an object of moderate mobility, such as life, for instance, or even volcanoes. It was thus through a narrow crack (that of "natural history," then in its infancy) that from the eighteenth century onwards light began to seep down into the great depths beneath our feet. In these initial estimates, the time considered necessary for the formation of the world was still very modest. But at least the impetus had been given and the way out opened up. After the walls of space, shaken by the Renaissance, it was the floor (and consequently the ceiling) of time which, from Buffon onwards, became mobile. Since then, under the unceasing pressure of facts, the process has continually accelerated. Although the strain has been taken off for close on two hundred years, the spirals of the world have still not been relaxed. The distance between the turns in the spiral has seemed ever greater and there have always been further turns appearing deeper still.

Yet in these first stages in man's awakening to the immensities of the cosmos, space and time, however vast, still remained homogeneous and independent of each other; they were two great containers, quite separate one from the other, extending infinitely no doubt, but in which things floated about or were packed together in ways owing nothing to the nature of their setting.

The two compartments had been enlarged beyond measure, but within each of them the objects seemed as freely transposable as before. It seemed as if they could be placed here or there, moved forward, pushed back, or even suppressed at will. If no one ventured formally as far as this play of thought, at least there was still no clear idea why or to what extent it was impossible. This was a question which did not arise.

It was only in the middle of the nineteenth century, again under the influence of biology, that the light dawned at last, revealing the *irreversible coherence* of all that exists. First the concatenations of life and, soon after, those of matter. The least molecule is, in nature and in position, a function of the whole sidereal process, and the least of the protozoa is structurally so knit into the web of life that, such is the hypothesis, its existence cannot be annihilated without *ipso facto* undoing the whole network of the biosphere. The *distribution, succession and solidarity of objects are born from their concrescence in a common genesis.* Time and space are organically joined again so as to weave, together, the stuff of the universe. That is the point we have reached and how we perceive things today.

Psychologically what is hidden behind this initiation? One might well become impatient or lose heart at the sight of so many minds (and not mediocre ones either) remaining today still closed to the idea of evolution, if the whole of history were not there to pledge to us that a truth once seen, even by a single mind, always ends up by imposing itself on the totality of human consciousness. For many, evolution is still only transformism, and transformism is only an old Darwinian hypothesis as local and as dated as Laplace's conception of the solar system or Wegener's Theory of Continental Drift. Blind indeed are those who do not see the sweep of a movement whose orbit infinitely transcends the natural sciences and has successively invaded and conquered the surrounding territory—chemistry, physics, sociology and even mathematics and the history of religions. One after the other all the fields of human knowledge have been shaken and carried away by the same under-water current in the direction of the study of some *development.* Is evolution a theory, a system or a hypothesis? It is much more: it is a general condition to which all theories, all hypotheses, all systems must bow and which they must satisfy henceforward if they are to be thinkable and true. Evolution is a light illuminating all facts, a curve that all lines must follow.

In the last century and a half the most prodigious event, perhaps, ever recorded by history since the threshold of reflection has been taking place in our minds: the definitive access of consciousness to a *scale of new dimensions*; and in consequence the birth of an entirely renewed universe, without any change of line or feature by the simple transformation of its initimate substance.

Until that time the world seemed to rest, static and fragmentable, on the three axes of its geometry. Now it is a casting from a single mould.

What makes and classifies a "modern" man (and a whole host of our contemporaries is not yet "modern" in this sense) is having become capable of seeing in terms not of space and time alone, but also of duration, or—and it comes to the same thing—of biological space-time; and above all having become incapable of seeing anything otherwise—anything—*not even himself.*

This last step brings us to the heart of the metamorphosis.

## SUMMARY OF POINTS FOR DISCUSSION

In this chapter, with totally opposed points of view on the interpretation of science at stake, it is not likely that any very satisfying conclusion will be reached. However, each side should be able to make some telling points against the other, and together the two points of view do converge on one overall conclusion:

*1.* It should be possible to prove that a reductive approach, deriving energy from substance rather than the other way around—here represented by Aristotle (brought up to date)—can come up with a concept that is capable of handling evolutionary unfolding. In Aristotle's case this is the dynamic notion of nature, *physis*, now interpreted as *radically relative*, relative not only to the changes Aristotle would have recognized but also, and perhaps more fundamentally, to evolutionary change. True reductionists, in the contemporary sense of the word, would be dissatisfied with Aristotle's conception, but presumably they would also be able to come up with a sufficiently dynamic concept to account for the radical character of evolution in contemporary thinking about science. (They would probably take the direction suggested by the dynamics of wave packets and space-time fields.)

*2.* Process philosophers have the upper hand in the debate, however, for it is easy and natural to assume that contemporary dynamic interaction theories—from particle physics to the development of astrophysical systems and even of the universe as a whole, to the unquestioned cohesiveness of biological evolution—point to an *ontological structure* of process and unfolding. At the very least, such philosophers would be able to demonstrate the untenability of a static view of the universe, on the ontological level, in the light of present scientific knowledge.

*3.* Finally, both sides in the discussion should be able to carry this last-mentioned point into a general metaphysics. A so-called "Greek static" view of the universe (which, as has been shown repeatedly, is not an apt characterization of at least some of the Greek philosophers) is totally unreconcilable with evolution interpreted as a scientific fact rather than a merely hypothetical theory.

## BIBLIOGRAPHY

Browning D. (ed.): *Philosophers of Process*, Random House, New York, 1965.

Dobzhansky, T.: *Genetics and the Origin of Species*, 3d ed., Columbia, New York, 1951.

————: *Mankind Evolving*, Yale, New Haven, Conn., 1962.

Harris, E.: *The Foundations of Metaphysics in Science*, Humanities Press, New York, 1965.

Nogar, R.: *The Wisdom of Evolution*, Doubleday, Garden City, N.Y., 1963.

————: *Evolutionism: Its Power and Limits*, Thomist, Washington, D.C., 1964.

————: *The Lord of the Absurd*, Herder and Herder, New York, 1966.

Northrop, F., and M. Gross (eds.): *Alfred North Whitehead: An Anthology*, Macmillan, New York, 1961.

Simpson, G.: *The Meaning of Evolution*, Yale, New Haven, Conn., 1949.

————: *This View of Life*, Harcourt, Brace & World, New York, 1964.

Teilhard de Chardin, P.: *The Phenomenon of Man*, Harper & Row, New York, 1959.

————: *The Future of Man*, Harper & Row, New York, 1964.

Whitehead, A.: *Science and the Modern World*, Mentor paperback, New York, 1948 (original edition, 1925).

————: *Process and Reality*, Harper & Row, New York, 1960 (original edition, 1929).

# Chapter
# 10*

# The Physical
# Interpretation of
# Causality

EMERGENCE, ACTIVITY, ENERGY, INTERACTION—all these must necessarily be related to problems of causality. If causal connections are empirically unverifiable, then the sort of complexity interaction demanded by Teilhard de Chardin, for instance, is at best nonempirical, at worst some sort of metaphysical or mystical mumbo jumbo. At the other end of the scale, science itself would be utterly impossible without causal connections, no matter what Humean skepticism might say.

Hence the problems of this chapter. Without causal connections of some sort, the search for scientific explanations becomes a meaningless game. Yet causal connections, since the time of Hume, have seemed to philosophers notoriously difficult to justify—except possibly pragmatically.

Little more than this bare statement of the odds at stake is needed here as an introduction. The first selection, from Edward H. Madden, is intended to suggest the sort of difficulties philosophers encounter when they attempt to deal with the notion of causality. The tone throughout is decidedly empiricist.

The second selection, on the other hand, from Mario Bunge, is notably impatient with the standard (empiricist) philosophical interpretation of causality. Bunge is not simply an anti-empiricist; he does not simply assert "causal connections" or "unobservable forces" or "ontological ties." What he does propose is that science is the criterion in matters of causality, and science knows more forms of *determination* than just the causal. Of such determinations, "causality" in the narrow Humean sense is only one kind, and a kind with a limited scope and importance in science.

Madden is thus presented here as summarizing the philosopher's concerns, Bunge as suggesting what he thinks are the true (though most often implicit) concerns of the scientist.

## THE MEANING OF "CAUSE" AND "LAW"[1]

*Edward H. Madden (1925– )*

### 1

We use the concepts of cause and effect widely in everyday discourse; in fact, they are among our most familiar terms. Scientists also use these notions in trying to explain how or why things come about as they do, although they use the terms more carefully than we, in the sense that they demand more evidence, and more carefully derived evidence, for their use than we do in ordinary affairs. Some philosophers of science, it is true, insist that scientists do not bother with the notion of cause at all. Cause-and-effect generalizations, they say, hold only within ranges whose limits are unclear and tacitly assume that certain unmentioned factors remain constant; therefore, scientists disregard the concept of causality in favor of the more sophisticated notion of lawfulness or functional connection. In logically sophisticated sciences like physics, to be sure, one infrequently finds the word "cause" used; but the matter is quite otherwise in biological, psychological, and social science where explanation is frequently described as the confirmation of hypotheses of causal connection. Actually, however, it matters little for our purposes whether scientists talk about "causes" or "laws" or whatever, since, as we shall see, the very same difficulties beset one no matter which of these terms he tries to define or clarify.

In the context of everyday language we find many familiar but not altogether clear notions of the meaning of "cause." If someone who knew nothing about philosophy or science were asked what he meant when he says "x is the cause of y," whatever "x" or "y" may be, he would probably reply that he means x is *responsible for bringing about* y, or x *produces* y, or x *makes* y *happen*. These definitions are not very helpful, however, since it is doubtful if "responsible for bringing about," or "produces," or "makes happen" is any more understandable in this

---

[1] From Edward H. Madden (ed.), *The Structure of Scientific Thought*, Houghton Mifflin, Boston, 1960, pp. 201–207.

context than "causes." Nevertheless philosophers have not been able to ignore these vague common-sense definitions in their efforts to produce more precise ones.

Let us begin our philosophical analysis of causality with the metaphysical or "necessary connection" viewpoint. This view is called metaphysical since it denies that the concept of cause can be fully understood or defined in terms of experience alone. A proponent of this view agrees readily that part of the meaning of "cause" is defined in experiential terms; whatever else we mean when we say "x causes y," we mean that x and y are always correlated in our experience, x and y always occur together and never apart. This idea is variously formulated; sometimes it is said that x and y are constantly conjoined, or x and y are functionally related, or, in the symbols of modern logic, $x \supset y$, that is, whenever x, then y. However constant conjunction, or whatever one calls it, is only part of the meaning of cause, the metaphysical proponent says; it is, in a sense, only the symptom of a causal connection. Mere constant conjunction can never give us a complete understanding, or be an adequate definition, of the cause-effect relationship. True, I experience a constant conjunction between willing to raise my arm and the upward movement of my arm, but in such cases of volition I also directly experience the causal relation itself: I experience the volitional force or energy which *makes* an event—in this case, the movement of the arm—occur. The full meaning of "cause," then, is the constant conjunction of x and y, plus a force that necessarily binds x and y together. X and y are not simply conjoined, but connected; they do not simply occur together, they belong together.

In the physical realm, of course, the metaphysical advocate continues, we do not have any direct experience of the causal connection between x's and y's, but nevertheless we must postulate the existence of some unobservable force or ontological tie which binds together the cause and the effect so that we can say the events are connected and not simply conjoined. On the level of common-sense we do feel that a cause and effect are connected in the sense that given the cause, the effect *must* occur; but mere constant conjunction can never explain this notion of *mustness* which we feel intuitively is present in all causal relationships.

In addition, the metaphysical proponent says, constant conjunction cannot be the whole meaning of "cause" since some constant conjunctions are accidental or, at any rate, not causal in nature, while other constant conjunctions *are* causal. Night follows day, and day follows night universally, but we do not for a moment think that either is the cause of the other. They are both, we say, the effects of a third thing, namely, the illumination of the sun and the rotation of the earth. However, since some constant conjunctions are and some are not causal in nature, constant conjunction cannot be all that is meant by "cause." Constant conjunction is only a symptom of causality in the sense that it only provides evidence which makes it reasonable, in some cases, to postulate the existence of a force or tie which insures and explains the universality of that conjunction.

The empirical philosopher, on the other hand, believes that "cause" means constant conjunction, or lawfulness, and nothing more. To justify this belief he tries to meet, point for point, the metaphysician's reasons for believing in a necessary causal connection and to show, in addition, that this concept is really a nonsensical one, the outgrowth, in short, of a semantical mixup.

*First*   The empiricist denies that we are directly acquainted with causal connections even in volitional experience. As Hume already pointed out, willing to move my arm is not the (complete) cause of the movement since it is only one of a set of many conditions which together make up the cause. Certain physiological conditions must be satisfied also before the movement occurs. If the muscles of my arm are paralyzed, regardless of how much willing I do, the arm will not move. Consequently, since in some cases the movement of the arm does not follow upon the volition, one is not able to say there is a necessary connection between the volition and the movement.

*Second*   The empiricist denies that it is *necessary* to presuppose or postulate causal forces or ontological ties between elements or events in the physical world; it is unnecessary since one can make the required distinctions between connected and unconnected events and causal and non-causal constant conjunctions within the ambit of experience itself.

A. What, after all, do we mean when we say events A and B are *connected* except that there is a chain of intermediate events so that A-a-b-B is perfectly continuous in space and time? However, since there is no gap in space or time between b and B, there is no further connection for these events to exhibit. Consider the example of a doctor administering a drug to his patients. After a reasonable lapse of time, let us say, they invariably recover from their illness. Still, even though we have a constant conjunction between administration of the drug and the recovery of patients, nevertheless we have not succeeded in connecting the events. We would have done the latter only if we knew how the gap between the two types of events is replaced by a continuous series of events which are contiguous in space and time. We would know how this gap is filled, how the events are connected, if we knew for example that the drug is injected into the veins, comes into immediate contact with blood particles, which undergo a chemical change, travel through the body, and come into contact with some organ, thereby changing it in a particular way, etc. The conclusion of the matter, according to one modern empiricist, is this:

> We learn that the causal relation between two separate events is actually explained or understood when we can conceive the two as being connected by a chain of intermediate events. If some of these are still separated, we have to look for new events between them, and so on, until all the gaps are filled out and the chain has become perfectly continuous in space and time. But evidently *we can go no further*, and it would be nonsense to expect more of us. If we look for the causal link that links two events together, we cannot find anything but another event (or perhaps several). Whatever can be observed and shown in the causal chain will be the links, but it would be nonsense to look for the linkage. This shows that we are perfectly right when we think of cause and effect as *connected* by a causal chain, but that we are perfectly wrong when we think that this chain could consist of anything but events, that it could be a kind of mysterious tie called "causality." [M. Schlick, "Causality in Everyday Life and in Recent Science," in H. Feigl and W. Sellars (eds.), *Readings in Philosophical Analysis*, Appleton-Century-Crofts, New York, 1949, p. 522.]

*B.* The way we distinguish those constant conjunctions which *are* causal from those which are *not*, says the empiricist, is by reference to an overall deductive context, not by invoking an unobservable force. We say that day-night and night-day are not causal correlations because we know that they are both *effects* of a common cause. That is, we know there is a constant conjunction or universal correlation between sources of illumination and the rotation of spheroid bodies from which we can deduce the sequences day-night and night-day as joint effects. If, however, there were no higher-order correlations from which we could deduce this consequence, then one would have to accept, until further notice, the correlation night-day-night as ultimate and so causal. The general conclusion is this: without a deductive context one would not be able to call any universal correlation non-causal.

Moreover, the empiricist asks, is there really a constant conjunction between day and night, albeit not a causal one? He thinks not; rather the higher-order correlation shows that the day and night relation is only an *apparent* or *conditional* constant conjunction, one which occurs only if the conditions specified in the higher-order correlation obtain. But a real constant conjunction, J. S. Mill wrote, is unconditional or exceptionless: a conjunction which occurs no matter what happens. Day and night, of course, would not follow each other no matter what happens. If the sun stopped shining or a screen were obtruded between the sun and earth, or whatever, the conjunction would be destroyed. Of course, we cannot actually destroy this conjunction, but we have good evidence from small scale systems that these conditions would destroy it.

Let us return for a moment to the concept of a deductive hierarchy of correlations in science. The more highly developed a science is, like physics, the more highly articulated is its deductive hierarchy. The important point, however, is that in any science the higher-order correlations necessarily imply the lower-order ones. One is thus able to say: Given the higher-order correlations the lower-order ones *must* follow; given the correlation between sources of illumination and the rotation of bodies, the sequences day-night-day etc. *must* follow. However, there is no mustness in the highest-order correlations; unless they contain theoretical terms the only evidence we have finally for their truth is the universality of the correlation of their terms. This analysis has led some empiricial philosophers to say we can never be certain that anything is really the cause of something else. Even our highest-order correlations might turn out eventually to be non-causal in the sense that we might discover a still higher correlation from which the terms of the previous correlation could be deduced as joint effects.

*Third*   The empiricist claims that the metaphysician's notion of mustness or necessary connection makes no sense in a causal analysis; it is literally the outgrowth of a semantical mix up. Logic and mathematics are the only contexts in which the notion of necessary connection has any meaning. A conclusion follows as necessarily true from its premises if the premises and the denial of the conclusion are self-contradictory. So, if what the metaphysician means by mustness is logical necessity, then he would have to say that the denial of a causal assertion is self-contradictory. But this position is absurd since if I say "wet feet always cause colds" I am clearly uttering a false sentence and so could not be uttering a self-contradictory one.

The metaphysician might reply that by mustness he does not mean logical connection; rather he means something like the cause *forcing* or *making* the effect occur, or being responsible for the occurrence of the effect. But if this is the case, the metaphysician has confused prescriptive and descriptive laws. A prescriptive law is the statement of a norm, that is, what must be done if one is to avoid sanctions. Of course, it makes perfectly good sense to say that the sanctions of a prescriptive law force a person to accept it or make him follow it, since he might well prefer on other grounds not to accept or follow it. However, this notion of forcing or making is inappropriate in the context of descriptive laws, since this type of law simply describes what is the case, not what must be the case. It is simply a little odd to talk about making or forcing physical objects to act in the required lawful way as if they might really prefer something else.

Some empiricists, trying to make the concept of cause more precise, have offered this string of definitions: "cause" = "sufficient condition"; "sufficient condtions" = "set of necessary conditions"; "necessary condition" = "condition without which the effect would not occur." Let us use the example of a forest fire to clarify these definitions. A forest fire will occur, one says, if these conditions obtain: some means of ignition, dry underbrush, a prevailing wind, oxygen in the air, etc. Each condition is necessary, not in the metaphysicians' sense, but only in the sense that without it the effect—the forest fire—would not occur. It is, of course, very difficult to find the whole set of necessary conditions, but this whole set, whatever it may be, is the condition sufficient or able to produce the effect and thus is the cause of the effect.

It is doubtful, however, that this analysis of "cause" carries one any farther than the constant conjunction interpretation. For, after all, the only empirical meaning that can be given to the phrase "a condition without which the effect would not occur" is this: when C happens (along with other conditions), E also happens; and when C does not happen, E does not happen.

## 2

Before we try to discover what the concept of scientific law means, we might be wise to look at several examples of scientific law in order to give a modicum of concreteness to our investigation. ($L_1$) All metals are conductors of electricity. ($L_2$) All gases, at constant pressure, expand with increasing temperature. ($L_3$) All surfaces colder than the surrounding air have moisture condense on them, etc. The aspect about all these laws which strikes one first is their universal form—All x's are y's, or if anything is an x then it is also a y. Some philosophers and most scientists, consequently, have defined scientific law, or simply law, as the universal conjunction of terms, or—since most of them can be given a mathematical formulation—the functional correlation of terms.

Many writers have objected to this straightforward definition of "law," and for a reason somewhat similar to an objection advanced against the empirical definition of "cause." Universal correlation, they say, is a necessary part of the definition of law but not itself a sufficient definition. There are, after all, many universal correlations which we simply would not consider laws: consider, for example, the statements that all apples in basket $b$ at time $t_1$ are red or that all the books on the top shelf of my bookcase are English novels of the nineteenth century. Even though these two sentences assert universal correlations we would not call them laws, since we would not say that any apple, chosen at random, put into basket $b$ at time $t_1$ would be red, or that any book chosen at random from a library shelf and put on the top shelf of my bookcase would be an English novel of the nineteenth century.

However, some empiricists answer, the difficulty with the statements about apples and English novels is simply that their universality refers to a finite class of objects. These statements, to be sure, assert universal correlations, but the items correlated do not belong to an infinite class. So we need to modify the definition of "law" only slightly: A law is the universal conjunction of terms which belong to a non-finite class. In this way, the sentence "All metals are conductors of electricity" is a law, since it asserts a universal conjunction between "metals" and "conductors of electricity," each of which can be infinitely exemplified; but "All apples in basket $b$ at time $t_1$ are red" is not, since it asserts a universal conjunction between terms of which an exhaustive inventory can be taken.

At this point, however, a difficulty arises for this amended definition of law. Consider this sentence: "All sixteen ice cubes in the freezing tray of this refrigerator have a temperature of less than 10° centigrade." This statement refers to a finite class of objects, sixteen ice cubes in a tray in *this* refrigerator, and so, on this new definition, should not qualify as a law; but nevertheless we are certain intuitively that the correlation it asserts *is* lawful in a way that the correlation between red apples and basket $b$ is not. This difficulty can be overcome in a simple way; the statement about ice cubes qualifies as lawful because it is known to be the deductive consequence of more comprehensive laws which contain only terms of an unlimited or non-finite scope. Accordingly the definition of law must be amended slightly again: A law is the universal conjunction of terms which belong to a non-finite class or the universal conjunction of terms which belong to a finite class but are deductively derivable from other universal conjunctions which contain only terms of a non-finite scope.

There is another difficulty with this empirical or Humean type of analysis of "law" which is not so easily overcome. Let us return to the statement about the apples in basket $b$ and the English novels on the top shelf of my bookcase. The trouble with these statements, what keeps them from being lawful universal conjunctions, is not simply that the correlated terms are not infinite in scope but rather that there is no connection, causal or non-artificial or whatever, between basket $b$ and the color of apples or between the top shelf of my bookcase and being English novels of the nineteenth century. The correct way for the empiricist to meet this difficulty is to show—in these cases quite easily— that we have a good deal of information from which we can deduce the artificial relationship of the correlations—or, what is the same thing, the accidental relationship of the correlations in *rerum natura*. This account of the problem and its solution, however, quite clearly brings us back to the central problem of causality—that is, is it possible to distinguish between accidental and causal correlations by experiential concepts alone?

—and the full circle of our analysis demonstrates the intimacy of the notions of cause and law.

Some philosophers have thought that lawfulness must be analyzed in terms of *counterfactual inference*; that is, a universal statement is a law if and only if it permits a corresponding counterfactual inference. For example, "All gases at constant pressure expand with increasing temperature" qualifies as a law since it permits this corresponding counterfactual inference, "If this pencil had the property of being a gas it would expand with increasing temperature." On the other hand, "All the books on the top shelf of my bookcase are English novels of the nineteenth century" does not qualify as a law since it does not permit this corresponding counterfactual inference, "If this chemistry book on my desk had the property of being on the top shelf of my bookcase it would be an English novel of the nineteenth century." Empiricists or Humeans, however, do not accept this interpretation, since to admit "what would be the case, but is not" as a basic concept would violate their notion that an unobservable concept must have some relationship, however tenuous, with the concepts of direct experience. Consequently, the empiricist, who offers a regularity view of lawfulness, claims that counterfactual inference must be analyzed in terms of lawfulness rather than the other way around. If one can distinguish between a lawful correlation and an accidental one by the use, say, of a deductive hierarchy of laws, inductively established, then, according to the empiricist, he can legitimately make the corresponding counterfactual inference for the former correlation but not for the latter. But then again in the context of lawfulness we have come to the same problem we had in defining "cause"—namely, that of distinguishing between lawful and accidental correlations. It is wise to keep in mind, if you continue to explore the concepts of this chapter, that it is this context of lawfulness and counterfactuality in which the identical problem of analyzing lawfulness and causality usually occurs in contemporary philosophical writing.

Laws, at any rate, whatever else one holds, are universal conjunctions of terms or variables. This statement does not tell us enough, however, because variables can exhibit several different kinds of universal conjunctions.

*First* Variables may exemplify either process or syndromatic universal relations. A process law, as its name suggests, consists of a general statement of regularity between variables as a function of time. Given such a law, and the statement of present conditions, one can predict subsequent conditions. There are process laws of varying degrees of generality, from a simple "If A, then B" sort of generalization to a complicated mathematical formula. A syndromatic law, on the other hand, consists of a statement of co-existing properties of the form "If x is present, then other specifiable elements y and z co-exist with x." The laws of physics are primarily process laws, while the taxonomic or classificatory phases of biological science are syndromatic in nature.

*Second*   Process laws may be further divided into systematic process laws and historical process laws. In the former, no historical or past information about systems is needed for the formulation of a law. Or, putting it the other way around, when a law is applied to a given case the initial conditions are specifiable from the present state of a system and do not have to be supplemented by historical information. In physics, for example, given the present state of a system of $n$ bodies at $t_1$, and the laws of mechanics, one can predict the subsequent state of the system at $t_2$. However, in an historical process law information about past histories is needed for the formulation of a law; and, in any application of it, past information about the initial conditions of that system. The laws or regularities of learning psychology, for example, are historical process laws. We must know how organisms have been affected in the past before we can predict how they will act in the future. That is, the present state of an organism is not open to inspection like physical systems, and can only be inferred through its past experience. However, in principle, it is logically possible that the historical process laws of learning psychology could be explained by the systematic process laws of a perfected physiological psychology. As a matter of factual expectation, however, this perfected psychology is remote indeed.

*Third*   Variables may exemplify either causal or statistical relations, where "causal" is not used in any sense that prejudges its meaning. In the present context, all "causal law" means is a universal statement which, with a statement of initial conditions, allows one to predict the occurrence or behavior of any particular event or individual. A statistical law, on the other hand, is the statement, say, of the percentage of times a certain item turns up in a whole class of items. It allows one to predict that percentage of occurrences in the group in the future but does not permit one to specify what individuals will be included in the percentage.

*Fourth*   Variables may occur in higher-order or lower-order laws; but since we have already seen that this distinction is at the heart of the empiricist analysis of causality and lawfulness we need make nothing more of it here.

Finally, let us qualify the uncontested minimum of meaning in the notion of law—which, you recall, was this: a law is a universal conjunction of terms or variables. The qualification we need to add is "independently defined terms or variables." Consider the following sentence: "Only the fit survive." It apparently asserts a regular sequence between two terms—if x is fit, then x survives. Yet if there is no other criterion of the occurrence of fitness than survival, then the two concepts are not independently meaningful and consequently they stand in a definitional rather than a lawful relationship.[2]

2 Note that this selection from Madden is an introduction to a series of articles or selected passages on causality and lawlike statements. His selections are taken from A. C. Ewing, Curt Ducasse, Roderick Chisholm, and Gustav Bergmann, among recent philosophers; and from John Stuart Mill and David Hume among standard figures in the history of philosophy. In general, the representation is very good, from an empiricist's point of view.

## THE PLACE OF THE CAUSAL PRINCIPLE IN MODERN SCIENCE[1]

*Mario Bunge (1919–     )*

### Causality: Neither Myth nor Panacea

The problem of causation divides philosophers into roughly three camps: causalists or panaitists,[2] who may be regarded as the conservative party; acausalists or anaitists, who exhibit the nihilistic tendency; and semicausalists or hemiaitists, whom I take pleasure in imagining to be representatives of the progressive or constructive trend. Causalism is the traditional attitude of disowning all noncausal categories of determination, holding dogmatically that every connection in the world is causal. The nihilistic party, on the other hand, declares that the concept of causal nexus is a "fetish" (Pearson: *The Grammar of Science* [1911]), an "analogical fiction" (Vaihinger: *The Philosophy of "As If"* [1920]), a "superstition" (Wittgenstein: *Tractatus Logico-Philosophicus* [1922]) or a "myth" (Toulmin: *The Philosophy of Science* [1953]). This view is usually accompanied by the phenomenalist rejection of *every* kind of explanation, including of course causal explanation, in favor of description.

Needless to say, the denial of the existence of genetic bonds among events is vital for every kind of subjectivism; in the case of laic empiricism, the sole admissible link among events is the experiencing subject, whereas in the case of Neoplatonist, Malebranchian, or Berkeleyan idealism, there can be no other bond than God. In either case a person, human or divine, is assigned the role of glue among facts that would otherwise be disconnected or simply nonexistent. The entirely negative attitude taken by indeterminism and by empiricism toward the principle of causation is inconsistent with the very goal of science, which is the

1 Reprinted by permission of the publishers from Mario Bunge, *Causality: The Place of the Causal Principle in Modern Science*, Cambridge, Mass.: Harvard University Press, Copyright, 1959, by the President and Fellows of Harvard College, pp. 333–344 and 351–353.

2 Greek *aitia*, "cause," originally in the sense of an imputation of responsibility.

search for the objective forms of determination and interconnection. To declare that the sole verifiable relations are those obtaining among sense data, concepts, and judgments, and to hold that it is vain to try to disclose autonomous interconnections and real modes of production, is an anthropomorphic attitude blocking scientific advance; it is a regressive attitude, even if most of its upholders sincerely believe that they are in the van of modern thought, just because they substitute modern dogmas for traditional ones. On the other hand, the recognition that causation is more than a psychological category akin to habit, the acknowledgment that genetic links, among them those of the causal type, do exist in the external world, is an attitude that, far from being anthropomorphic, helps to avoid the pitfalls of subjectivism, whether sensationistic or spiritualistic.

Many who wish to resist the phenomenalist and indeterminist attack on rational knowledge have found no better way than to repeat with obstinacy the traditional view according to which no scientific knowledge worth its name is possible apart from causal lawfulness and apart from explanation and prediction on the basis of laws which, like Newton's or Maxwell's, are wrongly supposed to be purely causal laws just because they are not statistical—the truth being that they have a causal component combined with doses of self-movement and reciprocal action. This conservative attitude, often rooted in a sound desire to preserve the right to understand the world—a right denied by indeterminists—has proved powerless in the face of philosophical criticism and the increasing realization of the importance of other types of determinacy, such as reciprocal causation, self-determination, and random interplay. The course of science has not confirmed the conservative hope that all the noncausal types of determination would finally be seen to be reducible to causation. Quite the contrary, a richer variety of types of determination is being recognized.

We are not, then, faced with the dilemma indeterminism-causalism. Just as in the problem of moral freedom, in intellectual affairs it is not always a question of choosing among two given alternatives; sometimes the act of choice is replaced by the creation of a third alternative. The right way of resisting the combined attack of phenomenalism and indeterminism upon rational and objective knowledge is not, I believe, to take refuge in the past by dogmatically disowning all noncausal types of scientific law, explanation, and prediction, regarding them as mere temporary contrivances—as is so often done in connection with statistical determinacy. The right and progressive attitude is to face the agreeable fact that science has advanced to such a point that, without dispensing entirely with the causal principle, it has assigned it a place in the broader context of general determinism—a role that is neither the principal nor the meanest, neither that of "main pillar of inductive sciences" (Mill) nor that of a "superstition" (Wittgenstein). The causal principle is one of the various valuable guides of scientific research and, like most of them, it enjoys an approximate validity in limited ranges; it is a general hypothesis with a high heuristic value—a fact suggesting that, in certain domains, it does correspond rather closely to reality.

## The Domain of Causal Determinacy

1. Conditions of Applicability of Causal Hypotheses:
The statement that the causal principle has a limited range of validity raises at once the following questions: What is the causal range? and When is it permissible to apply causal hypotheses? The first question refers to the objective operation of causation; the second concerns the conditions under which the use of causal ideas is valid. The answer to the first question depends on the answer to the second one, as the scientific way of drawing the stripe demarcating (rather vaguely indeed) the domain of causal determinacy is to ascertain the degree of adequacy of our causal ideas about the world, that is, to ascertain to what extent they are confirmed, a task that is of course performed by science in every particular case.

It is a consequence of what has been said in the foregoing chapters, and especially in Part III, that some of the conditions for the applicability of specific statements fitting the necessary-production formula of causation are the following:

(i) *That the main changes under consideration be produced by external factors*, that is, when the system is largely (never entirely) at the mercy of its environment, so that inner processes are not the main sources of the change in question—although external conditions will be efficient solely to the extent to which they succeed in modifying those inner processes. The predominance of external over internal factors finds frequent illustrations in technique and in industry—which, as Bacon would have said, are just concerned with turning the *natura libera* into a *natura vexata*.

(ii) *That the process in question can be regarded as isolated*, that is, when it is permissible to regard the given process as torn out from its actual interconnections—which are usually numerous, but often irrelevant to the aspect that is being investigated; in other words, when such an isolation does not affect essentially the feature that is being investigated, or (what amounts to it from a pragmatic viewpoint), when the perturbations can be corrected for. This is often possible for limited intervals of time.

(iii) *That interactions can be approximated by agent-patient relations,* that is, when reciprocal actions either do not exist or, far from being symmetrical, are such that the action is considerably more important than the reaction; in other words, when reactions either are absent, or are negligible for all practical purposes. It is, again, typical of human production and technology to regard the raw material as a patient on which human work is exerted.

(iv) *That the antecedents and the consequents be uniquely connected to each other*, that is, when each effect can be considered as following (not necessarily in time) uniquely from a fixed cause (simple causation, as contrasted to multiple causation). This is particularly the case when the relevant causes are not all equally important in the concerned respect, but may on the contrary be arranged in a hierarchical gradation (chief cause, first-order perturbation, and so on).

It should be noticed that all of these conditions concern facts rather than our cognitive "grasp" (reconstruction) of them; in other words, the conditions for the validity of causal ideas depend primarily on the nature of the object (or on what is assumed to be its nature). All of them seem necessary for causal hypotheses to work, none being sufficient by itself. Probably further clauses would be found on closer inspection; but what is more important to our present concern is that none of these conditions can *exactly* be fulfilled in real cases.

In fact, external conditions are not efficient no matter what the internal ones are, but act always in combination with them and impinge upon the specific characteristics of the object concerned; consequently changes are never exclusively produced by extrinsic determiners, as required by (i). Besides, there are no perfect enclosures guaranteeing complete isolation even in a given respect, as required by (ii). Further, there is nowhere an inert stuff performing the role of perfect patient in the style of the peripatetic *materia prima*, as demanded in condition (iii). Finally, owing to the many-sidedness and changeability of interconnections, as well as to inner lawful spontaneity, real cause-effect connections are never exactly one-to-one, as demanded by (iv).

In short, the foregoing conditions can sometimes be fulfilled to a sufficient approximation—never exactly.

2. Range of Validity of the Causal Principle:

We can now deal with the question concerning the range of validity of the causal principle. If the previous remarks are accepted, if at least one of the above-mentioned conditions is regarded as necessary, then the answer can be no other than this:

*Strict and pure causation works nowhere and never. Causation works approximately in certain processes limited both in space and time—and, even so, only in particular respects. Causal hypotheses are no more (and no less) than rough, approximate, one-sided reconstructions of deter-*

mination; *they are often entirely dispensable, but they are sometimes adequate and indispensable.*

To put it otherwise: in the external world there is always a wide class of processes the causal aspect of which is so important in certain respects and within limited contexts that they can be described as causal —although they are never *exactly* and *exclusively* causal.

A less vague delimitation of the domain of causal determinacy does not seem possible or even desirable. A few general conditions for the adequacy of causal hypotheses have been pointed out; but the decision about the range of every particular causal hypothesis should be the exclusive concern of science. To try to go much beyond the statement of the above-mentioned general conditions, in order to demarcate a priori and unambiguously the domain of causal determinacy in all fields of science, would be to come dangerously close to the traditional subjectivistic procedures. The adequacy of scientific and philosophic hypotheses has to be ascertained a posteriori, even though their probable adequacy can at times be assessed beforehand.

The notion of causal range of the laws of nature will next be clarified and illustrated, by analyzing in some detail a typical physical law with which every student of electricity is familiar. The few elementary mathematical symbols that will appear in the next section should not deter the nonmathematical reader, for they will be described in plain words, and are dispensable for a general grasp of the subject. (Mathematical signs do not replace physical concepts but ensure their clear, unambiguous, and accurate denotation.)

### Delimitation of the Causal Range of a Particular Law

1. Statement of the Problem:

Consider the elementary physical system constituted by an electrical circuit fed by a direct-current source, such as a battery. . . . When the connection is established, an electric current of intensity $i$ is set up, and this current in turn creates a magnetic field around the conductor. The relevant electrical properties of the wire are summarized in the constant $R$ (resistance); the over-all magnetic properties of the circuit are condensed in the constant $L$ (self-inductance). Notice that this is the simplest electrical circuit possible, for $R$ and $L$ never actually vanish, although in extreme cases either of them, or both, may become exceedingly small.

We make the usual assumption that our circuit is isolated enough from other physical systems that the above-mentioned parameters ($e$, $i$, $R$, and $L$) are the sole relevant ones and are moreover independent of external conditions. That is, we are assuming that condition (ii) above (isolation of process) holds. It is hardly necessary to point out that here, as everywhere else in scientific theory, we are concerned with an *ideal model* of an actual, concrete object; we are, in fact, neglecting a number of internal irregularities and external disturbances, such as small variations in the electromotive force, current losses, variations in the external magnetic field, random temperature fluctuations affecting $e$ and $R$, and so on.

The law that sums up the dynamic interdependence among the essential features of our system (represented by a parameter each) is the following: the sum of the applied electromotive force $e$ and the induced electromotive force $e_i$ (produced by the magnetic field) is equal to the fall of potential $Ri$. In symbols,

$$e + e_i = Ri$$

On the other hand, the law of induction reads,

$$e_i = -L\frac{di}{dt}$$

Substitution of the second statement into the first yields

$$e = L\frac{di}{dt} + Ri \tag{I}$$

One is tempted at first sight to regard this as a typical causal law, stating that the *cause* $e$ (applied electromotive force) produces the current $i$ (effect). A closer examination will, however, show that this causal interpretation of law (I) is valid solely in connection with a limited domain, namely, when the current $i$ has attained its final steady value $i_s$ (given by Ohm's law, which is a particular case of law (I), applicable when the current does not vary). Before the steady state has been attained, and also after it has ceased, the actual connections among the relevant features of our system are *not* strictly causal, as will be seen presently.

2. First Stage of the Process: Cycle of Determinants:

In fact, as soon as the battery is switched on, the current increases continuously from zero till its final steady value $i_s$ . . . ; $i$ does not attain this value $i_s$ abruptly, the full effect does not follow immediately upon the cause, simply because in this case the effect $i$ *opposes* the cause, so that condition (iii) above is violated. Indeed, while the current increases $(di/dt > 0)$, it produces a magnetic field of increasing strength that surrounds the coil and reacts back on the current in it. The variable magnetic flux $\phi$, due to the increasing current, produces in turn an induced emf ($e_i = -d\phi/dt = -Ldi/dt < 0$), which in this case opposes the applied emf. This back emf induced in the wire by the growing magnetic field is what prevents the current from attaining the final value $i_s$ without any time lag.

This process is an instance of (natural) negative feedback with a variable total effect. . . . From an ontological point of view, this stage of the process illustrates the *cycle of determinants,* in which the cause-effect nexus is but a side or a moment of a more complex loop of reciprocal actions. In this first stage of our process, the *interaction* category is the dominant determinant.

3. Second Stage of the Process: Causal Nexus:

The first stage goes over continuously and asymptotically into the second stage, which is definitely causal. In this second case, the action of the cause is no longer counteracted by its effect; the magnetic flux produced by the current is now constant ($d\phi/dt = 0$), so that the effect does not react back on the cause ($e_i = 0$). We now have a linear, unidirectional cause-effect bond, summarized in the following law (Ohm's law), which is a particular case of law (I), namely, the applied emf (the cause) maintains the constant current $i_s$ (the effect), which is proportional to it. The precise form of this law is

$$e = Ri_s \tag{II}$$

The steady state is, then, the *causal domain* of the process of electric conduction in metals; or, again, the special law (II) covers the *causal range* of the more general law (I). This does not mean, however, that the steady state of electric conduction is an *entirely* causal process. Quite the contrary, the theory of electronic conduction in solids—that is, the study of the lower-level motions giving rise to the macroscopic process covered by Ohm's macroscopic law (II)—shows that several categories of determination come into play; among them are self-determination (inertia of electrons and fields), interaction (mutual action among electrons, the crystal lattice, and the impurities), statistical determination (collective behavior of the electron gas), and so on. Still, these noncausal categories are finally masked in such a way that the average motion of the electrons "obeys" such a typically causal law as Ohm's—the causal nature of which is especially manifest in the form given to it by Drude, namely $E = (1/\sigma) j$, which is Aristotelian-like. The self-motion of the electrons again becomes apparent at very low temperatures, where instead of the law of Ohm and Drude we have London's law, $E = \Lambda \partial j/\partial t$, which accounts for superconductivity and is of the Newtonian type.

Only the *net effect* $i_s$ is connected in the simple form (II) to the cause $e$. When we say that the law (II) that characterizes electric conduction in metals at ordinary temperatures is causal, we imply that it is causal *on its own level,* quite aside from its roots in the more complex laws characterizing electron conduction inside a crystal lattice subjected to an externally impressed electric field. Here we are, in short, analyzing the causal range of a definite law belonging to a definite level; we are concerned with the causal component of a given law, rather than with the causal aspects of a given event or string of events—as every single phenomenon is the locus of a whole *set* of laws belonging to various levels.

4. Third Stage of the Process: Self-Determination:

Let us now turn to the third and last stage of our process. When the battery is switched off ($e = 0$), the current does not cease immediately but dies gradually, thus falsifying the well-known scholastic maxim *causa cessante cessat effectus.* The associated magnetic field decreases ($d\phi/dt < 0$), thereby producing an induced electromotive force acting now in the direction of the formerly applied emf (while the current decreases, that is, while $di/dt < 0$, $e_i = -Ldi/dt > 0$). This induced emf is what maintains the current $i$; it is a typical aftereffect, for the cause $e$ has now vanished. The pattern of this stage of the process is the following particular case of law (I):

$$0 = L\frac{di}{dt} + Ri \tag{III}$$

According to Maxwell's field theory (which explains the "phenomenological" circuit theory), in this last stage the causal component has entirely concentrated in the decreasing magnetic field—which is not, however, an *externally* acting cause but an *intrinsic* determinant of the whole system (of which the coil is only a part). But from the point of view of circuit theory, the process of dying out of an electric current has not even a causal component because, unlike stages I and II, in stage III the cause ($e$) has ceased to operate. From an ontological point of view this stage of the process is consequently dominated by the *self-movement* category, which characterizes predominantly or exclusively self-determined processes, whose ideal model is inertial motion.

To sum up, in the process of growth, maintenance of the steady state, and dying out of an electric current in the simplest possible metallic circuit, three stages must be distinguished, each characterized by a peculiar category of determination. These stages are:

*(i) Domain of reciprocal action (beginning of current)*  The effect $i$ has not yet fully developed, and reacts back on the cause $e$, in the manner of negative feedback. The differential law of this process of reciprocal action is (I); the corresponding integral law is

$$i = i_s (I - e^{-(R/L)t}), i_s = e/R$$

As time passes, the effect reacts less and less on the cause (that is, $di/dt$ decreases, and the corresponding back emf dies away) until finally the causal stage has fully developed.

*(ii) Domain of causation (steady state)* The (constant) cause $e$ maintains the (constant) effect $i_s$ in accordance with Ohm's law (II). This steady state lasts until, for one reason or another, the battery is switched off and the process goes over into its last stage.

*(iii) Domain of self-determination (dying away of the current)* The cause has disappeared ($e = 0$); but the effect does not vanish immediately; it dies away gradually, maintained by the decreasing magnetic field. The differential law of this process is (III); the corresponding integral law is

$$i = i_s e^{-(R/L)t}$$

The foregoing example was *not* meant to illustrate the claim that the range of *every* law of nature splits unambiguously into nonoverlapping domains each dominated by a single category of determination; this contention is definitely untrue, as will be realized by recalling the various types of law discussed in the previous chapters. Some laws have no causal component at all (as is the case with the classificatory, kinematical, and conservation laws) and others have a causal component that is not additively combined with other categories of determination. What the consideration of the electrical circuit discussed is expected to support is the central thesis of this book, namely, that the causation category is indispensable in science but, like every other category of determination, has a limited range and, moreover, works in combination with other determination categories. The analysis is also expected to have shown that the causal range—if any—of the laws of nature cannot be determined a priori once and for all for all types of law, but must on the contrary be the outcome of detailed analyses of specific laws. . . .

### General Conclusions

The net effect of the nihilistic criticism of causality was to encourage fortuitism and its epistemological partner, namely, irrationalism. On the other hand, the intention of the present book is to show that, just like every other category of determination, causation has a limited range of operation; that the causal principle holds a place in the broader context of general determinism; and that failures of the causal principle in certain domains by no means entail the failure of determinism *lato sensu*, or the breakdown of rational understanding.

The realization of the limited scope of the causal principle supports neither skepticism nor irrationalism; every failure of causality *stricto sensu* can be regarded as the victory of a different principle of determination, and it simply marks the breakdown of outdated ontologies that are too narrow to make room for the unlimited richness of reality, as progressively disclosed by the sciences. What in contemporary science has taken the commanding place once held by the causal principle is the broader *principle of determinacy,* or of lawful production. The two components of this principle, under which the general law of causation is subsumed, are the genetic principle (*Nothing springs out of nothing or goes into nothing*) and the principle of lawfulness (*Nothing unconditional, arbitrary, lawless occurs*). The principle of determinacy just states that reality is not a chaotic aggregate of isolated, unconditioned, arbitrary events that pop up here and there without connection with anything else; it states that events are produced and conditioned in definite ways, though not necessarily in a causal manner; and it asserts that things, their properties, and the changes of properties exhibit intrinsic patterns (objective laws) that are invariant in some respects.

The principle of determinacy, often mistaken for the law of causation, is the common ground of all forms of scientific determinism (from which fatalism is excluded, since it involves supernaturalistic elements violating the genetic principle). To reduce determinism to causal determinism is to have either a poor opinion of the resources of nature and culture, or too high an opinion of philosophical theories. Those who assign to causality the exclusive appurtenance of characteristics that are actually shared by all kinds of scientific determinism either fail to resist the attacks of indeterminism and irrationalism or—to the extent to which they succeed in the defense—inadvertently clothe noncausal types of determination in a causal language.

If there is some truth in what has been said in this book, the right policy with regard to the causal problem can be summarized in the following rules: (a) to employ the causation category whenever permissible, without fearing to be accused of fetishism, mechanism, or what not; (b) to recognize the limited character of causal hypotheses; (c) to make room for further categories of determination whenever they contribute to afford a truer account of being and becoming; and (d) to abstain from terming "causal" all those categories which, like self-determination, reciprocal action, and so forth, clearly overflow causality and belong instead to general determinism.

According to Descartes [*Principles of Philosophy,* I, 24], the perfect science was the precise knowledge of effects by their causes, that is, the deduction or explanation of (observed) effects from their (assumed) causes. This Peripatetic norm may still be regarded as the paradigm of science—but, paradoxically enough, with the following essential qualification: (a) the *link* between causes and effects need not always be causal (that is, unique, unsymmetrical, constant, external); (b) nothing warrants the presumption that we shall ever attain more than a *hypothetical* (but improvable) knowledge of causes, effects, and their links (whether causal or not). The causal principle reflects or reconstructs only a few aspects of determination. Reality is much too rich to be compressible once and for all into a framework of categories elaborated during an early stage of rational knowledge, which consequently cannot account for the whole variety of types of determination, the number of which is being increased by scientific research and by philosophical reflection upon it.

What has been rejected in this book is not the principle of causation, but its unlimited extrapolation, as asserted by the doctrine of causalism, or causal determinism—a primitive, rough, and one-sided version of what I took the liberty of calling *general determinism*. To use picture language, we may say that causal determinism is the ray-optics approximation of general determinism. Or, if a mathematical metaphor is preferred, determination is a vector in a space of a large, as yet unknown number of dimensions, causal determination being just one of its components or projections.

The causal principle is, in short, neither a panacea nor a myth; it is a general hypothesis subsumed under the universal principle of determinacy, and having an approximate validity in its proper domain.

## SUMMARY OF POINTS FOR DISCUSSION

The basic chasm separating the vantage points of these two selections is perhaps unbridgeable. It is always possible for the empiricist to retort to Bunge that he has simply missed the point: however complicated he may make the cause-effect relationship, his "causal stage" is as empirically unverifiable (the empiricist would say) as that of any less complicated causal-nexus theory. On the other hand, Bunge must ultimately side with those who insist, against the empiricists, on the rationality—and thus also the causal nature—of scientific knowledge. He may disagree with their simple causality-or-indeterminism dilemma, but he must agree with their anti-empiricism.

However, all discussion between the two points of view is not ruled out:

1. Madden's presentation of the Humean dilemma leans strongly on the notion of *lawfulness*, and ultimately like a good empiricist he must equate lawfulness with universal conjunction (of some sort), and this with causality. Bunge, similarly, emphasizes lawfulness: "What in contemporary science has taken the commanding place once held by the causal principle is the broader principle of determinacy, or of *lawful* production." Why, then, if both Madden and Bunge subsume causality under lawfulness, do they end up with such divergent views?

2. Bunge, while analyzing a simple example from physics, succeeds in showing the enormous complexity of any instance of supposed causality in science. Does the Humean or empiricist analysis do justice to this complexity?

3. Bunge ends up with a view that recognizes a genuine "genetic principle" —"events are produced and conditioned in definite ways." Can this view be justified apart from a more fundamental debate on the *epistemology* of induction or scientific method?

## BIBLIOGRAPHY

### General

Bunge's work (pp. 354–364) includes an excellent bibliography, though he introduces it with a disclaimer: "This bibliography is not a guide to the enormously wealthy literature on the problem of causality; it is merely a list of the books quoted in the text."

### Empiricists

Madden's work (p. 375) includes a good though selective bibliography; cf. also H. Feigl and M. Brodbeck (eds.): *Readings in the Philosophy of Science*, Appleton-Century-Crofts, New York, 1953, pp. 791–793.

### Pertinent Psychological Data

Michotte, A.: *The Perception of Causality*, Methuen, London, 1963.
Piaget, J.: *The Child's Conception of Physical Causality*, Kegan Paul, London, 1930.

# APPENDIXES

# Appendix

# Methodological and Epistemological Issues in Science

CAN A BELIEF IN GENUINE GENETIC causal principles *within* things be justified other than by an epistemological consideration of induction and the experimental method? This was the question left unanswered at the end of the discussion of physical causality in Chapter 10. A fully adequate answer to the question—and to similar questions about the methodology and epistemology of science—must be reserved for a more advanced course than the one presented in this book. However, it may serve a purpose to introduce some questions to suggest the sorts of things that will come up in such a course.

### Causality as an Epistemological Problem

A good place to begin an introduction of advanced topics is with the problem of causality. As mentioned at the very beginning of this book, a standard topic for discussion among logical empiricists is the manner of characterizing lawlike, causal statements in science. The discussions often tend to center around so-called "counterfactual conditionals" and the way in which lawlike statements seem to permit inference to such counterfactual conditions, whereas nonlaw statements do not.

Implicit in these discussions is an assumption—that causal propositions are "lawlike statements"—i.e., that causality means lawfulness. Consider the following from the Madden selection in Chapter 10:

> Some empiricists, trying to make the concept of cause more precise, have offered this string of definitions: "cause" = "sufficient condition"; "sufficient conditions" = "set of necessary conditions"; "necessary condition" = "condition without which the effect would not occur." Let us use the example of a forest fire to clarify these definitions. A forest fire will occur, one says, if these conditions obtain: some means of ignition, dry underbrush, a prevailing wind, oxygen in the air, etc. Each condition is necessary, not in the metaphysicians' sense, but only in the sense that without it the effect—the forest fire—would not occur. It is, of course, very difficult to find the whole set of necessary conditions, but this whole set, whatever it may be, is the condition sufficient or able to produce the effect and thus is the cause of the effect.
>
> It is doubtful, however, that this analysis of "cause" carries one any farther than the constant conjunction interpretation. For, after all, the only empirical meaning that can be given to the phrase "a condition without which the effect would not occur" is this: when C happens (along with other conditions), E also happens; and when C does not happen, E does not happen.[1]

As Madden acknowledges, this represents a straightforward and respectable empiricist view. Opponents would take a less favorable stand; they would say Madden is presenting pure and simple epistemological positivism. Bunge, for instance (in a passage not included in Chapter 10), characterizes this sort of view as "grounded in the original sin of empiricism, namely . . . the reduction of the meaning of a proposition to the mode of its verification."[2] Elsewhere Bunge says this conception of causality is the one "most positivists have held."[3]

Bunge's objection is that, "Such a reduction involves a confusion of epistemology (and, more particularly, of scientific methodology) with . . . ontology." Again, "Such a reduction of an ontological category to a methodological criterion is the consequence of epistemological tenets of empiricism, rather than a result of an unprejudiced analysis of the laws of nature."[4]

What would such an "unprejudiced analysis" reveal? Bunge's own answer has been given in Chapter 10. An idealist's response to positivism would be to reduce causality to a mental category of one kind or another. Another realist answer is the following:

> The first problem that we shall consider is to analyse more carefully

---

[1] Edward H. Madden, *The Structure of Scientific Thought*, Houghton Mifflin, Boston, 1960, p. 204. With respect to this and the remaining notes in this chapter, see the bibliographical note at the end.

[2] Mario Bunge, *Causality: The Place of the Causal Principle in Modern Science*, Harvard University Press, Cambridge, Mass., 1959, p. 45.

[3] *Ibid.*, p. 68.

[4] *Ibid.*, p. 46.

the relationship between causality and a regular association of conditions or events. For a regular association between a given set, A, of events or conditions in the past, and another set, B, in the future does not necessarily imply that A is the cause of B. Instead, it may imply that A and B are associated merely because they are both the result of some common set of causes, C, which is anterior to both A and B. For example, before winter the leaves generally fall off the trees. Yet the loss of the leaves by the trees is not the cause of winter, but is instead the *effect* of the general process of lowering of temperature which first leads to the loss of leaves by the trees and later to the coming of winter. Clearly, then, the concept of a causal relationship implies more than just regular association, in which one set of events precedes another in the time. What is implied in addition is that (abstracted from contingencies, of course) the future effects come out of past causes through a process satisfying *necessary* relationships. And, as is evident, mere association is not enough to prove this kind of connection.

An important way of obtaining evidence in favour of the assumption that a given set of events or conditions comes necessarily from another is to show that a wide range of *changes* in one or more of the presumed causes occurring under conditions in which other factors are held constant always produces corresponding changes in the effects. The more co-ordinations of this kind that one can demonstrate in the changes of the two sets of events, the stronger is the evidence that they are causally related; and with a large enough number one becomes, for practical purposes, certain that this hypothesis of causal connection is correct. To obtain such a demonstration, however, an active interference on our part by means of experiments will usually be required, although in some cases enough changes of the right kind will occur naturally so that it will be adequate to make a wide range of observations in the phenomena that are already at hand.[5]

This formulation depends upon the trust a realist epistemology has in observation, whether or not the observation requires experiments. For the realist, observation can reveal not only immediate data of experience but also genuine laws (some causal) that are truly descriptive of reality. Positivism denies this, reducing laws ultimately to the status of probable hypotheses which only *may* be descriptive of reality. What is the basis of the realist's trust, and of the positivist's lack of trust, in this law-revealing aspect of observation?

## The Problem of Induction

Questions about the confidence that should be placed in observation and sense knowledge are as old as philosophy itself. In the form in which they bear on contemporary philosophy of science, however, they go back to the British empiricist, David Hume.

Hume states the problem in deceptively simple terms:

When it is asked, *What is the nature of all our reasonings concerning*

[5] David Bohm, *Causality and Chance in Modern Physics.* Copyright 1957, D. Van Nostrand Company, Inc., Princeton, N.J., pp. 5–6.

*matter of fact?* the proper answer seems to be, that they are founded on the relation of cause and effect. When again it is asked, *What is the foundation of all our reasonings and conclusions concerning that relation?* it may be replied in one word, *experience*. But if we still carry on our sifting humor, and ask, *What is the foundation of all conclusions from experience?* this implies a new question, which may be of more difficult solution and explication.[6]

Hume's answer to his own question is indeed "of more difficult solution and explication." In his own summary:

> *What, then, is the conclusion of the whole matter?* A simple one; though, it must be confessed, pretty remote from the common theories of philosophy. All belief of matter of fact or real existence is derived merely from some object, present to the memory or senses, and a customary conjunction between that and some other object. Or in other words; having found, in many instances, that any two kinds of objects—flame and heat, snow and cold—have always been conjoined together; if flame or snow be presented anew to the senses, *the mind is carried by custom to expect heat or cold, and to believe* that such a quality does exist, and will discover itself upon a nearer approach. This belief is the necessary result of placing the mind in such circumstances. It is an operation of the soul, when we are so situated, as unavoidable as to feel the passion of love, when we receive benefits; or hatred, when we meet with injuries. All these operations are a species of natural instincts, which no reasoning or process of the thought and understanding is able either to produce or to prevent.[7]

A realist like Bunge or Bohm would simply repudiate Hume's conclusion as incompatible with the experience on which he claims to base it. The modern empiricist, however, continues to believe that Hume has proved his point, however crudely. A great deal of attention is thus given in contemporary philosophy of science to the "the problem of induction." What should be pointed out here is that these discussions have now become a great deal more sophisticated than the problem as originally suggested by Hume.

> In the philosophical discussion of induction, one problem has long occupied the center of the stage—so much so, indeed, that it is usually referred to as *the* problem of induction. That is the problem of justifying the way in which, in scientific inquiry and in our everyday pursuits, we base beliefs and assertions about empirical matters on logically inconclusive evidence.
> This classical problem of justification, raised by Hume and made famous by his skeptical solution, is indeed of great philosophical importance. But more recent studies, most of which were carried out during the past two or three decades, have given rise to new problems of induction, no less perplexing and important than the classical one, which are logically prior to it in the sense that the classical problem cannot

[6] David Hume, *An Enquiry Concerning Human Understanding*, sec. 4, part 2.

[7] *Ibid.*, sec. 5, part 1.

even be clearly stated—let alone solved—without some prior clarification of the new puzzles.[8]

Hempel gives a summary of these "new puzzles" which, as logically prior to, must be solved before the classical problem of induction:

> For a clear statement of the classical problem of justification, two things are required. First, the procedure to be justified must be clearly characterized—this calls for an explication of the rules governing the inductive appraisal of hypotheses and theories; second, the intended objectives of the procedure must be indicated, for a justification of any procedure will have to be relative to the ends it is intended to serve. Concerning the first of these tasks, we noted that while there are no systematic mechanical rules of inductive discovery, two other kinds of rule have to be envisaged and distinguished, namely, rules of support and rules of application. And in our discussion of the objectives of inductive procedures we noted certain connections between rational belief on one hand and valuation on the other.
>
> Whatever insights further inquiry may yield, the recognition and partial exploration of these basic problems has placed the classical problem of induction into a new and clearer perspective and has thereby advanced its philosophical clarification.[9]

For the procedure of inductive inference to be justified, Hempel is maintaining, it must first be clearly characterized in terms of *precise criteria* of what counts as acceptable inductive reasoning in science. And here Hempel notes that "this is one objective of Carnap's inductive logic."[10] Carnap's purpose can also be stated in his own words:

> *The purpose of this work.* This book presents a new approach to the old problem of induction and probability. The theory here developed is characterized by the following *basic conceptions:* (1) all inductive reasoning, in the wide sense of nondeductive or nondemonstrative reasoning, is reasoning in terms of probability; (2) hence inductive logic, the theory of the principles of inductive reasoning, is the same as probability logic; (3) the concept of probability on which inductive logic is to be based is a logical relation between two statements or propositions; it is the degree of confirmation of a hypothesis (or conclusion) on the basis of some given evidence (or premises); (4) the so-called frequency concept of probability, as used in statistical investigations, is an important scientific concept in its own right, but it is not suitable as the basic concept of inductive logic; (5) all principles and theorems of inductive logic are analytic; (6) hence the validity of inductive reasoning is not dependent upon any synthetic presuppositions like the much debated principle of the uniformity of the world. One of the tasks of this book is the discussion of the general philosophical problems concerning the nature of probability and inductive reasoning, which will lead to the

---

[8] Carl G. Hempel, "Recent Problems of Induction," in Robert G. Colodny (ed.), *Mind and Cosmos,* University of Pittsburgh Press, Pittsburgh, 1966, p. 112.

[9] Hempel, *loc. cit.,* pp. 132–133.

[10] *Ibid.,* p. 119.

conceptions just mentioned. However, the major aim of the book extends beyond this. It is the actual construction of a system of inductive logic, a theory based on the conceptions indicated but supplying proofs for many theorems concerning such concepts as the quantitative concept of degree of confirmation, relevance and irrelevance, the (comparative) concept of stronger confirmation, and a general method of estimation. This system will be constructed with the help of the methods of symbolic logic and semantics. . . . In this way it will for the first time be possible to construct *a system of inductive logic that can take its rightful place beside the modern, exact systems of deductive logic.*[11]

Viewed as an attempt to characterize, in clear logical terms, what counts as acceptable inductive reasoning in science, Carnap's inductive logic seems a noble ideal as well as a definite contribution toward clarifying Hume's problem in a way that might allow it finally to be solved. Unfortunately empiricists have found all sorts of difficulties with Carnap's inductive logic,[12] even to the point of claiming to find a contradiction in its very first premise:

The most important of the criticisms of Carnap have been levelled against his basic concept of degree of confirmation. Ernest Nagel, for instance, has argued that the completeness, in terms of primitive predicates, required by [this concept] is "thoroughly unrealistic" and, in fact, contrary to the whole purpose of inductive logic ["Carnap's Theory of Induction," in *The Philosophy of Rudolf Carnap,* ed. P. A. Schilpp (La Salle, Ill.: Open Court, 1963), pp. 792–794]. Wesley Salmon has argued that Carnap's concept violates a "criterion of linguistic invariance" which he thinks is essential to the pragmatic justification of induction ["Vindication of Induction," in H. Feigl and G. Maxwell (eds.), *Current Issues in the Philosophy of Science,* Holt, Rinehart, and Winston, New York, 1961, pp. 245–256]. Karl Popper goes even further, finding a contradiction in the very identification of degree of confirmation (with Carnap's or any other c-function) with probability [*The Logic of Scientific Discovery* (New York: Harper Torchbooks, 1965), New Appendix IX; [12] cf. Carnap's rejoinder in *The Philosophy of Carnap,* pp. 995–998].

Two other criticisms are interesting especially in that they propose alternatives to Carnap's formulation of inductive logic. Henry Kyburg rejects Carnap's view as unnecessary and idealistic, and prefers an "informal formalization" in terms of ordinary language, a "protosyntactical" view rather than Carnap's formal semantical view [*Probability and the Logic of Rational Belief* (Middletown, Conn.: Wesleyan, 1961), p. 331; cf. also Introduction; pp. 47–54 give a number of criticisms of Carnap from the literature, as well as Kyburg's own]. Hilary Putnam attempts to set out a formal logical proof that scientific method includes features which are incompatible in the strict sense with a quantitative degree of confirmation; in the process he introduces a "method M" which (especially when improved according to methods proposed by John Kemeny and Nelson Goodman) is not incompatible with these features of actual scien-

---

[11] Rudolf Carnap, *Logical Foundations of Probability,* 2d ed., University of Chicago Press, Chicago, 1962, p. v. Italics in last sentence added.

[12] Popper's acerbic comments on his controversy with Carnap can be found on pages 394–395.

tific practice ["Degree of Confirmation and Inductive Logic," in *The Philosophy of Carnap*, pp. 761–783].

A more fundamental criticism, not only of Carnap, but of all attempts to use probability in solving the problem of induction, can be made. The basic idea behind an attempt to justify induction through probability is this: Induction can be viewed as a scientific *prediction* of future successes of a theory on the basis of a sufficiently large number of successes in the past—the prediction does not say with certainty what will happen in any individual case, but only that there is a denumerable probability of success. Similar attempts have been made before to justify induction in terms of predictions on the basis of past success, but very often these have been aimed at predicting with certainty and have been based on a principle of the uniformity of nature. Carnap attempts to avoid the difficulties implicit in this view, and in particular he claims that his view is not based on the uniformity of nature. However, it is difficult to accept this: a *probability* of success in the future is no less dependent on the uniformity of nature than any other prediction of success would be, if in either case it is presumed that the future will be like the past [cf. Israel Scheffler: *The Anatomy of Inquiry* (New York: Knopf, 1963), p. 231].[13]

Thus, the solution of Hempel's first "new puzzle" seems nowhere in sight. What about his second puzzle? It concerns the *objectives* of inductive reasoning, the reasons for utilizing it in science in the first place, and Hempel recognizes that this brings up the difficult problem of *values* in science. The following passage ends with one of the most disarmingly frank concessions to the opposition in all of empiricist literature:

> What will have to be taken into account in constructing or justifying inductive acceptance rules for pure scientific research are the objectives of such research or the importance attached in pure science to achieving certain kinds of results. What objectives does pure scientific research seek to achieve? Truth of the accepted statements might be held to be one of them. But surely not truth at all costs. For then, the only rational decision policy would be never to accept any hypothesis on inductive grounds since, however well supported, it might be false.
>
> Scientific research is not even aimed at achieving very high probability of truth, or very strong inductive support, at all costs. Science is willing to take considerable chances on this score. It is willing to accept a theory that vastly outreaches its evidential basis if that theory promises to exhibit an underlying order, a system of deep and simple systematic connections among what had previously been a mass of disparate and multifarious facts.
>
> It is an intriguing but as yet open question whether the objectives, or the values, that inform pure scientific inquiry can all be adequately characterized in terms of such theoretical desiderata as confirmation, explanatory power, and simplicity and, if so, whether these features admit of a satisfactory combination into a concept of purely theoretical or scientific utility that could be involved in the construction of acceptance rules for hypotheses and theories in pure science. Indeed, it is by no means clear whether the conception of basic scientific research

---

[13] Paul R. Durbin, *Logic and Scientific Inquiry*, Bruce, Milwaukee, 1967, pp. 21–23.

as leading to the provisional acceptance or rejection of hypotheses is tenable at all. One of the problems here at issue is whether the notion of accepting a hypothesis independently of any contemplated action can be satisfactorily explicated within the framework of a purely logical and methodological analysis of scientific inquiry or whether, if any illuminating construal of the idea is possible at all, it will have to be given in the context of a psychological, sociological, and historical study of scientific research. [Footnote: Such an alternative conception is represented, e.g., by T. S. Kuhn's work, *The Structure of Scientific Revolutions*.][14]

This concession to the avowedly anti-empiricist interpretation of Kuhn, with his dependence on historical and sociological factors, might suggest that the next topic for consideration ought to be the question whether or not non-logical considerations should enter into philosophy of science. However, there are reasons for postponing this question and treating it in a separate appendix. One of these reasons is that there is another fundamental point of disagreement between realists and positivists that is too important to pass over. This is the question of "theoretical entities" in science.[15]

## The Reality of Theoretical Entities

Some realists have been naïve in the way in which they assigned the note of physical reality or physical significance to such theoretical entities as atoms, molecules, wave functions, and even such limit concepts as perfect elasticity and inertial motion. But these naïve assumptions of reality for any objects postulated by a well-supported empirical theory are not the only realist interpretations. The following is a very careful and precise realist interpretation:

> A critical realist . . . in the style of the present author avoids the two extremes, on the one hand of identifying the real strict object of physical science with sensible data interpreted in common sense terms, and on the other of identifying it with theoretical models. Sensible data when interpreted within the noetic-noematic structures of common sense reveal of course the common sense realities of the laboratory environment. No one would wish to deny that the pointer position is a *real* pointer position and the dial a *real* dial. But, when the noetic-noematic structure of physical science is brought to bear on these common sense events and objects, they take on the character of observable symbols revealing the existence of another horizon, that of scientific reality, the noemata of science. The critical realist on the other hand also refuses to identify the realistic aim of science with the construction of theoretical models. This latter was the explicit aim of Cartesian rationalism which many influences, historical, philosophical and not least scientific have to a great measure overthrown. It lingers on however in the minds of phenomenologists who consider erroneously in the present author's opinion that the scientific method is irrevocably and irredeemably tied to Cartesianism.

[14] Hempel, *loc. cit.*, pp. 131–132.

[15] See the Introduction, above, pp. xxi–xxii.

> What then is the terminal object of scientific inquiry? In what does its
> realistic aspect consist? The terminal object of scientific inquiry is a
> strict object in the horizon of reality attained by using theoretical models
> to render intelligible the dynamic pattern of physical interactions be-
> tween objects of that horizon as manifested in and through the observ-
> able symbols produced by the measurement process. Science exercises
> its realistic function when it uses theoretical models to reveal the
> interrelatedness of things among themselves.[16]

At the opposite pole from this critical realist interpretation of theoretical
entities is the extreme phenomenalist positivism of Ernst Mach:

> In our view of the matter, natural laws are the consequence of our
> psychological need to find our way in nature, and to avoid having to
> confront it as a confused stranger would. This is clearly demonstrated
> by the standards which these laws are expected to meet, though such
> standards express the current cultural situation as well as the above-
> mentioned psychological need. The earliest attempts at self-orientation are
> mythological, demonological, and poetic. The period of the rebirth of natu-
> ral science, the period of Copernicus and Galileo, strove for a primarily
> qualitative, preliminary orientation, and ease of comprehension, sim-
> plicity, and aesthetic satisfaction were accordingly the principles govern-
> ing the search for those laws which might contribute to the mental recon-
> struction of the observed facts. Research of a more precise quantitative
> sort aims at as complete a specificity as possible, at *unambiguous speci-
> ficity*—an objective already apparent in the early history of mechanics.
> With the accumulation of information, the demand for laws diminishing
> the effort required for assimilating it, the demand for intellectual economy,
> continuity, permanence, and as general an applicability and practicality
> as possible becomes particularly pressing. The later history of mechanics
> or of any advanced part of physics amply illustrates this development.[17]

This interpretation of theories as "economies of thought," though it has
a respectable history in philosophy of science, is now generally discredited
because of its assumption that all theoretical terms can, at least in principle,
be translated into observational terms. In place of this interpretation, then, a
new one called "instrumentalism" has grown popular among empiricists. One
author who clearly inclines toward instrumentalism, even though he claims
its differences with respect to a realist interpretation are of "only terminologi-
cal interest," is Ernest Nagel. The following passage, which Nagel takes to
be a proof of his point that the instrumentalist-realist differences are termi-
nological, would be taken by the realist as expressing clearly positivistic
leanings, however cleverly disguised:

> More specifically, if [a certain criterion] is adopted for specifying the

---

[16] Patrick A. Heelan, "Horizon, Objectivity and Reality in the Physical Sciences," *International Philosophical Quarterly*, vol. VII (September 1967), p. 412; cf. also Heelan, *Quantum
Mechanics and Objectivity*, Nijhoff, The Hague, 1965.

[17] Ernst Mach, "The Significance and Purpose of Natural Laws," in Arthur Danto and
Sidney Morgenbesser (eds.), *Philosophy of Science: Readings*, Meridian, New York, 1960,
pp. 270–271.

sense of "physically real," it is quite patent that the instrumentalist view is entirely compatible with the claim that atoms, say, are indeed physically real. In point of fact, many instrumentalists themselves urge such a claim. To make the claim is to assert that there are a number of well-established experimental laws related in a certain manner to one another and to other laws by way of a given atomic theory. In short, to assert that in this sense atoms exist is to claim that available empirical evidence is sufficient to establish the adequacy of the theory as a leading principle for an extensive domain of inquiry. But as has already been noted, this is in effect only verbally different from saying that the theory is so well confirmed by the evidence that the theory can be tentatively accepted as true.[18]

Nagel may still be right in maintaining that there is only a verbal difference between realist and instrumentalist interpretations of theoretical entities—that "what often divides them are, in part, loyalties to different intellectual traditions." In any case, by making this point he brings up another interesting question: To what extent are options in the interpretation of science influenced by more fundamental philosophical commitments?

## Are There Metaphysical Presuppositions in Science?

Perhaps the most famous discussion of this question is that of E. A. Burtt: *The Metaphysical Foundations of Modern Physical Science*.[19] However, the most consistent school of thought on the matter is associated with the neo-Thomists at Louvain University.[20] An example of their a priori assumption that there *must be* a metaphysical component in science is the following:

In speaking here about the fundamental structure of material reality, we do not intend to take this term in the sense in which it is used in physical science. For this book is not a treatise of physical science but a study about physical science itself. In a treatise of physical science the first chapter dealing with the fundamental structure of material reality would probably speak about atoms and molecules, the second about atomic nuclei and electrons, the third about protons and neutrons, etc. It would thus give us a progressively more profound analysis of the structure of matter, as it reveals itself in physical research. Accordingly, atomic and sub-atomic structures are, as we noted in Chapter 1, *results* of physical research, but not structures which condition this research itself.

What interests us is a philosophical consideration of matter, and this means here that we ask ourselves in what way matter must be constituted if it can be at all object of the method used by physical science.[21]

[18] Ernest Nagel, *The Structure of Science*, Harcourt, Brace & World, New York, 1961, p. 151.

[19] Edwin A. Burtt, *The Metaphysical Foundations of Modern Physical Science*, 2d ed., Doubleday, Garden City, 1954 (original edition 1924).

[20] Désiré Nys, Fernand Renoirte, Henry Koren, Andrew van Melsen, and Henry van Laer are perhaps the best known; though not all directly associated with Louvain, they are recognized among Thomists as the "Louvain School."

[21] Andrew G. van Melsen, *Science and Technology*, Duquesne University Press, Pittsburgh, 1961, p. 93.

This assumption of metaphysical presuppositions in science—taken so much for granted by Thomistic and other philosophers who feel at home with the notion of metaphysics—can evoke a passionate reaction on the part of antimetaphysicians. Ernest Nagel treats several versions of the idea among "recent evaluations of science" that have "had an obviously malicious intent." These are strong words. But Nagel means for them to be taken seriously. His chief objection is to ideas that are "frankly based upon explicit theological and metaphysical commitments for which no experimental evidence is invoked." He argues as follows:

> The assumption that there is a superior and more direct way of grasping the secrets of the universe than the painfully slow road of science has been so repeatedly shown to be a romantic illusion, that only those who are unable to profit from the history of the human intellect can seriously maintain it. Certainly, whatever enlightenment we possess about ourselves and the world has been achieved only after the illusion of a "metaphysical wisdom" superior to "mere science" had been abandoned. The methods of science do not guarantee that its conclusions are final and incorrigible by further inquiry; but it is by dropping the pretense of a spurious finality and recognizing the fallibility of its self-corrective procedures that science has won its victories. It may be a comfort to some to learn that in so far as man uses "wisdom" he can aim only at the good, since the most diverse kinds of action—kindly as well as brutal, beneficent as well as costly in human life—are undertaken in the name of wisdom, such a testimonial will doubtless enable everyone engaged in such an undertaking to redouble his zeal without counting the costs. But it is not wisdom but a mark of immaturity to recommend that we simply examine our hearts if we wish to discover the good life; for it is just because men rely so completely and unreflectively on their intuitive insights and passionate impulses that needless sufferings and conflicts occur among them. The point is clear: claims as to what is required by wisdom need to be adjudicated if such claims are to be warranted; and accordingly, objective methods must be instituted, on the basis of which the conditions, the consequences, and the mutual compatibility of different courses of action may be established. But if such methods are introduced, we leave the miasmal swamps of suprascientific wisdom, and are brought back again to the firm soil of scientific knowledge.[22]

These strong words, obviously, depend upon an assumption that knowledge "for which no experimental evidence is invoked" is knowledge where no "objective methods" have been instituted. For Nagel states explicitly that "if such methods are introduced, we leave the miasmal swamps of suprascientific wisdom." The Thomist against whom Nagel is directing this attack is Jacques Maritain, and Maritain would object strenuously, claiming that there are "objective methods" other than the scientific. Furthermore, Maritain

[22] Reprinted with permission of Free Press from *Sovereign Reason* by Ernest Nagel. Copyright 1954, p. 32.

has no deliberate intention of being antiscientific. He even recognizes, with Nagel, that science can be disparaged in the name of wisdom:

> We are not forgetting that science is good in itself. Like everything else which derives from spiritual energy in quest of truth it is naturally sacred. And alas for those who fail to recognise its proper dignity. Every time that the fragile representatives of wisdom thought themselves authorised to despise science and its humble and plebeian truths, in the name of a higher truth, they have been severely and rightly punished.[23]

However, he goes on immediately to qualify the last statement in a way that could evoke Nagel's hot response:

> But science is like art in this that though both are good in themselves man can put them to bad uses and bad purposes: while in so far as man uses wisdom—and the same is true of virtue—he can only use it for good purposes.[24]

But even this assertion, that "man can only use wisdom for good purposes," though it obviously rankles Nagel, would not fully explain his anger. What does explain it can be seen in the following passage:

> I will use [knowledge] in the more usual and purer sense, in the classical sense which makes it mean a certain type of knowing and a certain perfection of the intelligence; where we have to do with the knowledge of the causes of things; with a knowledge which is as such a certain nobility of mind; and which has a certain dignity.
>
> Thus, the word knowledge has three meanings. In a superior sense it means *knowing in a firm and stable way*. It is not exhaustive, of course (except in God), but is armed for certitude and capable of advancing endlessly in the way of truth. In this sense wisdom is comprehended in knowledge, and is its highest region. We speak of the "knowledge of the saints" as we speak of "the wisdom of the saints." In this first sense, which is the most comprehensive, we may speak of "knowledge or understanding."
>
> In an intermediate sense the word knowledge is taken in opposition to the highest regions of our understanding. In this sense it means science in contradistinction to wisdom, and has to do with the less exalted regions of our understanding. We do not describe botanical or linguistic knowledge as wisdom, but as science. Wisdom is knowledge through the highest sources and in the deepest and simplest sense. But knowledge or science in this second sense means *knowing in detail and by proximate or apparent causes*. In this sense we speak of "science, or the special sciences."
>
> And finally there is a third and inferior sense, an unclassical sense, which is not used and ought not to be used by the *philosophia perennis*, though it has its place in the common speech of men. In this sense the word knowledge no longer connotes a firm and perfect mode of under-

23 Jacques Maritain, *Science and Wisdom*, Geoffrey Bles, London, 1940, p. 32.
24 *Ibid.*

standing, but a way of knowing that is curious of detail and that likes the tang of created things, savouring them and entering into a kind of connivance with them. In this sense knowledge is more than ever in opposition to wisdom.[25]

Maritain certainly had no intention, in writing this passage, of being deliberately provocative or annoying—however much opposed he was to positivism. He was simply stating what he took to be a standard use of terms. And indeed the usages he describes are still prevalent, in some sense, in many Catholic intellectual circles. Maritain is simply stating a straightforward and classical form of the subordination and hierarchy of intellectual disciplines.

All of this suggests that the question, "Are there metaphysical presuppositions in science?" cannot be answered apart from the "loyalties to different intellectual traditions" to which Nagel refers. And this brings us back to the question left unanswered earlier, as to whether or not nonlogical (especially psychological, sociological, and historical) considerations should enter into the interpretation of science.

[25] *Ibid.*, pp. 4–5.

# Appendix

# B*

# Historical and Sociological Issues in Science

THE CLASH BETWEEN THE VIEWS of Maritain and Nagel clearly illustrates the extent to which general cultural backgrounds influence an author's interpretation of science. In addition, there are good reasons for believing that the very work of the scientist himself is affected by social, cultural, and historical influences.

The contemporary discipline devoted to the study of these influences is the sociology of science. It has been said, with respect to the importance of the sociology of science, that "because science is of such central social and cultural importance in our society, no one is properly educated today if he does not have an understanding of science equal to his understanding of other major social institutions."[1] The field is, however, a relatively new one, as yet only moderately developed.

It has been said, quite accurately, that there has been a definite neglect of the sociology of science:

> Colleges and universities with courses in this subject or with professors who devote a major part of their research efforts to it are a

[1] Bernard Barber and Walter Hirsch (eds.), *The Sociology of Science*, Free Press, New York, 1962, Introduction, p. 1. See also Bernard Barber, *Science and the Social Order*, Free Press, New York, 1952.

handful at the most, despite the fact that among the few scholars who do seriously cultivate the sociology of science are included men like Robert K. Merton and Talcott Parsons.[2]

What sorts of questions should be asked about the cultural and social influences in science? An excellent list is provided by Robert S. Cohen:

> The impacts of the sciences *on the social order* have perhaps been most often examined, and are known to take many forms, direct and indirect. I will, in view of this, turn my attention to the impact of the social order *on science.* In studying the role of the social environment, past and present, vis-a-vis science, it is just as well to state boldly what we want to know about the state of science in some detail, namely, why the following aspects exist as they do: (i) the social position of the scientific enterprise; (ii) the internal social characteristics of science, the variety and quantity of talent, the institutional forms, including professional societies and mediums of communications, forms of training and education of scientists, and of the public, and so forth; (iii) why certain problems are dealt with; (iv) why certain solutions (concepts and theories) are offered at the time they are offered; (v) why certain solutions are accepted; and (vi) why a mode of explanation is accepted, dominating the judgment of a man, a school or an epoch.
>
> It is, of course, important to distinguish the sources of problems from the sources of answers and solutions to these problems. Likewise it is necessary to realize that we seek the historical genesis of these problems and of their solutions. Explanation of the history of scientific thought and practice will be genetic explanation (at least until historical explanation generally advances to now unknown characteristics).
>
> The source of problems and solutions are of only two kinds, which may operate jointly in complex fashion and may be difficult to disentangle: (i) those due to previous stages of science, including of course other scientific activities, not logically connected to the particular scientific activity we seek to explain, and (ii) those due to nonscientific factors.
>
> There is another way of typifying the sources: (i) those internal to the science, and that generate a problem logically, and (ii) those that pose problems only by external circumstance, in which case the neighboring sciences form part of the external group. Authors who have explored the external factors have suggested a wide variety of social influences on science.[3]

Cohen then lists a number of these influences, along with classic contributions to each: the influence of religion, as documented in Max Weber's *The Protestant Ethic and the Spirit of Capitalism,* Robert K. Merton's "Puritanism, Pietism, and Science" (reprinted in his *Social Theory and Social Structure*), etc.; the influence of art, of social institutions, and of philosophy as suggested

---

[2] Barber and Hirsch, *op. cit.,* p. 2.

[3] Robert S. Cohen, "Alternative Interpretations of the History of Science," in Philipp G. Frank (ed.), *The Validation of Scientific Theories,* Collier paperback, New York, 1961, pp. 200–201. The article appeared originally in *Scientific Monthly,* (February, 1955), and is here reprinted by permission of The American Association for the Advancement of Science.

by, for instance, Maritain's *Science and Wisdom* or F. S. C. Northrop's *The Logic of the Sciences and the Humanities;* the influence of the economic order, as suggested in Marx; and the influence of irrational forces as suggested, for instance, in Freud's *Civilization and Its Discontents.* (This is only a very limited selection from Cohen's copious documentation.) Cohen then goes on:

> All of these have been documented sufficiently and we may now ask that some comparative analysis be made. The significant hypothesis today, and for some time past, would be one which tries to determine the relations of dominance—for a specific period of science, or even a specific scientific event—among the many factors that have been suggested. The sweeping views of a Whitehead that the bifurcation of mind-body can be traced to Cartesian philosophy; or of Northrop that the science and general culture can be determined by an epistemological decision about the apprehension of nature; or of Freud's irrational determinants, or of the others, need to be put to a test which is somewhat different from that which they themselves offer. By this I mean that their exposition seems to be incomplete.
>
> We must ask Koyré and Whitehead why a new philosophy of the cosmos, a science that uses material, unspiritual, and non-mental substance, gains dominance? Why and where does it arise? We must ask Northrop, why should an epistemological policy be *proposed* in the first place—surely not because of a previous epistemological decision—and why should it have been *accepted* as orthodox or normal in the second place? Or, would Northrop claim that the history of epistemology has an independent development from which the history of culture, and indeed general history, is derivative?[4]

The bearing of all this on the philosophy of science becomes obvious in the new view of science that emerges from applying sociology and history to its interpretation. Most recent discussions of the issue center around the professedly anti-empiricist work of Thomas Kuhn. He writes:

> The man who takes historic fact seriously must suspect that science does not tend toward the ideal that our [empiricist] image of its cumulativeness has suggested.[5]

And again:

> It is hard to see how new theories could arise without . . . destructive changes in beliefs about nature. Though logical inclusiveness remains a permissible view of the relation between successive scientific theories, it is a historical implausibility.
>
> A century ago it would, I think, have been possible to let the case for the necessity of revolutions rest at this point. But today, unfortunately, that cannot be done because the view of the subject developed above cannot be maintained if the most prevalent contemporary interpretation of the nature and function of scientific theory is accepted. That interpretation, closely associated with early logical positivism and not cate-

---

4 *Ibid.,* pp. 201–202.

5 Thomas S. Kuhn, *The Structure of Scientific Revolutions,* University of Chicago Press, Chicago, 1962, p. 95.

gorically rejected by its successors, would restrict the range and meaning of an accepted theory so that it could not possibly conflict with any later theory that made predictions about some of the same natural phenomena.[6]

Kuhn's essay is thus both anti-empiricist and historically oriented. Though he omits references to the "external social, economic, and intellectual conditions in the development of the sciences," he acknowledges a debt to social scientists for helping him to find the key to his interpretation. In particular, in a key passage, he appeals to the model of political revolutions:

> The remainder of this essay aims to demonstrate that the historical study of paradigm change reveals very similar characteristics in the evolution of the sciences. Like the choice between competing political institutions, that between competing paradigms proves to be a choice between incompatible modes of community life. . . . Each group uses its own paradigm to argue in that paradigm's defense.
> The resulting circularity does not, of course, make the argument wrong or ineffectual. . . . Yet, whatever its force, the status of the circular argument is only that of persuasion. It cannot be made logically or even probabilistically compelling.[7]

It is at this point, as also in his belief that the scientific data before and after a revolution are incommensurable, that logical empiricists have found Kuhn vulnerable. Dudley Shapere in particular has returned to the attack in several places. He claims:

> Yet if the meanings of all the terms are theory- (or paradigm-) determined to the extent that all the meanings even of the same terms in different theoretical contexts cannot be compared, we must wonder . . . how those theories are to be judged against one another, and how the replacement of one theory by another can be said to constitute "progress."[8]

And in another place:

> By hardening the notion of a "scientific tradition" into a hidden unit, Kuhn is thus forced *by a purely conceptual point* to ignore many important differences between scientific activities classified as being of the same tradition, as well as important continuities between successive traditions.[9]

Nevertheless, even if one must admit that Kuhn has overstated his case (as is true of most revolutionaries), it must also be admitted that he has injected a challenging new note into philosophy of science. It could once be

[6] *Ibid.*, p. 97.

[7] *Ibid.*, p. 93.

[8] Dudley Shapere, *Philosophical Problems of Natural Science*, Introduction, p. 18. Reprinted with permission of The Macmillan Company. Copyright © Dudley Shapere 1965.

[9] Dudley Shapere, "Meaning and Scientific Change," in *Mind and Cosmos* (see footnote 8, above), p. 71.

fashionable to reject a contribution to philosophy of science with the disparaging remark that it was "sociopsychological."[10] Now, instead, we have Hempel recognizing that:

> One of the problems here at issue is whether the notion of accepting a hypothesis independently of any contemplated action can be satisfactorily explicated within the framework of a purely logical and methodological analysis of scientific inquiry or whether, if any illuminating construal of the idea is possible at all, it will have to be given in the context of a psychological, sociological, and historical study of scientific research.[11]

## BIBLIOGRAPHY

**Editor's Note:** The appendixes were designed in such a way as to introduce, simultaneously, both some of the leading issues in contemporary philosophy of science and the literature in which these issues are presented. Thus the footnotes already represent a good bibliography.

However, a number of important collaborative efforts could not be fitted in, either because the articles are too technical or for some similar reason. These additional references are mentioned here:[12]

Baumrin, B. H. (ed.): *Philosophy of Science: The Delaware Seminar*, 2 vols.,* Wiley, New York, 1963 ff.

Cohen, Robert S. and Marx Wartofsky (eds.): *Boston Studies in the Philosophy of Science*, 3 vols.,* ff. Reidel, Dordrecht, Holland, Humanities Press, New York, 1963 ff.

Feigl, Herbert *et al.* (eds.): *Minnesota Studies in the Philosophy of Science*, 3 vols.,* University of Minnesota, Minneapolis, 1956 ff.

Nagel, Ernest, Patrick Suppes, and Alfred Tarski (eds.): *Logic, Methodology, and Philosophy of Science*, Stanford University Press, Stanford, 1962.

Smith, Vincent E. (ed): *Philosophy of Science*, vol. I of Philosophy of Science Institute Lectures,* St. John's University, Jamaica, N.Y., 1960 ff.

Edwards, Paul (ed.): *The Encyclopedia of Philosophy*, 8 vols., Free Press, New York, 1967. This encyclopedia includes excellent material on all the issues in the appendixes.

---

[10] See, e.g., Paul K. Feyerabend, "Comments on Hanson's 'Is There a Logic of Scientific Discovery?' " in Herbert Feigl and Grover Maxwell (eds.), *Current Issues in the Philosophy of Science*, Holt, Rinehart and Winston, New York, p. 38.

[11] Hempel, "Recent Problems of Induction," in *Mind and Cosmos*, p. 132.

[12] Several of the series continue in operation, and new volumes are to be expected in the future. These are marked with an asterisk.

# INDEX